THE CHILD
FROM FIVE TO TEN

BOOKS BY ARNOLD GESELL

THE NORMAL CHILD AND PRIMARY EDUCATION (WITH B. C. GESELL)

EXCEPTIONAL CHILDREN AND PUBLIC SCHOOL POLICY

HANDICAPPED CHILDREN IN SCHOOL AND COURT

THE PRE-SCHOOL CHILD FROM THE STANDPOINT OF PUBLIC HYGIENE AND EDUCATION

THE RETARDED CHILD—HOW TO HELP HIM

THE MENTAL GROWTH OF THE PRE-SCHOOL CHILD

INFANCY AND HUMAN GROWTH

GUIDANCE OF MENTAL GROWTH IN INFANT AND CHILD

AN ATLAS OF INFANT BEHAVIOR—TWO VOLUMES, 3,200 ACTION PHOTOGRAPHS

INFANT BEHAVIOR—ITS GENESIS AND GROWTH (WITH THOMPSON)

THE PSYCHOLOGY OF EARLY GROWTH (WITH THOMPSON)

BIOGRAPHIES OF CHILD DEVELOPMENT

THE FIRST FIVE YEARS OF LIFE:—A GUIDE TO THE STUDY OF THE PRE-SCHOOL CHILD

WOLF CHILD AND HUMAN CHILD

TWINS T AND C FROM INFANCY TO ADOLESCENCE (WITH THOMPSON)

DEVELOPMENTAL DIAGNOSIS: CLINICAL METHODS AND PRACTICAL APPLICATIONS (WITH AMATRUDA)

A GUIDE TO THE STUDY OF THE YALE FILMS OF CHILD DEVELOPMENT (WITH AMES)

THE EMBRYOLOGY OF BEHAVIOR

HOW A BABY GROWS

FEEDING BEHAVIOR OF INFANTS—A PEDIATRIC APPROACH TO THE MENTAL HYGIENE OF EARLY LIFE (WITH ILG)

INFANT AND CHILD IN THE CULTURE OF TODAY (WITH ILG)

VISION—ITS DEVELOPMENT IN INFANT AND CHILD (WITH ILG AND BULLIS)

STUDIES IN CHILD DEVELOPMENT

THE CHILD
FROM FIVE TO TEN

*(From the former Clinic of Child Development
School of Medicine at Yale University)*

BY
ARNOLD GESELL, M.D.
FRANCES L. ILG, M.D.

IN COLLABORATION WITH
LOUISE BATES AMES, Ph.D.
GLENNA E. BULLIS

HARPER & ROW · PUBLISHERS

New York and Evanston

CONTENTS

PART THREE

THE GROWTH COMPLEX

CONTENTS

PREFACE

MANY minds have gone into the making of this book,—especially if we include the multitude of infants and children whose growing minds have been our subject of study over a long period of years. The authors of this volume have been associated on the staff of The Yale Clinic of Child Development from ten to twenty years. They have had common interests converging on the universal problem which confronts all children from the moment of birth: the problem of development.

The most basic and dramatic phases of that development are concentrated in the first five years of life. The outward manifestations of early mental growth are remarkably patterned and lawful. In comparison the years from five to ten seemed relatively undefined, for the available literature on these years tended to lump them together in broad generalizations. We were naturally interested to learn whether the precise patterning processes so evident in infancy also project themselves into the school years.

At this point the aforementioned infants and pre-school children came forward to make their contribution! They grew up. The baby, who at 28 weeks had raked at a pellet, and who at 40 weeks plucked it pincerwise, in due course acquired his sixth year molars. He then applied the forceps of his mind (i.e. of his action-system) upon things more abstruse,—on the alphabet and numbers, on crumbs of information and moral proprieties. True to his former self his behavior patterns changed with aging. The transformations were gradual and not dramatically obvious; but when our numerous behavior records were analyzed it became evident that the growth of the mind is lawfully patterned in the years from five to ten. The patterns may not be as sharply defined to ordinary observation, but we were amazed at their consistent characteristicness when they were comparatively studied by clinical methods. This volume attempts to set down the characteristicness disclosed.

The logic of our biographic-clinical approach to the study of child development is more fully indicated in the *Introduction*. Knowledge of the dynamic morphology of behavior must be gained by intimate, consecutive, individualized contacts, rather than mass studies. The normative researches, the diagnostic and advisory services of the clinic, the guidance nursery and the systematic pattern analysis of cinema records, —all gave direction and form to the present investigation.

A preliminary work on *The Feeding Behavior of Infants*, reported in a previous volume (1937), proved to be a kind of pilot study for later elaboration. The junior author, Dr. Ilg, as a pediatrician, has had a uniquely rich and varied clinical experience with normal children of all ages up to ten years. Additional experience with deviate and problem children has helped to sharpen her insight into the typical expressions of development.

Mrs. Ames, curator of the Yale Films of Child Development, has devoted special attention to the objective analysis of behavior patterns infallibly recorded in cinema film. She has become an expert in this methodology, which has directly and indirectly illumined the processes of child development at all ages.

Miss Bullis, as assistant in research and in other capacities has been closely identified with our developmental research over a period of twenty years. Her critical judgment and her familiarity with the lives and homes of the children have been invaluable in the prosecution of our study. She has also conducted the visual skills examinations which furnished many side lights on the behavior characteristics of children of kindergarten and school age.

The senior author, as director of the clinic, can testify to a long standing interest in infants and young children. Indeed a special interest in children of school age dates back to the turn of the century; and to his first published volume, written with Mrs. Gesell. May he be permitted a smiling nod to that volume and its co-author?

This preface must deal heavily with acknowledgements, for our indebtedness has been heavy. We are indebted to all our colleagues on the clinic staff, past as well as present. Immediately we owe much to Miss Janet Learned, principal of the guidance nursery and to her associates for their knowledge of the individualities of the children as displayed in the pre-school years.

The parents of the children deserve very special mention for their unstinted cooperation in exploring the characteristics of their children. These parents assimilated our developmental point of view and became very skillful in reporting observations which concerned the mechanisms of the growth process. The rapport between home and clinic was close and marked by mutual confidence and interest. We wish to record our admiration of the attitude of the parents and our deep appreciation of their contribution.

Most of our children were studied in New Haven and in the clinic. But in 1942 we made a very fortunate association with The New Canaan Country School, in New Canaan, Connecticut. Here again we became the beneficiaries of a mutual interest in the welfare of the children. The staff of this excellent school gave generously of their time and enthusiasms, and even made special adjustments of their programs in our behalf. We also benefitted from healthy skepticism and criticism. We are indeed grateful to the whole teaching staff, to Mr. Henry Welles, headmaster, and also to Mrs. Paulina Olsen, head of the Lower School, who was formerly chief guidance worker in our own guidance nursery.

For illustrations of the present volume we have made moderate use of diagrammatic and abstract devices. Special thanks are due to Mrs.

Rudolf F. Zallinger for her interest and skill in rendering the sketches which we placed at her disposal.

Since the work of the clinic has deep roots in the past, we would like to refer again to the supports given by Rockefeller funds, The Carnegie Corporation and Yale University. The current enterprises of the clinic have been made possible by continuing support from the Yale School of Medicine; and a generous grant of American Optical Company, through its Bureau of Visual Science.

Why did we write this book which was begun during a war and completed in its aftermath? Perhaps our task was somewhat motivated by a war which has wrought such tragic destruction and injustice upon children. It is no longer trite to say that children are the one remaining hope of mankind. For the rest of our preface may we refer the reader to The Philosophic Postscript with which this book ends.

But one more word about the children themselves. They carry the hope of mankind, because in a democratic culture they give ample evidence of the potentialities of the human spirit, and of its engaging qualities. If we could but capture their transparent honesty and sincerities! They still have much to teach us, if we observe closely enough. Indeed when the child of five reaches the age of ten he becomes so articulate that he can actually tell us something directly about himself and about ourselves. Perhaps at this significant transition age of ten, near the brink of adolescence, we must begin to take children more completely into our confidence.

Meanwhile, we hope that this book will help you to get better acquainted with your children in the years from five to ten.

Many readers have reminded us that their fives-to-tens are trending into the teens. We may report that a further volume, dealing with the years from ten to sixteen, is in the early stages of preparation by the authors, who are now on the staff of the Gesell Institute of Child Development. This Institute was founded in 1950 by the research members of the former Yale Clinic of Child Development.

Gesell Institute of Child Development
New Haven, Connecticut, U. S. A.

THE CHILD
FROM FIVE TO TEN

INTRODUCTION

How this book is built and how it may be used.

Books have origins. And origins often help to answer the inevitable questions as to aims, scope and method. This particular book was not written with design deliberately aforethought, nor yet as a mere after thought. In retrospect we have become aware that it grew from some inner necessity as a developmental sequel of the earlier volume *Infant and Child in the Culture of Today* (1943). The two volumes supplement each other and they may be considered companion volumes; but each is constructed to stand independently.

In a still earlier volume entitled *The First Five Years of Life* (1940), the staff of the Yale Clinic set forth a somewhat systematic summary of the behavior characteristics of normal infancy and pre-school childhood. The data were based on extensive clinical and normative studies, and were presented in the form of age characterizations and genetic sequences.

The present volume follows the same general pattern reflected in previous publications. Indeed in basic arrangement of subject matter, scheme of treatment and format it closely parallels the companion volume (*Infant and Child in the Culture of Today*),—for the very good reason that the laws of child development do not undergo any real change at the age of five.

Our continuing interest in children whom we had studied during

[1]

their infancy and pre-school years, led to annual follow-up observations of these same children during the years from five to ten. The present volume, therefore, is in large measure a biographic-developmental study of the patterning of behavior throughout the first ten years of life. The approach is definitely longitudinal, and our findings are presented in the form of *growth gradients* embracing some seventeen age levels, and ten major fields of behavior. For convenience of reference, as well as an aid to interpretation, the findings are also presented in cross sectional age summaries.

In the Preface we have alluded to the favorable circumstances which have surrounded this survey of the psychological growth of the school child. The cohesion and cooperativeness of the staff over a long period of years have enabled us to do some group thinking in the interpretation of our voluminous data. One-way-vision screen facilities made auxiliary observations possible, while the basic contacts with the children and their parents were highly individualized. These contacts, moreover, were cumulative, so that children, observers, examiners and parents all came to understand each other. The organic growth of mutual understanding and rapport over a period of ten years or more must be mentioned as an important element in the validity of our investigation.

In spirit and technique our methods were clinical, rather than statistical, or rigorously experimental. We used standardized procedures for measurement and observation, but they were freely supplemented with naturalistic observations, stenographically recorded. In harmony with the clinical approach the procedures were not kept altogether uniform from age to age, but were shifted in context and emphasis to meet the shifting contexts and accents of development. As the child changed with maturity we adapted the procedures accordingly. By noting the form and direction of these adaptations, the outlines of the maturity traits were sharpened. Since we were always dealing with a gradient (that is a progressive series of data) this method of clinical appraisal was essentially comparative and self-corrective. It applied to the information gained by interview, as well as to the direct observations.

Fifty or more children were examined at 5, 5½, 6, 7, 8 and 9 years, and a smaller number at 10 years. Most of these children were of high average or superior intelligence, and came from homes of good or high socio-economic status. Three-fourths of the children had attended the guidance nursery of the clinic; some had also been developmentally examined during infancy. Nearly all the children attended a public elementary school, and were in this sense representative of a prosperous American community. A special group of 14 children, who attended an excellent private school in a small Connecticut town, were examined at semiannual intervals from six through nine years. These children were not only examined individually, but were observed as members of their schoolroom groups. There were numerous observations and discussions with the teachers relative both to individual and group behavior.

The case-record for each child grew to considerable size before the end of the study. It included for each periodic contact the following materials: a) a psychological examination based on the Yale developmental schedules and Stanford Binet scale, b) performance tests, including the Arthur series, c) reading readiness tests, including Monroe, d) visual skills tests including pursuit fixation, fusion, acuity, etc., e) naturalistic observations of the child's play behavior and incidental postural and tensional behavior, and f) a wide-ranging interview with the mother, concerning behavior at home and school. The incidental, naturalistic observations often proved revealing when brought into relation with the more formalized observations. All the records were carefully analyzed, age by age, situation by situation, and child by child. Percentage frequencies were noted, but were not made the sole basis for the final conclusions, and are not reported in this volume. Sometimes a single, but revealing behavior led to the identification of a significant developmental trend. The ultimate criterion of credibility and validity was developmental:—Does the given behavior have an assignable status in a gradient of growth as indicated by the converging evidence of the total data for all the children of all the ages?

This criterion is frankly clinical, but due care was exercised to secure

ample objective data. The gradients, the individual items of the gradients, and the growth trends were discussed in detailed conferences. All
this involved subjective estimates, but with self-correcting safeguards.
The very complexity and diversity of the data required that we use the
method of progressive approximation. An unqualified statistical report
of frequencies would not have served our purpose. Our task was to
make the data intelligible and to extract meanings, so that the reader
might gain a better insight into the nature of child development.
Although we have made a survey which has taken years of application,
our primary purpose is not to report the findings as mere facts, but to
give the reader the benefit of what we have learned through the unique
opportunities of the investigation. It was a rare privilege to become so
well acquainted with a fine group of young Americans.

The construction of the book, therefore, explains itself. For this is a
book which was at every step built with the interests of the readers in
mind, particularly parents and teachers; also physicians, nurses and
others who are professionally responsible for safeguarding the developmental welfare of children from five to ten.

PART ONE is intended to give the reader preliminary orientation to
the central theme of development. Growth or development (the two
words can be used interchangeably) remains an empty abstraction, unless it is envisaged as a concrete process which produces patterns of
behavior. The patterns change in shape and character as the child
matures. They can be arranged in growth gradients. To understand
the general significance of the years from five to ten, Chapter 1 considers their relation to the total life cycle. The nature of psychological
growth is treated in Chapter 2. The mental attitudes of parents and
teachers, in turn, depends upon an appreciation of these growth factors,
as indicated in Chapter 3.

PART Two delineates the progressive stages in the growth of the
child's mind, by means of a series of cross sectional characterizations.
The mental growth of the first four years is summarized in twelve
thumb nail sketches. The purpose of this summary is to give foundation
and perspective to the portrayal of the years from five to ten. Each of

these yearly age levels is treated more elaborately and always with systematic reference to ten major fields of behavior: §1. Motor characteristics §2. Personal hygiene §3. Emotional expression §4. Fears and dreams §5. Self and sex §6. Interpersonal relations §7. Play and pastimes §8. School life §9. Ethical sense §10. Philosophic outlook.

These ten categories are fairly comprehensive. They were not decided upon in advance. They were the natural outgrowth of the data when the basic records were analyzed. They determine the *Maturity Traits* which are concretely formulated in the double columns of chapters 5, 6, 7, 8, 9. For convenience of reference they are always identified by the same sectional numbers.

The maturity traits are *not* to be regarded as rigid norms, nor as models. They simply illustrate the kinds of behavior (desirable or otherwise) which tend to occur at this age. Every child has an individual pattern of growth, unique to him. The behavior traits here outlined may be used to interpret his individuality and to consider the maturity level at which he is functioning.

Each of the age levels covered in PART Two is treated as a unit, but not as an independent unit. Throughout we have emphasized the dynamic sequences which preserve the continuity of the total stream of development. The reader who wishes to get acquainted with any given age period will probably be interested to read the two adjacent periods to sense the past and the future trends.

The chief aim of this volume is to impart a sense of growth trends. Although the subject matter is arranged by ages, our purpose has *not* been to set up rigid age norms or a static yardstick. Growth is motion. We should be mainly concerned with the position of the child in a forward moving cycle.

PART THREE deals with the total growth complex. We take the reader onto ten closely connected platforms, so that he may get a panoramic view of the flowing slopes of development, with trends which date back to infancy. The trends are also formulated in tabulated *gradients of growth*. The platforms represent the ten major fields of behavior (Chapters 11-20). Each field constitutes a terrain of growth territory distinguishable enough to be considered as a separate topic. To comprehend a landscape one must look at it from varied angles. So these chapters often reveal a single subject in different aspects. It will be found, for example, that motor characteristics affect emotional expression and tensional outlets. They may even enter into the sense of self, and thereby influence interpersonal relations, which in turn concern ethics and school life. It is very important to grasp the unitariness of the growth complex. We hope that the very multiplicity of the growth gradients (over forty in number) and the parallelisms in these gradients will throw light upon the growth process as a living integrated reality.

Here again we would emphasize that the gradients are always relative and not absolute. They are *not* offered as norms of absolute ability, but as approximate norms of developmental sequence. The gradients will become an aid to child guidance only if they are used to locate the position of a child with respect to certain aspects of behavior in the total growth complex. Your problem, as a lay person, is not to measure the mind, but simply to get a sense of direction.

Do not be surprised if you find that your child does some things that are not even mentioned in the book! We know that every child is an individual and that he travels by his own tailor-made time schedule. Nevertheless, we have given you in the characterizational profiles the descriptive maturity traits and in the seriated growth gradients a frame of reference to consult. If you do not use this reference frame too rigidly, it should help to make your child more intelligible; and if he is at all normal, as he probably is, then you will have the reassurance that he is steadily (though not evenly) moving forward to higher levels of maturity. This reassurance will also place you in a better position to give the backward-mindful and forward-constructive guidance best suited to him at one particular phase of his development. And you will always be confronted by a phase at a time! The total ground plan is beyond your control. It is too complex and mysterious to be altogether entrusted to human hands. So Nature takes over most of the task, and simply invites your assistance.

PART ONE

   . . . Could you tell me
   how to grow,
   or is it unconveyed,
   like melody or witchcraft?

       —EMILY DICKINSON
          (1862)

1

THE CYCLE OF DEVELOPMENT

THE years from five to ten occupy an important position in the scheme of human development. To appreciate their significance we may look down two vistas; one vista reaches into the past, the other into the future. A diagram will help us to see these middle years of childhood in true perspective.

It takes, on the average, somewhat over twenty years before a newborn infant becomes an adult. Birth was itself preceded by ten lunar months of growth in which the zygote became an embryo, and the embryo a fetus. Soon after the beginning of the fetal period, that is, eight weeks after conception, the nervous system and the muscular system show signs of organization. The fetus stirs with body, head, arm and leg muscles. Presently eyes and hands become active with mild but patterned movements. By the twentieth prenatal week the future infant is already in possession of the billions of nerve cells which are to govern his behavior throughout life.

As early as the eighth week of intrauterine life the beginnings of the differences between a boy and a girl become recognizable. Long before birth the future infant is already stamped with individuality. Every child is born with potentialities which are peculiar to him or to her. Each child has a unique pattern of growth, determined by these potentialities, and by environmental fate.

There are, however, certain basic traits and growth sequences, which are typical of the human species in a modern culture. These general characteristics are indicated in the accompanying diagram, which is so drawn that one may look into the long vista which stretches toward the future, and also into the deep vista which reaches downward into the formative past.

The general course of development is similar for girls and for boys. But girls mature somewhat more rapidly and earlier. Our diagram, therefore, shows two separate curves.

Seven stages are pictured. They correspond only partly to Shakespeare's seven ages of man. The distant stages of senescence and senectitude are not included. Emphasis is placed on the progressive developmental advance which proceeds as follows:

1) Stage of the Embryo (0-8 weeks)
2) Stage of the Fetus (8-40 weeks)
3) Infancy (from birth to 2 years)
4) The Pre-School Age (2-5 years)
5) Childhood (5-12 years)
6) Adolescence (12 to 20-24 years)
7) Adult maturity

Man, of all creatures, has the longest period of relative immaturity. He is so complex that it takes him over twenty years to grow up, physically and mentally. Not without reason is the right of franchise in our democratic culture postponed to the age of twenty-one.

24 years

10 years

5 years

2 years

O

MAN

Adult

WOMAN

Adolescent

Puberty

COMMUNITY

School Child

Grade Five

SCHOOL

Grade One

Second Dentition

Pre-School

Kindergarten

Seven Stages of the
Cycle of Development.

1. Embryo
2. Fetus
3. Infant
4. Pre-School
5. School Child
6. Adolescent
7. Adult

Infant

Nursery School

HOME

BIRTH

Prenatal Period

Boy

Fetus

GIRL

Fetus

Embryo

The years from five to ten occupy a middle position in this long span of immaturity. These middle years are intermediate both in a biological and in a cultural sense. During them the child sheds his milk teeth, a biological event. At six years he cuts his first permanent tooth, a molar at that. We may call it a school-entrance molar for it punctuates his induction into the elementary school system, which is a sociological event.

Puberty is the next great landmark on the pathway of development. It marks the beginning of adolescence, which continues for some ten years, until the attainment of maturity. They are years of completion; the first five years of life are years of preparation. The middle years of childhood lie between. They can be understood only in terms of the past in which they are rooted, and in terms of the future toward which they trend.

Being intermediate years they lack the dramatic vividness of infancy on the one hand and of adolescence on the other hand. In consequence the psychology of the five to ten period has been somewhat slighted by elision. The literature reflects a tendency to generalize for the period as a whole without recognizing the age differences within the period. The elementary school to be sure, promotes its children on an annual basis; but curriculum and methods are too largely determined by a narrow psychology of learning instead of a liberal psychology of development. The institutional pressures of the school tend to obscure or to overlook both the individual and the age differences in growth processes. The child is not only advancing in strength and skills, but he is changing in the interior patterns of his private psychology.

Knowing too little about these subtle and hidden changes, parents are prone to blame the school for maladjustments; and teachers in turn are prone to blame child and parent. Often no one is to blame. Ignorance of the ways of growth lies at the basis of many of our difficulties. If only the child himself could tell us more about how he feels, how he thinks, how he acts. We judge too much by the superficial evidences of "success" or "failure," and then further distort our judgments by an overweening attitude of competitiveness projected upon the child.

Here, again, more insight into the laws and the concrete ways of growth will humanize our adult-child relationships. We shall find that even such a simple (?) task as the recognition of words on a printed page is not so simple that it can be solved through sheer drill and training (with a little discipline, and not too much nonsense!). The function of visual perception in man equals that of speech in its unique complexities. We have much to learn about the development of this function in its manifold relations to life and education. The alarming increase of visual defects and reading disabilities in the early school years testifies to the complexities of development in these years.

Perhaps we have exaggerated the perturbation of adolescence and also the steadiness and stability of childhood. More goes on than frankly meets the eye between five and the teens: there are alternations of relative equilibrium and of transitional disequilibrium; there are rhythms of accent in introverted versus extroverted activity, in home versus school, in self versus group interests, in fine motor versus gross motor movements, in the to and fro shifts, in the delicate controls of eye movements. Only by identifying the developmental shifts in such counterbalanced traits can we arrive at a more accurate picture of what these somewhat inscrutable boys and girls are really like. Development does not advance on a straight line.

Whence come these developmental trends and fluctuations? They are not the product of the contemporary environment; they are primarily the expressions of the ancient processes of evolution. Man was not made in a day. It took vast ages to bring to their present form his capacities to walk, to talk, to manipulate with his hands, to contrive with his brain, and to see with such rich perception, and to foresee with far reaching imagination. In some condensed way the child must retraverse these immense ages. This too takes time. His organism must gather up and reweave the essential ancestral threads. In the vast complexities of his nervous system he matches the vastness of his ancestral past.

At the age of five he has already come a long way. He has surmounted a hilltop. He is no longer a mere baby. He is "a little fellow"! He is almost self-dependent in the elementary routines of life at home. He is ready for the simple community life of a schoolroom. In his emotional traits, in his general intelligence and adaptability he evinces a well organized, well rounded action-system. It is as though Nature had momentarily completed what she undertook to create. The 5-year-old at least presents a preliminary version of the ultimate adult. Perhaps he registers in a dim way what was once a plateau of full maturity in the remote racial past.

Five, therefore, is a nodal age. For a brief period the child remains in a phase of balanced adjustment to himself and to his environment. It is as though his problem of development had been solved. But the push of growth and the pressure of cultural demands build up new tensions. Sometimes these demands are excessive. It is as though the culture were bent on appropriating the child. He on his part is also bent on assimilating the culture; because, of course, he is destined to graduate from his five-year-oldishness.

It is not, however, easy to strike a smooth and steady balance between himself and his multifarious environment. At six years, he seems less integrated than he was at three years. He is more like the 2½-year-old child, who has not fully found either himself or his environment and is therefore in a fluctuating two-way equilibrium. The 6-year-old likewise is in a bipolar phase, trying at one and the same time to find himself and to find out his new environment. Choice and reconciliation between the two poles create tensions and hesitations. He is solving new problems of development. This is the key to understanding some of his difficulties and instabilities at the threshold of his formal education.

The 7-year-old has himself better in hand. He shows less lability, and a greater capacity to absorb and organize his new cultural experiences. He establishes more firm relationships with his companions and his teacher. He is decidedly more unipolar. He is better able to take what comes. There is less disequilibrium. This is, comparatively speaking, an absorptive and assimilative phase. Day by day he grows in mental stature.

By the age of eight, the budget of income and outgo shows new balances. The child has built up a firmer body of experience and is able to give as well as to take. He shows more initiative and spontaneity in going out to meet the environment. He can fraternize with his co-equals. At nine he is detaching himself still more from apron strings, and domestic tethers. With a mounting indifference to his elders when he is away from them he dwells in a culture of his own selection.

By the age of nine and ten this indifference reaches new heights. Boys and girls alike are amazingly self-dependent. Their self-reliance nas grown, and at the same time they have acquired intensified group feelings. Identification with the juvenile group promotes the complex process of detachment from the domestic family group. This is part of the method of maturing.

At the same time the divergence between the two sexes is widening. By the age of ten, the tendency toward segregation is well defined. Girls, somewhat earlier than boys enter upon the pre-pubertal period, marked by changes in body proportions, metabolism and endocrine secretions. These changes become yet more marked during adolescence, which is a prolonged period of diminishing immaturity. The child thus becomes a youth, the youth an adult.

For boys the stage of adolescence lasts about ten years, for girls a year or two less. Adolescence, therefore, is almost as long as infancy and childhood combined. From a cultural standpoint it is an extremely critical period; because it is that time of life when youth is progressively initiated into the responsibilities of citizenship and into the meaning of marriage. With marriage the first great sector of the cycle of development comes to full circle. For then a new home is founded. A new infant is born. A new generation starts on its life career, which again pursues the age old sequence of infancy, childhood, adolescence and parenthood.

We can scarcely expect the carefree child to contemplate the full sweep of this cycle of development. He is deeply immersed in the present. Parents and teachers must make up for his lack of foresight. Being adults they can better understand the scope and the trends of the cycle. They can have confidence in these trends; they can use knowledge and skill to direct the trends. In countless ways they can give infant, child and youth intimations of the future which is in store.

For all these reasons it is extremely important that teachers and parents should see the whole cycle of development in its imposing perspective. A developmental outlook upon the everyday problems of child behavior imparts meaning and dignity to these problems. It lessens their irritation. We cannot comprehend child life with a sense of proportion or of humor unless we see that life through the stereoscopic lenses of development.

When we put on those lenses we see things in their third dimension: the shortcomings, the strivings, and the immaturities of children take on new meaning. Each child's behavior is then appraised in terms of *his* development history, and *his* unique patterns of growth. External pressures will be modulated to *his* changing growth needs. He will be reared through guidance based on sympathetic understanding.

The purpose of this volume is to increase understanding. We begin with a panoramic view of the cycle of development. We see the broad sequences which are characteristic of the human species in general. Within these sequences are many variations of emphasis and patterning which lie at the basis of individuality.

There is also a pageant of the changes that come with the years. In later pages we shall characterize these changes in some detail. None of the changes are ushered in with dramatic abruptness, and there are numerous personal variations in tempo and in timing. But it will be profitable to delineate the changes, so that we may have a frame of reference which will bring the growth processes into focus.

This makes it necessary to adjust our own interpretive lenses from year to year; because the 6-year-old child *is* significantly distinguishable from the 7-year-old, and the 7-year-old in turn from the 8-year-old.

When we can define the trend of these year-by-year differences we can adapt our practices and our expectations to the nature and the needs of the individual child.

How else can we avoid the ever present dangers of authoritarianism in home and school? How else can we realize the spirit of democracy, which above all pays tribute to the dignity of the individual?

2

THE GROWING MIND

"I WISH to understand my child." This is the desire of every right-minded parent. "I wish to understand so far as possible the individuality of each of my pupils." That is the goal of the modern teacher. Such understanding requires some appreciation of *how the mind grows.* This book deals with the minds of growing children.

The mysterious relationships between mind and body (sometimes called psyche and soma) need not concern us. It is enough to know that the psychology of the child, which includes all of his behavior, is inseparably bound up with his nervous system, and indeed with his entire organism. We cannot separate "the mind," from the total child; and it would lead us far astray if we considered the psyche to be an occult force, which operates behind the scenes. The child is a unit.

The nervous system makes him so. It consists of multi-billions of neurons which connect with every sensitive and every moving part of the whole organism. Vegetative neurons pervade blood vessels, heart, lungs, gastro-intestinal tract, genito-urinary organs, the sphincters of rectum and bladder, the mucous, sweat, salivary and tear glands and the ductless glands of internal secretion. *Sensory* neurons supply countless end organs of skin, mucous membranes, joint surfaces, tendons, and a dozen highly specialized organs of sense, of which vision is the most intricately contrived. *Motor neurons* supply the extensive muscular system, which numbers some 600 paired muscles and many billions of contractile fibrils. *Associative neurons* register, coordinate, inhibit and organize the immense internal traffic of the entire system into patterns of memory, speech, imagery, symbolism and volition. Whether we think in terms of chemistry or of electronics we can envisage the human action-system as a vast network of wired and wireless arrangements which make the infant a prodigious creator and the child a marvelous walkie-talkie.

The growing mind is part and parcel of this vast network of living tissue. The mind grows because the tissue grows. Neurons have prodigious powers of growth. They multiply at a rapid rate in the embryonic period and fetal period when the foundations of behavior are laid. The 5-month-old fetus is already in possession of the full quota of twelve or more billions of nerve cells which make up the nervous system. These cells continue to grow and organize throughout the cycle of development.

One may think of the child's mind as a marvelous fabric of some kind,—a growing fabric. Physically its structure is represented by a great maze of nerves and nerve tracts, and a microscopic feltwork of branching fibers and exquisite fibrils. Functionally the mind consists of propensities and patterns of behavior. We cannot see the underlying feltwork; but we *can* see the outward behavior patterns. These patterns have so much design and are so lawfully related to each other, that the mind is indeed comparable to a fabric which is richly woven and interwoven,—an organic fabric which continues to *grow*, creating new patterns while it grows.

Parents and teachers who think that a child is so plastic that he can be made over by strenuous outside pressure, have failed to grasp the true nature of the mind. The mind may be likened to a plant, but not to clay. For clay does not grow. Clay is moulded entirely from without. A plant is primarily moulded from within through the forces of growth. The present volume will stress these forces.

Intelligent guidance begins with the concept of growth. To understand a child whether in infancy or in the school years, one must become acquainted with the gradients of growth which determine the trends and patterning of his behavior.

What is a growth gradient? It is a series of stages or degrees of maturity by which a child progresses toward a higher level of behavior. A few concrete illustrations will show how growth gradients operate in the first year of life, in the pre-school years, and also in the years from five to ten.

For example, during the first year of life a baby acquires the ability to pick up objects. This is a very important part of his behavior equipment. It takes a long time to mature the muscle and neuron connections necessary for prompt and precise prehension. We can test these growing powers of *Prehension* by placing a little red cube before a baby. At first he can "pick up" the cube only with his eyes, but not with his hands. Reduced to simplest terms this growth gradient runs as follows:

PREHENSORY BEHAVIOR

1) *12 weeks* Looks at cube.
2) *20 weeks* Looks and approaches.
3) *24 weeks* Looks and crudely grasps with whole hand.
4) *36 weeks* Looks and deftly grasps with fingers.
5) *52 weeks* Looks, grasps with forefinger and thumb and deftly releases.
6) *15 months* Looks, grasps, and releases to build a tower of two cubes.

This simple gradient exemplifies the basic mechanism of all psychological development,—not only the mental growth of the infant but also that of the school child. Let us, therefore, examine a little more closely how the patterns in this particular growth fabric are built up. Recalling that the mind grows not unlike a plant, we have drawn a tree-like diagram to show how the patterns of prehensory behavior elaborate and differentiate by branchings and sub-branchings. Each new pattern grows out of the old and yet retains a connection with the old. The final pattern of tower building is a condensed culmination of all the growth that went before. The gradient begins with the comparatively simple pattern of looking. With increasing maturity one refinement follows another in lawful sequence: 1. Ocular focus 2. Arm approach 3. Manual grasp 4. Finger grasp 5. Release 6. Tower. At 15 months the infant unreels this sequence in a flash, but this skillful flash of behavior is the patterned end-product of a whole year of constructive growth.

All school skills have a similar pre-history of growth. They are always subject to the principle of developmental readiness. They are never the sole product of training or drill. For example consider another simple six step gradient in the field of *Reading Behavior.* The 15-month-old child who has just attained the sensori-motor skill of building a tower is also at the lower threshold of reading. He can already help to turn the pages of a picture book. He can definitely identify the circular hole in a circle-triangle-square form board. Surely this is the growth rudiment of the capacity to recognize the round letter O, which is the beginning of all reading! Moreover he can read some of the pictures of a book

A symbolic diagram of the growth processes which underlie the patterning of behavior.
Six stages in the development of prehensory behavior are pictured: **1.** At 12 weeks the infant
merely *looks* at the cube; **2.** at 20 weeks he *approaches* it with a bent arm; **3.** at 24 weeks he
grasps it with a palmar squeeze; **4.** at 36 weeks he *grasps* with his fingertips; **5.** at 52 weeks with
forefinger and *thumb opposition*; **6.** at 15 months he both *grasps* and *releases* adaptively;
placing one cube upon another. He builds the tower in a twinkle. The twinkle is based on 15
months of post-natal growth time.

These reactions are made possible by patterned connections between countless neurons and
muscle fibers. The connections are symbolically represented by the outgrowths of variegated
neurons in brain and spinal cord. Neurons sprout and grow not unlike plants and trees. They
put forth branches, sub-branches, end-tufts and terminal aborizations. Threadlike fibrils extend
from fingertips to cord and to cortex. A million nerve fibers unite the eye to the vastly complex
jungle of neurons in the cortex. This living, patterned and patterning tissue affords an inti-
mation of *how the mind grows.*

to this extent: He pats a picture which he recognizes. Our illustrative growth gradient begins with that pattern of behavior,—an elementary perception of a picture on the printed page.

READING BEHAVIOR

1) *15 months* Pats identified picture in book.
2) *18 months* Points to an identified picture in book.
3) *2 years* Names 3 pictures in book.
4) *3 years* Identifies 4 printed geometric forms.
5) *4 years* Recognizes salient capital letters.
6) *5-6 years* Recognizes salient printed words.

The ages assigned to the stages in the foregoing gradient represent average, normative trends. All gradients are subject to individual variations, with respect to age values, but the sequence of a gradient tends to remain the same for all children in spite of such variations. As we shall demonstrate later in this volume growth gradients have a double usefulness: a) they define the developmental traits characteristic of childhood in general; b) they enable us to determine in an individual child the attained levels of maturity for these traits. In this way we become acquainted both with the individual and with the group to which he belongs.

As a child grows older his patterns of behavior become more complex, and they seem to embody to an increasing degree the impress of cultural influences. The mechanisms of development, however, do not change; and the child remains true to his own unique patterns of growth and of adaptation. We may illustrate this with still another six step gradient which outlines certain progressions in the field of *Acquisitive Behavior*. Under this term we include patterns and propensities which concern the appropriation and ownership of things, and the collection of possessions.

This acquisitiveness gradient no doubt ought to begin with prehensory behavior, because the infant is a very grasping creature! He seizes and holds objects with intense avidity. Often he resists removal of an object which he has acquired; but his possessive relation to the object is so fleeting that we scarcely think of him as an owner of his toys! They simply "belong" to him. He does not have a strong sense of personal ownership. In the 5-year-old child, however, we see a personal pride in *his* belongings, which bespeaks an altogether higher form of acquisitive behavior. The growth gradient for the next five or ten years runs somewhat as follows:

ACQUISITIVE BEHAVIOR

1) *5 years*   Takes pride in certain personal possessions
(e.g. hat or a drawing of his own).

2) *6 years*   Collects odds and ends rather sporadically
(e.g. Christmas cards).

3) *7 years*   Collects with purpose and specific, sustained interest
(e.g. postal cards).

4) *8 years*   Collects with zeal and strong interest in size of collection
(e.g. comics, paper dolls).

5) *10 years* Collects more formally with specialized, intellectual interests
(e.g. stamps).

6) *15 years* Saves money with discriminating thrift and interest in money
values.

Analysis of the foregoing gradient will show that the cultural determinations are not as powerful as they appear to be on the surface. To be sure hats, postal cards, comics, stamps and moneys are cultural goods. But the value which the child instinctively places on these goods, how he collects and cherishes them, how he disposes of them,—all this depends upon his developmental (and temperamental) characteristics. A similar relationship between maturation (biological) and acculturation (environmental) will prove to hold in all fields of behavior. The primary growth gradients hold the key to the wisest methods of guidance and education.

In PART THREE of this volume we shall assemble numerous gradients, covering a wide diversity of behavior areas. The developmental patterning of personality, as well as the growth of school abilities and of

A Locomotor Gradient

A. Lifts head   X

B. Swims   X

C. Pivots   ↻

D. Crawls backward   ⟶

E. Kneels   X

F. Creeps backward   ⟶

G. Rocks   ←X→

H. Creep - Crawls   ⟵

I. Creeps   ⟵

J.-K. Gets on feet   ⟵

school interests will be included. It is hoped that a study of these varied gradients will impart substance to the reader's envisagement of the child's mind. The nature of that mind eludes us unless we manage to think of the psyche as a growing, organic action-system, patterned in all its arrangements, both latent and manifest. Profound laws govern the forms and the sequences of those patterns. The significance of any child behavior must be adjudged in terms of its form and of its position in a sequential gradient.

The growth gradients are frames of reference which can be used to locate the stage of maturity which a child has reached in a given field of behavior. The gradients are not applied to ascertain a mental age, or to measure the child in an arbitrary way. The purpose is rather to find his approximate position in various sequences of development. That enables us to estimate the developmental ground he has already gained and the ground which lies just ahead. Educational and guidance measures can then be adapted to the maturity of the child. Failure to interpret his maturity status leads to waste effort, to harmful interference and unjust discipline.

Sometimes, of course, the child's behavior is so unexpected and so contradictory that it is very difficult to understand. He may even seem to go backward when the growth gradients demand that he should go forward. In such a situation, whether it arises at home or at school, it is especially important to interpret the problem in terms of development. It must be remembered that the mind does not grow on a straight and even front. The course of development is uneven (in some children more so than others). It zigzags, and sometimes it spirals backward in a way which suggests retreat and regression. But if the child is normal, the ultimate and all-over trend is toward a higher level of maturity. Development is like a stream; it carves the best possible channel; it flows onward; it reaches a goal.

A child may be making good progress even when his development seems to be taking a devious course. This is transparently shown by the manner in which a baby learns to creep. Careful observation has disclosed that a baby goes through some twenty stages or sub-stages in achieving this locomotor ability. Ten of these stages are pictured in the accompanying pictographic gradient. The developmental goal is forward locomotion, prone progression on all fours. But note how often the behavior at a given stage seems to disappoint the goal and even goes contrary to it. Yet in due season the child scoots across the floor on hands and knees, then on hands and feet, and yet later on feet alone.

The following stages are depicted in the diagram (over a dozen intervening stages are omitted):

Stage	Behavior Pattern	Progression	Code
A	*Lifts head—legs passive*	None	x
B	*Swims* (head rears, legs extend)	None	x
C	*Pivots* (arms alternately flex and extend)	Circles	x
D	*Crawls backward* (arms push)	Backward	→
E	*Kneels creepwise* (lifts trunk)	None	x
F	*Creeps backward* (lowers trunk)	Backward	→
G	*Rocks* (in high creep position)	Oscillates	⇆
H	*Creep-crawls* (pitches forward)	Forward	←
I	*Creeps* (on hands and knees)	Forward	←
J	*Creeps plantigrade* (on hands and feet)	Forward	←

From the foregoing sequence, which is virtually universal for the human species, it is clear that Nature does not always go directly to her goal. She takes a round about path, and sometimes she seems to be poised midway as though she did not know where to go! At stage G the child is all set to go places, but instead he rocks back and forth, oscillating between two alternatives. At stage C he spun around in a circle; at stages D and F he actually went backward; at other stages he remained completely on location. And yet when we view the entire gradient in perspective we know that he was making *developmental headway* all the time, even when he was pushing himself backward. Nature has a devious cunning which is beyond our logic.

The child is so closely in league with Nature that we must respect his innate gradations of growth. Who would think of punishing an infant because he propelled himself backward instead of forward, or because he vacillated between forward and backward; or because he combined crawling and creeping patterns instead of adopting the "proper" method of locomotion?! In the naive immaturities of his prone behavior, we see that Nature herself needs time to refashion in the individual a complex type of behavior, which required aeons of evolution in the race.

The patterning of prone behavior supplies an instructive example of the mechanisms which govern child development at all ages. The baby betrays his immaturities as he solves the problems of locomotion. When he becomes a school-beginner he will be confronted by other problems, but he will exhibit comparable immaturities. In his writing he will go in wrong directions, he will produce astonishing reversals, and at times he will seem to make no progress at all. But ultimately he achieves the necessary coordinations of posture, eyes and hands to enable him to write straightforward. His rate of progress will always depend primarily upon the maturity of his nervous system. It is doubtful whether he should be "disciplined" for his motor shortcomings. And in interpreting his "failures" in writing, reading and arithmetic, it is well to recall the tortuous gradations by which the baby "learns" to creep.

From this preliminary discussion it is clear that the significance of a child's behavior depends upon the position of that behavior in a developmental sequence. In any given situation we ask: What growth preceded? What growth is likely to follow? In the management of children, we do not so much need rules of thumb; we need orientation. Growth gradients will give us bearings in the latitude of maturity levels and in the longitude of age.

As a child advances in age, he not only gains in height and weight, but his body proportions, and even his body chemistries undergo change. Most importantly of all, his behavior equipment changes. The changes are gradual; so gradual, indeed, that they often escape notice. They come as softly as a thief in the night.

For this very reason it is advantageous to demarcate the changes in a way which will make them evident. This we have attempted to do in PART TWO. For each year from five to ten, we have drawn up a type portrait which delineates the distinctive behavior characteristics of that age. It is not assumed that this portrait will snugly fit any one child; but it will suggest the traits by which he may be appraised. A series of such annual portraits will also define the concrete trends toward maturity. Just as the eye needs two overlapping images in order to see depth, so we need two adjacent maturity levels to secure a stereoscopic view of the child's development.

These year by year behavior profiles provide the basic points of departure for the growth gradients assembled and partly codified in PART THREE. The profiles outline a total behavior picture. The gradients may be used analytically, singly and in various combinations. They are designed to serve as *interpretational devices*. Properly applied they will help the adult to appraise the problems of growth with which every child is faced. The child can scarcely formulate his problems for us. We must watch his behavior and use it as a clue to understanding. If he reverses his digits he may well be in the equivalent of a backward-crawl stage in locomotion.

A growth gradient may tell us where he has arrived and whither he is trending. By applying several gradients to their several fields of behavior, we get a better view of his total maturity status. We may even get an indication of his strongest assets,—and his characteristic liabilities if he has any. We do not necessarily expect him to be equally advanced in all behavior fields. We know that there are many entirely normal variations in the chronological age at which school abilities are attained. We know that every child has a unique pattern of growth. And just because basic development proceeds in sequences which are nearly universal, the growth gradients help us to discover and to describe that unique pattern.

The child is his own best norm. He is never so much like himself as when he is changing, because his growth characteristics are the truest index to his individuality.

Growth gradients also tell us something about the psychological differences between boys and girls. Girls are more advanced and more generalized in some types of behavior. Boys are more intense and more channelized; for example, in certain aspects of acquisitive behavior. Some of these differences are subtle, but they are significant and they should influence our attitudes as parents and educators.

Growth gradients deal with relativities rather than absolutes. Nothing can be more misleading than an absolute, particularly in the management of children. Absolutism leads to authoritarianism and this in turn leads to blindness,—a blindness toward the developmental status and to the developmental needs of the child. From an absolute standpoint "stealing" is always *stealing,* but even a crude use of a simple gradient of acquisitive behavior will indicate that there is a difference between the "pilfering" of a 7-year-old and a specific "theft" of a 10-year-old.

Growth gradients therefore, make possible a developmental outlook upon the frailties of human efficiency and of childhood conduct. Far from encouraging a policy of indulgence, a developmental philosophy re-enforced by concrete growth gradients will make us more alert to the developmental needs of children. Such a philosophy has far reaching implications for the harmony of relationships between parent, teacher and child.

3

THE PARENT-CHILD-TEACHER RELATIONSHIP

WHEN a baby is born he is still almost completely merged with the cosmos. Which is to say that he has no sense of self-identity, no sense which distinguishes between the *World of Things* and the *World of Persons*. As he matures he gradually makes distinctions. He learns to discriminate between what is animate and inanimate. Slowly he discovers his physical self. He becomes dimly aware of his personal self. He discovers his parents. He differentiates friends from strangers, children from adults, aggressors from benefactors. He finds that he is a personal agency who acts and is acted upon.

He does not say all this in words, but he builds interpersonal attitudes into his growing personality, chiefly through his experiences with other persons. Indeed his personality is the end-product of all the interpersonal relationships in which he becomes involved. When this intricate web of relationships is wholesome, his personality tends to be wholesome. Needless to say the basic organization of personality takes place in the first five years of life.

The parent-child relationships of family life, therefore, are of determining importance in the early patterning of personality. A well ordered home which provides normal parental care is the best guarantee of mental health in the growing child. The school naturally can accomplish maximum results only when it works in harmony with such a home. But this should be a two-way harmony, with the child more than an innocent bystander. In fact the child from five to ten is at the apex of a triangle of interpersonal forces. Life apparently would be easier for him if he had to adjust only to his parents or only to his teachers. But he has to adjust to both sets of adults. Sometimes the task is doubly difficult when the home and the school adults fail to see eye to eye. The adjoining diagram with its two-way arrows shows the triangular field in which all these interpersonal forces function.

Perhaps the best way to understand the meaning and mechanism of the teacher-pupil relationship is to compare it with its prototype, namely the relationship between parent and child. What are the similarities? What are the differences?

(1) The parent-child relationship is based on heredity, or kinship. The teacher-child relationship is based upon authority conferred by the State. This authority is very august. From an educational standpoint it confers upon the teacher a certain advantage, because it puts him or her in a position to regard the problems of child development in a realistic manner.

(2) The size of the teacher's "family" is large. This, of course, confers a fundamental advantage upon the parent-child relationship. But when we recall that only a portion of the parent's time can be directly devoted

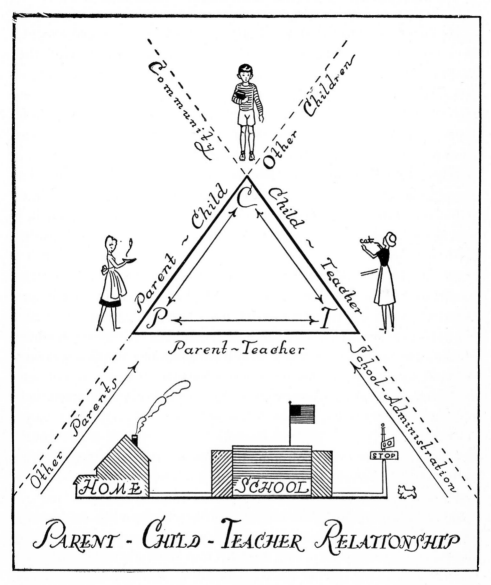

Parent - Child - Teacher Relationship

A diagrammatic representation of the interacting relationships of Parent (P), Child (C), and Teacher (T). The position of the child is focal. His welfare is affected not only by his relations with parent and with teacher, but also by the mutual relationships of teacher and parent. The outlook of parents and teachers is in turn influenced by the community, which in its turn determines the standards and policy of school officials. The professional status and practices of the teachers are greatly influenced by the character of the school administration.

to the task of rearing children, we see that the advantages are not all in favor of the home. The teacher, moreover, has the tremendous psychological reinforcement which comes from the impact of the school group upon the individual child. She can use the group to influence the child.

(3) The intimacy and restricted size of the home give the natural parents a maximum opportunity to become acquainted with the characteristics of their children. But here again the teacher is not at a complete disadvantage if she has been professionally trained to perceive individual differences. Moreover, the teacher observes the child as a member of a social group. This brings to light characteristics which the home cannot reveal.

(4) During the early school years the emotional bonds between parent and child are more intense than those between teacher and child. A wise teacher respects this difference and does not try to function as a substitute mother. She has an enlightened Platonic affection which she metes out to assist the developmental needs of her pupils, apportioning more to some than others. Hers is a wholesome, human friendliness. Unfortunate the child who attends a schoolroom where the very atmosphere is so unhomelike and so domineering that his sense of security is weakened.

The authoritarian schoolroom, like the authoritarian home of an earlier day has become inconsistent with the spirit of democracy. Since the second Great War we realize that the sources of the democratic spirit are to be found in the homes and the schools of the people,—in the interpersonal way of life which prevails in the parent-child and teacher-child relationships. Do not children need discipline? Yes, but discipline being a mode of government can be either autocratic or democratic in method. It can defy the laws of development. It can humanely defer to them.

If then we analyze the psychology of enlightened parent-child and teacher-pupil relationships we find three common components, namely: 1) Considerateness, 2) A sense of humor, and 3) A philosophy of growth.

1) *Considerateness.* Considerateness is the first essential. The very word considerateness conveys the idea of respect for the dignity of the individual. Considerateness, it has been well said, is in itself a social system. It certainly favors the development of democratic attitudes.

If parents (and teachers) begin with the assumption that they can make over and mould a child into a preconceived pattern, they are bound to become somewhat autocratic. If, on the contrary, parents begin with the assumption that every baby comes into the world with a unique individuality, they are bound to become more considerate. For their task will be to understand the child's individuality and to give it the best possible chance to grow and find itself. The same holds true for teachers.

Considerateness, as we use the term here, is not merely a social or domestic grace. It is something of an art, a kind of perceptiveness and imaginativeness, which enables one person to understand the attitudes of another person. It is an alert kind of liberalism which acknowledges distinctive characteristics in other individuals. It is an active form of courtesy.

2) *A sense of humor.* Fascist government is not distinguished for a sense of humor. It is so distinguished for lack thereof that we may well believe that a sense of humor has some significance for democracies.

The sense of humor is a pliant sense of proportion. Its function is to keep the individual from becoming mechanized and hardened. It is a play of the mind akin to the spirit of freedom. When a teacher has it she protects her own mental health and that of her pupils. Humor is a safeguard against undue tensions and the severities of unwise discipline. An over serious schoolroom violates for children the Jeffersonian right of pursuit of happiness.

3) *A philosophy of growth.* The child's personality is a product of slow and gradual growth. His nervous system matures by stages and natural sequences. He sits before he stands; he babbles before he talks; he says "no" before he says "yes"; he fabricates before he tells the truth; he draws a circle before he draws a square; he is selfish before he is

altruistic; he is dependent on others before he achieves dependence on self. All his abilities, including his morals, are subject to laws of growth. The task of child care is not to mould the child behavioristically to some pre-determined image, but to assist him step by step, guiding his growth.

This developmental philosophy does not mean indulgence. It is instead a constructive accommodation to the limitations of immaturity. Lacking such a philosophy, a teacher may use harsh methods of discipline, and false methods of instruction, designed to subdue her pupils and to bring them to a uniform level. Lacking such a philosophy, a parent may unjustly accuse the teacher for not keeping her child up to standards of achievement and of conduct.

Sometimes teacher and parent alike fail to understand that the child's behavior problems arise from conflicting attitudes which he has acquired toward the adults of the home and of the school. Needless to say, parents should avoid careless or confusing remarks about the child's teacher, and should do everything possible to support her legitimate status. There cannot be mutual understanding without a unity of goal and policy in the conduct of a school, whether it be a private or a public school.

The public school system in America has become an indispensable instrument for the perpetuation of our democracy. As early as 1935 the Educational Policies Commission (created by the National Education Association and the American Association of School Administrators) reached three fundamental conclusions:

1) The democratic way of life is being challenged at home and abroad.
2) The public schools are the foundation of democracy, and its first line of defense.
3) The most urgent and intensely practical problem facing the teaching profession is the achievement and maintenance of democracy through education.

Parent-teacher associations have accomplished an important pioneering work in bringing home and school into closer union. These associations still have a necessary service to perform. But they have depended too much on group meetings, exhibit days, formal programs and mass appeal to reach the desired ends. The public school system in the post-war era will be under new pressures to bring the education of parents and of their children into more intimate interrelation. This will require personalized individual conferences between teacher and parent. The conferences should not be merely on an incidental or emergency basis. They can be made a systematic feature of the total educational program, by relaxing the excessive emphasis on constant pupil attendance. In rural, village and city schools alike it is possible to modify the regular yearly schedule sufficiently to make room for interviews and consultations.

Such individualized arrangements would tend to humanize school practice and counteract the tendencies toward regimentation which are so inconsistent with a democratic culture. Our schools need this type of "interruption." They are becoming too compartmented into homogenous groupings, too stratified. There should be more mingling of young children and older children; more contacts between pre-parents of the secondary grades and the boys and girls in the primary grades, as well as more flexible interchanges between parents and teachers. The public school system has been called one of our most authoritarian institutions. If this is true, the condition can be corrected only by relaxing the rigidity of prevailing school administration, and by breaking down the barriers to freer human relationships.

These are the broad considerations which make the improvement of the parent-child-teacher relationship so vital to our culture. It is a three-way relationship. The child with his double bonds is an intermediate link, creating a third bond of responsibility between teachers and parents. The responsibility cannot become mutual without a common outlook upon the developmental welfare of the child. This requires more than academic achievement tests, intelligence scores and graded report cards. Home and school alike must lay less stress on competition and be more genuinely concerned with the nature and the needs of the child's personality.

The present volume undertakes to outline personality characteristics in terms of developmental maturity and of environmental culture. The emphasis is not on academic progress, but upon the fundamental behavior equipment of the child,—his motor skills and demeanors, his emotional life, his concepts of right and wrong, his social adjustments, his sense of self, his sex attitudes, his plays and games, his spontaneous activities, his school interests and his orientation to the world of Nature and the expanding world of human society.

These are the true fundamentals of civilized life. And these fundamentals alone can draw teacher, parent and child into vital interaction. We hear much about indoctrination of the ideals of democracy. Indoctrination has an important role. But even more basic is the application of these ideals as a way of life in the everyday relationship of parent, teacher and child.

A SPECIAL WORD TO FATHERS

A new era is opening for fathers. The status of children is changing; and the role of father in the home is coordinately changing. Not long ago he was truly a monarch. His word was law, and the law was stern. He held himself apart from the plain everyday affairs of his children, reserving his powers for higher occasions of discipline and admonition. He did not unbend. Even during the long prenatal period he maintained a befitting detachment.

All this is now changing under the irrepressible tide of cultural forces. Fathers are actively sharing in the numerous everyday tasks that go with the rearing of children. Participation rather than detachment is the trend. The careful mutual planning which now characterizes pregnancy and maternity hygiene marks a new advance in our ways of living. With the aid of the famous Broadway success *Life with Father* we wave a gay goodbye to the paterfamilias of the good old days.

The modern father is now in the process of finding his new role. He has already discovered that he is not satisfied by emergency help with night feeding and laundry, nor by sketchy contacts with his children at evenings or on Saturday afternoon. He is somewhat amazed to find

that at times his child does not respond to his well meaning and affectionate approaches. He finds that at some ages the child seems to be
better than at others. Perhaps he especially enjoyed the 3-year-old
or the 5-year-old period, and was simply dumbfounded by the 6-year-old
behavior. Some fathers do not get on a comfortable companionable
basis until a son reaches nine or ten years of age, when they arrive at a
man-to-man rapport.

Some ages are indeed smoother and pleasanter than others, but all are
equally interesting and significant. The father-child relationship will
not be on a fully enlightened level until both parents make a joint
effort to understand the ever changing characteristics of the child at
each advancing stage of maturity. This demands a developmental outlook upon all the problems of child care and child management. It
demands an increasingly penetrating acquaintance with the *mechanisms
of growth*.

We live in a technological age, and need not be frightened by the
concept of mechanisms. Fathers in particular know something about the
precision and beauty of engines and machines. They readily think in
terms of atomic structures, electronic orbits, short and long waves and
frequency modulation. They would like to know what makes the child
tick. It degrades neither child nor father to bring mechanical concepts
to bear upon the manifold wonders of the child's behavior and his individual development. These concepts do not solve the mystery of life;
but they do strengthen our faith in the lawfulness of life and growth.

They help us to understand why the pathways of child development
are so tortuous and yet so patterned and so ballasted by an overall trend
toward optimal realization. This kind of insight leads to a deeper understanding of individual differences. It makes for philosophic tolerance,
and a more vital appreciation of the meaning of infancy and childhood.

We respectfully invite fathers who may read this volume to regard
it as an introductory manual in psychotechnology! A technology which
deals with the mechanism of child development and thereby with the
improvement of parent-child relationships.

PART TWO

Growth of Man like growth of Nature
Gravitates within,
Atmosphere and sun confirm it
But it stirs alone.

—EMILY DICKINSON

4

THE FIRST FOUR YEARS

THE cycle of human development is continuous. All growth is based on previous growth. The growth process therefore is a paradoxical mixture of creation and of perpetuation. The child is always becoming something new; yet he always summates the essence of his past. His psychology at the age of five is the "outgrowth" of all that happened to him during the four years after birth,—and the forty weeks prior to birth. For all the past was prelude.

§1. THE NEWBORN INFANT

Birth marks the arrival but not the beginning of an individual. The true beginnings trace back to the embryonic and fetal periods when the tissues and organs of the body take form and when even the shape of the behavior to come is profoundly foreshadowed. Types of body build are prefigured: square and firm; round and soft; spindly and delicate. Modes of reaction characteristic of varieties of physique are likewise laid down.

The patterning of behavior gets under way remarkably early. By four weeks after conception the heart beats; by eight weeks, head and trunk make minimal movements; by twelve weeks, the hands flex; by twenty-four weeks the chest is capable of rhythmic movements; by twenty-eight to forty weeks all physiological functions may be sufficiently mature to insure survival in the event of birth.

Once the infant is born he must struggle for his very existence. With the assistance of Nature and caretakers, he must bring his various physiological functions such as respiration, temperature regulation, digestion, excretion, sleeping and waking into adequate coordination. While making these early life adjustments he appears unsteady, unstable. His thresholds of reaction are low and inconstant. He startles, sneezes, quivers, cries on slight provocation. His breathing and body temperature are irregular. He may even swallow in the wrong direction! Normally, he weathers the storms of adaptation and settles down to relative stability in a few weeks. But so exacting are these early transitions that we may say a baby is really not full-born until he is four weeks of age.

No sharp line can be drawn between "physiological" and "psychological" functions. A baby's satisfactions, needs, interests and drives are determined by the status of his entire organism, including his metabolism, the chemistry of his body fluids, and the tonus of his muscular system. Throughout infancy much of his behavior is directly related to the complex functions of feeding, sleeping and elimination. The acquisition of speech even involves a recombination of feeding and breathing behavior patterns,—a recombining which it took the race literally millions of years to perfect. The "lower" vegetative functions are thus incorporated into the growing action-system. They color emotional patterns and temperamental trends. The autonomic nervous system which presides over these functions operates in close conjunction with the cerebro-spinal nervous system which governs sensation and motion. The new born baby is already in possession of the basic equipment for feeling, sensing and moving. His mental growth is well under way.

In the next four years he will make prodigious progress. Never again will he advance with the same speed. He is laying the wide base of a pyramid which continues to ascend in the years from five to ten. During the first half of this first decade he is preeminently a home child. During the second half he is both a home and a school child. In rapid succession he progresses from bassinet to crib, to high chair, to play pen; to porch, sidewalk, nursery and schoolroom; to first, second, third, fourth and fifth grades. In a growth sense it is a long, as well as a swift journey.

The present chapter will briefly characterize the developmental ground covered during the first four years with milestones at 4, 16, 28, and 40 weeks; 12, 15 and 18 months; and 2, 2½, 3 and 4 years.* The child does not linger at any of these milestones; so we shall emphasize the unremitting sweep which bears him on his forward course. But with the aid of ten stop-motion sketches we can get an impression of his transforming behavior make-up as he travels toward his consecutive destinations.

§2. 4 WEEKS OLD

The month old baby is no longer a mere neophyte in the elementary art of living. He breathes with regularity, his heart has steadied its pace, his body temperature has ceased to be erratic. His muscle tone is less fluctuant than it was in the days of long ago when he was only a newborn. He has reserves of muscle tonus. He taps the reserves and responds with motor tightening when you pick him up. This makes him feel less molluscous and more compact. By virtue of his heightened

* For a detailed account of these stages of development the reader may be referred to the companion volume: "Infant and Child in the Culture of Today" (Gesell and Ilg. Harpers, 1943).

muscle tonus he is already more competent to meet the buffetings of fate.

His reactions since birth have become more configured. He sleeps more definitely, wakes more decisively. He opens his eyes widely and does not lapse so much into shallow, ambiguous drowsing. When awake he usually lies with head averted to a preferred side. Often he extends the arm on that side, crooking the other arm at shoulder level in a sort of fencing attitude. He holds and activates this tonic-neck-reflex posture from time to time as though it were a developmental exercise, as indeed it is. Nature is laying a foundation for a coordination of eyes and hands.

In a few more weeks the baby will begin to look in the direction of the extended arm and catch sight of his hand. Even now he will see and briefly follow a moving object dangled near his eyes. But his hands remain fisted. He is not yet ready for reaching.

He gives attention only in so far as his behavior capacities permit. This will always be true of him even after he reaches school age. Just now he manifestly attends to the sensations of gastric well-being which suffuse him after a meal; and to the massive warmth of a bath. Sometimes he immobilizes with interest as he regards the face of his mother. His emotional patterns are very simple, if we may judge by the general impassiveness of his physiognomy. Nevertheless he reacts positively to comforts and satisfactions; negatively to pain and denials. He cries. He listens. Occasionally small throaty sounds emerge from his larynx.

In all these behavior tokens we see the germs of language, of sociality, perception, intelligence, body posture and even locomotion. The neuro-motor system is organizing apace. The mind is growing.

§3. 16 WEEKS OLD

By 16 weeks the neuro-motor system has so elaborated that the child is no longer always content to lie on his back. He likes to be held for brief periods in a seated position, so that he may face the world eyes front. So held he can erect his head. This is the first component of the upright posture which in another year will enable him to walk alone. Command of head and eyes comes before command of feet.

The 16-week-old infant has gained considerable control over the six pairs of search-light muscles which move his eyes in their sockets. The eyes focus upon his own hand; they shift their focus to an object near by; they pursue a dangled toy moving through an arc of 180 degrees. Eyes are becoming nimble.

There is something prophetic in the way in which the 16-week-old infant relishes the sitting position. His eyes glisten; his pulse strengthens, his breathing quickens and he smiles as he is translated from horizontal to perpendicular. This is more than an athletic triumph. It is a widening of the visual horizon; it is a social reorientation.

Social behavior both personal and interpersonal has greatly expanded. He coos with personal contentment; he chuckles; he laughs aloud. He used to smile only on gastric occasions. Now he imitates a social smile. He also smiles responsively and vocalizes on social approach.

His hands are no longer predominantly fisted. They are uncurling; and soon they will be able to reach out. But at present the baby reaches with his eyes. He inspects, he looks expectantly; he even singles out small details in his visible environment. He associates sight and sound. He "notices" when he hears and sees his food prepared. He reacts to cues and clues. This always remains the essence of wisdom.

The 16-week-old child is usually well adjusted both to the world of things and to the world of persons. This is partly because he derives such great satisfaction from the free use of his eyes. He frets when his visual hunger goes unappeased. He quiets when ocular and social stimuli combine to feed his appetite for visual experience. But new demands are in the making. Soon he must satisfy the eagerness of his hands as well as that of his eyes.

§4. 28 WEEKS OLD

Touch hunger follows visual hunger. Or, rather, the two now combine; for the 28-week-old baby is bent on manipulating everything that he can lay his eyes and hands on. Whether he lies on his back or sits in his high chair he must have something to handle and to mouth. He likes to sit up, for he is gaining control of his trunk muscles,—another step toward the attainment of upright posture.

Note with what concentrated attention he exercises his growing powers. He sees a clothespin on his play tray. He grasps it in an instant, brings it to his lips and tongue for tactile impressions, bangs it on the tray for sound and motion, transfers it from hand to hand and back again for manipulatory experience, inspects it with a twist for visual perception. Such avid attention is born out of growth needs. The baby's play is work and his work is play.

So engrossing is his self-activity that he can amuse himself for long periods. But he can smile at onlookers and he is usually friendly both with familiars and strangers. Indeed he presents an amiable union of self-containedness and sociality. He alternates with ease between self-directed and socially referred activity. He listens to words spoken by others; he listens also to his own private vocalizations.

At this age the child's abilities are in good balance. His behavior patterns and trends are in focus. He is so harmoniously constituted, that he causes few perplexities on the part of his caretakers. It is a period of short lived developmental "equilibrium." There will be similar periods in his later growth career; but they likewise will be transient. The growth complex never fully stabilizes. New thrusts, new tensions of development produce imbalances which are in turn resolved and replaced by another temporary stage of comparative equilibrium.

The 28-week-old baby has numerous new problems of posture, locomotion, manipulation and personal-social behavior to meet before he reaches the age of 40 weeks. The course of true development can not always run smooth.

§5. 40 WEEKS OLD

Horizons widen with each advance in motor maturity. The 40-week-old infant can creep, and this greatly expands the scope of his initiative and of his experiences. But, significantly enough, he tends to keep head erect and eyes front while he creeps. He shows a special interest in vertical surfaces, by which he pulls himself to his feet; for the upright posture is his developmental goal. He is nearing this goal in gross motor control; he can sit quite alone and he can stand with support.

Fine motor control, also is advancing. Place a string on a table: he grasps it with prompt, precise pincer prehension. At 28 weeks he slapped the string with his flat palm. If he is more discriminating now it is because uncountable millions of delicate connections have silently organized in his network of neural and muscular fibrils. Nature is perfecting particularly the acuteness of his sensitive finger tips. He is under an irrepressible propensity to poke and pry and palpate with his extended index finger.

This is another method for widening the psychological horizon. By his inquisitive poking he probes into the third dimension of depth. He discovers the physical secret of container and contained. Place a cube in a cup: he thrusts his hand in and fingers the cube. His perceptual world is not as flat as it used to be.

He is also penetrating more deeply into his social environment. He discriminates more sharply between familiars and strangers. He imitates gestures, facial expressions and sounds. He heeds "No! No!" He echoes "Da, Da." He probably has learned a nursery trick. But if he now pat-a-cakes to everyone's delight, it is due not so much to the teaching of his elders, as to his own developmental readiness. At 28 weeks it was quite impossible to teach him this nursery game.

§6. 12 MONTHS OLD

Since the baby was born the earth has completed one full revolution around the sun,—chronological age: one year. The baby can now place

[49]

a cube into a cup and release it,—developmental age value: one year. A baby is as old as his behavior. From the standpoint of guidance and education he must be appraised in terms of the maturity level of his abilities. When a year old he can usually cruise around his pen by himself, but in walking he needs the guiding help of a supporting hand.

Gross motor skills show more individual variation than fine motor and adaptive behavior. Again place a string on a table. He plucks it with deft thumb and forefinger opposition and he dangles the object tied at the end of the string. He thus gives evidence of increasing perceptiveness of relations. He puts one and one together. He holds one cube and contacts another cube with it; or he puts a cube into a box; or into the receiving palm of his mother's hand.

Left to his own devices with a dozen cubes, he exhibits a very instructive behavior pattern. He picks up one cube and drops it; he picks up another cube and drops it; he picks up still another and drops it. All this is done in a somewhat disorderly manner; but by all the canons of development this one-by-one cube manipulation must be set down as the first step in the gradient of mathematics! It is nothing less than rudimentary counting. This remarkable behavior pattern is not the result of imitation nor of cultural impress; although the culture in due season will supply the appropriate labels, 1, 2, 3, 4, 5. . . . In time the labels will be true symbols and the child will entertain corresponding concepts,—but not yet!

In social situations, too, the yearling child puts one and one together. He likes an audience; he repeats performances laughed at; he enjoy' all sorts of to-and-fro household play. This social reciprocity is based on his increasing emotional perceptiveness which enables him to read more accurately the emotions of others.

§7. 15 MONTHS OLD

At 15 months the behavior picture seems to lose its harmony and equilibrium. This is the dart and dash and fling age. The give-and-take of to-and-fro rapport is superseded by one-way behavior. The 15-month-old child is no longer a mere creeping and cruising baby. He strains at the leash with his new found powers of walking and toddling. He likes to overturn waste baskets; he likes to pull off his shoes.

His gross motor drive is powerful: he is ceaselessly active with brief bursts of locomotion, starting, stopping, starting again, climbing and clambering. It is as though he were an aggressive jeep putting himself through all its paces.

If he is confined to a pen, he is likely to pick up each toy and fling it outside. This is a gross type of prehensory release,—a casting pattern which needs practice,—at least in his own estimation. Developmentally, crude casting precedes more highly coordinated forms of throwing. But this casting is not altogether crude; because the baby is casting with his eyes as well as with his hands. He is using his eyes alertly to see where an object falls, as it falls. This is a significant exercise in distance perception, in ocular accommodation and convergence. It requires agile coordination of his various eye muscles.

The 15-month-old child is not all bluster and bumble. Surprisingly enough he can poise one cube over another and release it with sufficient neatness to build a tower of two. In the ancient history of the race this was an important construction feat. It is a significant achievement in the history of the individual.

The release pattern is now so refined that the baby can pluck a pellet and drop it into the mouth of a small bottle. He does this without instruction or demonstration. We simply place the pellet beside the bottle. He responds with immediate spontaneity. Spontaneous behavior is often a key to developmental readiness.

§8. 18 MONTHS OLD

The 15-month-old toddler strains at the leash. The 18-month runabout is on the loose, colliding with new physical and cultural problems at every turn. The one-year-old, by reason of his locomotor immaturity and relative docility, is protected from excessive impacts of the culture. But the 18-month-old child is no longer a "mere" baby, and life is not so easy for him. Larynx, legs, hands, feet, bladder and bowel sphincters are all, concurrently, coming under cortical control. With such an extraordinary diversity of behavior patterns to coordinate, it is no wonder that he functions in brief spans and pulsations of attention.

His attention is sketchy, mobile, works in swift brief strokes. He lugs, tugs, dumps, pushes, drags, pounds, runs into nooks and corners and byways; goes up and down stairs; by one device or another, pulls a wheeled toy from place to place, abandons it,—and then resumes with variations, including walking backward.

He attends to the *here* and *now*. He has little perception for far off objects. He runs into them headlong, with scant sense of direction. He has little perception for far off events. No need to talk to him about the future. He may, however, understand and even execute a simple commission within his motor experience, such as Go-and-get-your-hat. He has a few favorite expressions of his own: "all gone," "bye-bye," "oh-my!"

Although he has meager pre-perceptions he has a significant sense of "conclusions." He likes to complete a situation. He puts a ball in a box with decision and caps the performance with a delighted exclamatory "Oh-My!" He closes a door; he hands you a dish when he has finished; —he mops up a puddle,—all with an air of conclusiveness, as if to say *now-that's-done.*

This is a most interesting growth phenomenon. It accounts for his punctuated demeanor. It reveals the operation of morphogenetic processes even in apparently trivial behavior. We are too blind to the significance of similar subtleties in the behavior patterning of the child of school age.

§9. 2 YEARS OLD

The 2-year-old is graduating from infancy. Since the age of 18 months he has gained two inches in height, three pounds in weight and four teeth in dentition. He can run without falling; he can turn the pages of a book singly; he can pull on a garment; he can keep a spoon right side up as he puts it into his mouth; he can frame a two word phrase or a three word sentence; he can even use words to express and to control his toilet needs. By all these tokens he is sometimes too readily considered to be ripe for promotion from home to nursery school.

More concessions ought to be made to his developmental immaturity. He is still an infant-child. There is a residual stagger in his walk. His running is amateurishly headlong. He can not slow down or turn sharp corners. (Motor abilities are rarely modulated while they are still new.) He delights in the grosser forms of muscular activity,—romping and rough and tumble play. He tends to express his emotions massively in dancing, clapping, stamping or captious laughter.

The facial muscles of expression, however, are more mobile. The muscles of the jaw are under better control. Chewing is no longer as effortful as it was at 18 months, and mastication is becoming rotary.

The fine motor coordination of the 2-year-old is obviously de-limited by certain selective immaturities of his nervous system. He can build a tower of five or six cubes; but he cannot rearrange them in a horizontal row to build a wall. He also has difficulty in making a horizontal stroke with crayon, even though he imitates a vertical stroke with the greatest of ease. This predilection for vertical over horizontal is based not on chance but on a foreordained geometry of growth. When somewhat older, he will show a comparable predilection for the horizontal. Yet older, he will be in full command of both dimensions. At the age of three he builds a bridge which combines both vertical and horizontal components.

Similar developmental delimitations show themselves in the sphere of personal-social behavior. He has a robust sense of *mine*, but a very weak sense of *thine*. He can hoard, but he can not share. Nevertheless, let us not lose hope, for he can smile at praise, and he can hang his head in disgrace!

§10. 2½ YEARS OLD

The 2½-year-old child also has difficulties with *thine* and *mine*,—difficulties which, by the way, have not been entirely mastered even by the adults of the human race. The 2½-year-old, however, has developed a stronger awareness of persons other than himself. He will bring a favorite toy to nursery school to display it with pride; but he finds he can not quite surrender it to his playmates. He will also be seized with an intense impulse to acquire a coveted toy; but once in possession he abandons it with indifference. The sense of ownership is evidently in a transitional, unmodulated phase of development.

The 2½-year-old does not have himself well in hand. He is reputed to be variously impetuous, imperious, contrary, hesitant, dawdling, defiant, ritualistic, unreasonable and incomprehensible. He does lack the equanimities of the classic self-containment of 28-week-old maturity.

His difficulties are due to the fact that he is just discovering a new realm of opposites. Life is no longer a one-way street as it was at 18 months. Life is charged with double alternatives. Every pathway in the culture has become a two way street. He has a great deal of intermediating to do between contrary impulses, and yet, he has to become acquainted with *both* opposites. Being inexperienced as well as immature he often makes two choices where he should make one; or he makes the wrong choice; or he makes none at all. Hence his reputation! Hence the impatience of his disciplinarians.

For the time being his action-system is in a stage of relatively unstable equilibrium. He has yet to acquire skill in balancing alternatives and in thinking of one alternative to the exclusion of another. He reminds us of the two-way rocking and the creep-crawl stages in the patterning of prone locomotion. Yet we know that he is forging ahead developmentally and we can predict that at the age of three years he will have himself in hand.

§11. 3 YEARS OLD

The 3-year-old has himself in hand because he has come out victorious in his struggle with diametric opposites. He is no longer as paradoxical and unpredictable as he was at two-and-a-half years. He has captured the power of judging and choosing between two rival alternatives. In fact, he likes to make a choice, within the realm of his experience. He is sure of himself. He is emotionally less turned in on himself. He takes his routines more sensibly and does not insist on rituals to protect himself. He has more flexible personal relations. Self-dependence and sociality are well balanced. Accordingly, he seems to fit into the culture more comfortably. His whole action-system, for the time, is in good working equilibrium. Hence his good reputation. Hence the approval of his elders.

THREE is a nodal age, a kind of coming of age. The conflict of opposites which a half year ago expressed itself in "negativism," "wilfulness," and "contrariness" gives way to a new realization of social demands. Far from being contrary he tries to meet and to understand these demands. He even asks, "Do it dis way?"

Much of this social amenability is based on sheer psycho-motor maturity. He is more sure and nimble on his feet; he no longer walks with arms outstretched (he swings them like a man); he can dodge, throw, stop-go and turn sharp corners. He has attained to the developmental rule of three: he can count to three; he can compare two objects, which requires a three step logic; he can combine three cubes to build a bridge; he can combine a vertical and horizontal crayon stroke to make a cross; he can barter commodity *a* for commodity *b*, which also requires a three step logic; in play and games he can wait his turn.

For all these reasons you can bargain with and on the 3-year-old! He marks both a culmination and a prophecy in the cycle of child development.

§12. 4 YEARS OLD

The 3-year-old is conforming. The 4-year-old is assertive and expansive. He bursts with motor activity: racing, hopping, jumping, skipping, climbing. He bubbles with mental activity, manifested in an abandoned use of words and in flights of fable and fancy. The 4-year-old tends to go out of bounds, notably in his speech and in his imaginative antics. He is blithe and lively, but he is more firmly based than may appear on the surface. Emotionally and intellectually he comes back to home base; he does not get too detached from his moorings. The mental consolidations achieved at the age of three serve to stabilize.

The key to the psychology of the 4-year-old is his high drive associated with a mental organization which is mobile at the margins. His mental imagery is almost mercurial. It moves from one configuration to another with great agility. In his dramatic play he doffs and dons his roles with the greatest of ease. In his drawing he is often a downright improvisor. He designates his drawings during and after execution rather than in advance. His drawing of a man is scarcely recognizable as such, and readily metamorphoses into something else with free comments.

The 4-year-old is voluble because the architectured neuron network which underlies language, is literally burgeoning with "outshoots" which take the form of new conjunctions, new adverbs and adjectives, expletives and novel syntax: *maybe*; *I guess*; *not even*; *enormous*; *suppose that*; *really*; and *I bet you can't do this, I hope*! Order finally emerges out of this linguistic luxuriance; but at four years we must expect some developmental *mal a propos*. Even though he can scarcely count to four, the 4-year-old blithely talks of seventy-seven.

This is a growthsome stage. He tells tall tales; he brags; he tattles; he threatens; he alibies; he calls names. But this bravado is not to be taken too seriously; his attractive traits more than compensate. He is fundamentally striving through these impulsions to identify himself with his culture and to penetrate its unknown. Sometimes he seems to be almost conscious of the growing up process. He is much interested in becoming five years old; he talks about it a lot.

*   *   *

We have now characterized in rapid sequence eleven ascending levels of maturity in the first four years of life. In succeeding chapters we shall describe at length six more maturity levels embracing the years from five to ten. At these later ages we shall encounter many new and interesting patterns of behavior, but we do not expect to find new mechanisms of development. The fundamental mechanisms have already revealed themselves in the transparent naivetes of infancy and preschool childhood.

A panoramic view of the eleven early stages of maturity gives us a deepened appreciation of the surety and the lawfulness of child development. Although there are innumerable contingencies in the environment, we see that the growth complex moves forward with certainty toward specific ends. Every child is unique; but every child is also a member of one human species. Obedient to these species characteristics there are growth sequences which are rarely or never circumvented. The motor control of the eyes precedes that of the fingers; head balance precedes body balance; palmar prehension precedes digital prehension; voluntary grasp precedes voluntary release. Banging comes before poking; vertical and horizontal hand movements before circular and oblique; crawling before creeping; creeping before upright walking; gestures before words; jargon before speech; nouns before prepositions; solitary play before social; perceptions before abstractions; practical before conceptual judgments. These are but a few simple examples of the sequential order inherent in the structuralization of child behavior, from its lowest to its highest manifestations.

The structuralization of behavior,—this is an important concept. It means that we must visualize the action-system of the child as a living structure, which is ingeniously fabricated through the architecture of growth. The lines of this construction are suggested by the behavior profiles which we have sketched.

From these sketches it is evident that the mind does not grow like an onion, nor like an artichoke by the addition of successive layers. It grows by weaving unimaginably complex patterns which correspond to the multiplicities of a world of things and a world of persons. All these patterns are incorporated into a single individuality.

The process of this *incorporation* is intriguing to everyone who wishes to understand the dynamics of psychological growth. The action system (the *corpus* of behavior) develops as a unitary whole. In general its organization proceeds in a head to foot direction; and from the central axis outward. The trunk is innervated before the shoulders; the shoulders before the arms; the arms before the hands. Opposed members and counterpoised functions must be brought into balance: flexor versus extensor muscles; right and left extremities; eyes and hands; forward and backward movements; vertical and horizontal movements; grasp and release; mine and thine; self-activity and sociality; good and bad, etc.

As it matures the action-system reconciles and counterbalances a host of opposites. But this process is so intricate that growth cannot take a straight line course. It seesaws, emphasizing now one and now another opposed function, but finally coordinating and modulating both. Self-regulatory fluctuation and reciprocal interweaving are outstanding methods of child development.

As we have seen from the eleven maturity profiles in this chapter, the growing action-system is in a state of formative instability combined with a progressive movement toward stability. Growth gains are consolidated in periods of relative stability. There is a somewhat rhythmic trend toward recurrent equilibrium. Witness the relatively stable equilibrium at 16 weeks, 28 weeks, and 3 years. Contrast the relatively instable equilibrium at 2½ years.

The trends of development tend to repeat themselves at ascending levels of organization; as though the cycle of development took a spiral course. It is an onward spiral, but the child at a given stage may show a strong resemblance to what he was at an earlier stage.

These parallels in the developmental spiral are very instructive. They indicate the logic of growth changes. Although the child always remains true to himself, we must expect him to pass through varying phases. It helps us to understand his behavior if we recognize that there are nodal periods when he is in focus, and other periods when he is in transition. Although we shall never apply age norms arbitrarily, it gives us a sense of perspective to know that there are fundamental correspondences in the dynamic makeup of the child at 16 and 28 weeks; at 3 years and 5 years; at 2½ years and 6 years. The maturity characteristics of the infant and pre-school child may well serve as touchstones for a more sympathetic insight into the inner psychology of children of school age.

5

FIVE YEARS OLD

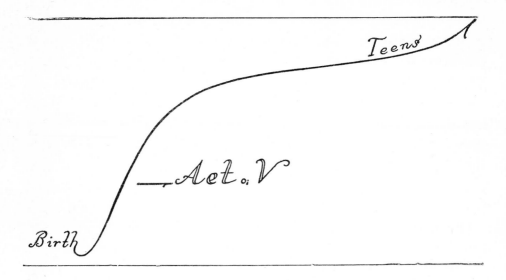

How can we best portray the rich and varied developmental transformations which take place in the growthsome years from five to ten? Most of these transformations come so stealthily that we are scarcely aware of them at the time at which they occur. Yet they come with such unremitting surety that each birthday marks a significant advance. Each year brings changes in the maturity picture.

AGES AND STAGES

In the chapters which follow we shall attempt to outline the patterns of these progressive changes. What the first four years have wrought has just been summarized. Our next task is to characterize the succeeding years in terms of their *developmental essence*. This means a series of delineations which will define the directions and the destinations of development. If in these delineations we make incidental comparisons between adjoining stages of maturity we should get a further insight into development as a process.

The concept of maturity, when applied to children is, of course, relative. A 3-year-old child is normally more mature than a 2-year-old. A 1-year-old baby is extremely mature when compared with a 16-week-old baby. Indeed, the maturity difference between them is very much greater than that between a 6- and 7-year-old child; for the rate of development has already slowed down by the age of five years.

The developmental changes which occur in the years from five to ten, therefore, are not as striking as those which occur in infancy. Being less dramatic, the changes are easily overlooked, both at home and at school. To become more aware of the developmental forces which bring about these changes, we need a frame of reference. Above all we need to know that the forces are working day in and day out, year in and year out. Growth is a process.

Our task is to point out the influence of age on the growth of behavior. The psychology of a child is determined by his maturity and by his experience. The experiences in turn are determined by his maturity as well as by the culture in which he lives. The variations both in child and culture are, of course, enormous. A child may be reared in Patagonia or on Park Avenue. That must make some difference. His color may be white, black or brown. In terms of endowment he may be idiot or genius. In physique he may be endo-, meso-, or ecto-morphic. In temperament, viscero-, somato-, or cerebro-tonic. In life career he may have enjoyed the affection and security of a happy home; or he may be one of those culturally disinherited "five-year-old people" of war-ridden Europe "who look like seventy because they have seen things no child should see."

With such a multiplicity of variables it would be fatuous to look for mathematical averages. It is possible, however, by comparing one age group with another to single out distinguishing behavior characteristics and developmental trends. On the basis of such systematic comparisons, we shall draw up a series of *behavior profiles,* devoting a separate chapter to each age level.

The profiles will present behavior characteristics which are typical of intelligent children of favorable socio-economic status in our American culture. A profile does not attempt to portray either an individual child or a statistical child. Each profile is a composite character sketch, which incorporates intimate cross sectional and longitudinal studies of a wide range of children. As such the behavior profiles may be used to identify and to interpret the changing developmental status of actual children as they mature in the years from five to ten. Our first profile outlines the developmental essence of the 5-year-old. Five is a nodal age which marks both the end and the beginning of a growth epoch. FIVE, himself, seems to be conscious of a culmination, for he announces somewhat assertively, "I am five!"

BEHAVIOR PROFILE

The 5-year-old has come a long distance on the upward winding pathway of development. He will have to travel fifteen years more before he becomes an adult, but he has scaled the steepest ascent and has reached a sloping plateau. Although he is by no means a finished product, he already gives token of the man (or the woman!) he (or she) is to be. His capacities, talents, temperamental qualities, and his distinctive modes of meeting the demands of development,—have all declared themselves to a significant degree. He is already stamped with individuality.

But he also embodies in his young person general traits and trends of behavior which are characteristic of a stage of development and of the culture to which he belongs. *These underlying pervasive traits constitute his 5-year-oldness.* They are the maturity traits which make him somewhat different from the 4-year-old and from the 6-year-old.

[62]

Five is a nodal age; and also a kind of golden age for both parent and child. For a brief period the tides of development flow smoothly. The child is content to organize the experiences which he gathered somewhat piecemeal in the less deliberate fourth year. As an expansive 4-year-old he was constantly going out to meet the environment, making his thrusts in an almost harum-scarum manner. In contrast, the 5-year-old is self-contained, on friendly and familiar terms with his environment. He has learned much; he has matured. He takes time to consolidate his gains before he makes deeper incursions into the unknown. At the age of about 5½ years a new form of developmental restlessness makes itself apparent.

Meanwhile there is an interlude when he feels quite at home in his world. And what is his world? *It is a here-and-now world*: his father and mother, especially his mother; his seat at the dining room table; his clothes, particularly that cap of which he is very proud; his tricycle; the backyard, the kitchen, his bed, the drugstore and the grocery store around the corner (or the barn and the granary if he is fortunate enough to live in the country); the street, and perhaps the big kindergarten room, with other children and with another "nice lady." But if his universe has a center, it is his mother who is that center.

He does not tolerate even a kindergarten well, if it makes too many pioneering demands upon him. Just now he is not in a pioneering phase of development. He has a healthy intolerance for too much magic and too much fairy tale. He has just barely discovered his actual world; and this has enough novelty and reality on its own merits. He is even something of a homebody. This is not because of abnormal dependence; but because the home is a complex institution, which invites and rewards his consideration. He is happy to play house, with all its domesticities, by the hour, which is not to his developmental discredit. And if while he is in kindergarten he particularly enjoys the dramatization of domestic situations, we cannot be amazed. He must make the familiar more familiar to himself; the familiar world is still new.

Even his infancy is relatively recent in time. He likes to have the experiences of his earlier childhood revived for him by his mother. He talks baby talk to his infant sister. All this helps him to detach himself from his babyhood and to become more completely identified with his present immediate environment.

His rapport with the environment is very personal. He is not yet ripe for the conceptual detachments and the abstract notions which adult ethics aspires to. He has a fairly robust sense of possession; for things that he likes he even has a pride of possession; but it is with reference to HIS *own*. He does not have a general notion of ownership. He tends to be realistic, concrete and first-personal; without, however, being aggressive and combative. "Do dogs run?" a 5-year-old was asked. "I don't have a dog!" was his polite answer.

Yet within the limits of the familiar and a narrow fringe of the unknown, he will ask questions of his own. What is it for? What is it made of? How does this work? Why does the bus come around this way? are favorites.

The 5-year-old makes a favorable impression of competence and stability, because he does not go off on wild tangents. Nor is he overdemanding. He likes to function well within the realm of his abilities. Although his spontaneous play is not stereotyped it tends to restrict itself to small, conservative variations. But these variations are numerous and in time they yield substantial developmental gains.

Self-limitation is almost stronger than self-assertion. Accordingly he demands adult help where needed. He likes little responsibilities and privileges to which he can do full justice. He is best managed on that basis rather than through challenges to efforts still beyond him. He may respond with little flashes of resistance or sensitiveness if overtaxed; but quickly resumes his habitual poise. There is often a vein of seriousness. He is much more deliberate than a 4-year-old. He thinks before he speaks.

Nevertheless, the 5-year-old may have a vein of humor. He likes to plan a "surprise-joke," even in the realm of moral conduct. His father asks him, "Have you eaten your dinner?" He says "No!", already betraying advance amusement in his deception. He adds, "No I won't!" And presently on investigation, to everyone's great joy, it proves that he has already eaten the dinner, every bit of it!

Five-year-olds like to fit into the culture in which they live. Their spontaneous activity tends to be under good self-control. They seek adult support and guidance. They accept adult help in making unfamiliar transitions. They are eager to know how to do things which lie within their capacity. They like to be instructed, not so much to please their elders, as to feel the satisfactions of achievement and social acceptance. They like to practice the social convention of asking for permission and of waiting for formal permission. Five is an age of conformity which sums itself up in the question, "How do you do it?"

This docility, however, does not mean that the 5-year-old, with all his attractive traits, is a highly socialized individual. He is too deeply immersed in his world to have a discriminating perception of his self among his peers and superiors. His cooperative play is usually limited to a group of three; and is conducted with chief concern for his individual ends rather than the collective ends. Boys and girls accept each other freely regardless of sex; though not without hierarchical competition as to who in housekeeping play should fill the role of mother and who that of the baby. Not being unduly aggressive and acquisitive, the 5-year-old tends to get along peacefully with playmates in simple group play.

The emotional linkage with his mother is strong. He obeys her readily. He likes to help about the house. He enjoys being read to by his mother. Should things go wrong, he may use her as a scapegoat, blaming her as a "mean mommie." On the other hand he will also accept punishment from her with a temporary change of course.

These emotional patterns are, of course, subject to great individual variations; but they suggest a strong matriarchal orientation. The mother, after all, is a rather important figure in the small world of the 5-year-old. She is obviously the Great Executive Agent of the household from whom proceed all blessings and authorizations. He is discovering the outlines of the social order,—outlines which emerge in the home.

And he signalizes his new sociological insight by asking his mother to marry him!

This proposal reflects the intellectual limitations as well as the emotional patterns of a typical 5-year-old. He represents an interesting combination of practical realism and primitive naivete. He has some appreciation of yesterday and tomorrow, but he understands *me—now –here* better than *you—then—there*. He is so completely immersed in the cosmos that he is unaware of his own thinking as being a subjective process separate from the objective world. He is factual and literal rather than imaginative. He can distinguish his left from his right hand in his own person, but he lacks that extra bit of projectiveness which would enable him to distinguish left from right in another person. Although he is beginning to use words with great facility he is so self-in-cosmos engrossed that he cannot well suppress his own point of view to realize by reciprocity the point of view of others. Yet he has an elementary sense of shame and disgrace. He seeks affection and applause. He likes to be told how nicely he is doing. He likes to bring home something he has made at school.

The 5-year-old is a pragmatist rather than a romanticist. He defines in terms of use: "A horse is to ride. A fork is to eat." Fairy tales with excessive unrealities vex and confuse him. He is serious, empirical, direct. Give him a crayon and he will draw a man for you with head, torso, extremities, eyes and nose. He may even supply five digits, for he can count to four or five. He can also copy a square. If he copies a few capital letters he is likely to identify them very closely with persons and objects. He almost makes personalities for certain words. His mechanics and his astronomy are likewise tinged with animisms. He is very innocent in the realm of causal and logical relationships. Clouds move because God pushes them, and when God blows it is windy.

Nevertheless, FIVE is a great talker. The volubility of the fourth year yielded an increased vocabulary of perhaps 2,000 words. He has overcome most of his infantile articulation. He uses connectives more freely when he narrates an experience. He can tell a tale. He may exaggerate;

but he is not given to over-fanciful invention. His dramatic play is full of practical dialogue and a kind of collective monologue. He is using words to clarify the multitudinous world in which he lives. In language perhaps, more than in any other field of behavior he shows a slight tendency to ramble out of bounds. This is a wholesome growth tendency, for words will help to detach him constructively from his mother and from the environment which holds him in its grasp.

In general the emotional life of the 5-year-old suggests good adjustment within himself and confidence in others. He is not without anxieties and fears, but usually they are temporary and concrete. Thunder and sirens awaken dread. Darkness and solitude cause timidity. Many a 5-year-old has fits of fearfulness lest his mother should leave him, or be gone when he awakens. His dreams may be pleasant, but he is often more subject to nightmares in which terrifying animals figure more prominently than persons.

All things considered, however, the 5-year-old in his waking hours is in excellent equilibrium. Somatically his health is good. Psychologically he is comfortably at home in his world, because he is at home with himself. He may be pushed off balance but he tends to return to counterpoise. Ordinarily he does not go off on tantrum tangents. A brief stamping of feet and a "No I won't" suffice. Although fond of climbing and gross motor activity, he shows composure in his standing and sitting postures. He does not shift or fidget while in a chair. He stands aplomb. Oftentimes we see unconscious grace and skill both in gross and fine motor coordinations. There is a finished perfection and economy of movement,—which again suggests that five is a nodal stage toward which the strands of development converge to be organized for a new advance.

Indeed the psychological nature of five-year-oldness becomes most apparent when we halt at this nodal milepost and look back at the developmental path by which the child reached his present estate. It is a winding, spiraling pathway. There were similar mileposts in the past; there will be others in the future. Five-year-oldness compares with

3-year-oldness and with 28-week-oldness in its general configuration and quality. Ten-year-oldness will resemble five. These are brief periods in which the assimilative, organizing forces of growth are in ascendancy. During intervening periods, at four, six and eight years the expansive, fermentive, forward thrusts of development are more prominent.

Needless to say these alternations in the accents of development are not sharply defined. The growth continuum is like the chromatic spectrum: each phase, each color, shades by imperceptible gradations into the next. Yet the seven colors of the rainbow are distinguishable. In a similar way the maturity traits of the 5-year-old are distinguishable from those of the 6-year-old.

And, gentle reader,—be forewarned, you will not understand your 6-year-old unless you make the distinction!

MATURITY TRAITS

A behavior profile aims to give us a composite picture of the child as a whole. We cannot do justice to his psychology unless we think of him as a total unit, as an individual. If we try to take him apart he vanishes; he ceases to be a person.

Nevertheless he is so many-sided that we cannot attend to every aspect of his complex behavior equipment at one glance. We must look at him from different angles, and seek out those characteristics which are of special significance. Since he is a unified personality we shall find that all his traits are more or less interdependent.

For practical purposes, however, we can group these traits into ten classifications which are shown on the accompanying table. We call them *maturity traits* because the emphasis, throughout, is not on the abilities of the child but upon the stages and mechanisms of his development.

The list of traits is fairly comprehensive and covers the most important areas of behavior with which home and school are concerned. Under the various headings we shall cite concrete examples of behaviors

CLASSIFICATION OF
MATURITY TRAITS AND
GRADIENTS OF GROWTH

§ 1. *Motor Characteristics*
    Bodily Activity
    Eyes and Hands

§ 2. *Personal Hygiene*
    Eating
    Sleep
    Elimination
    Bath and Dressing
    Health and Somatic
      Complaints
    Tensional Outlets

§ 3. *Emotional Expression*
    Affective Attitudes
    Crying and Related
      Behaviors
    Assertion and Anger

§ 4. *Fears and Dreams*
    Fears
    Dreams

§ 5. *Self and Sex*
    Self
    Sex

§ 6. *Interpersonal Relations*
    Mother-child
    Father-child
    Siblings
    Family
    Manners
    Teacher-child
    Child-child
    Groupings in Play

§ 7. *Play and Pastimes*
    General Interests
    Reading
    Music, Radio and Cinema

§ 8. *School Life*
    Adjustment to School
    Classroom Demeanor
    Reading
    Writing
    Arithmetic

§ 9. *Ethical Sense*
    Blaming and Alibiing
    Response to Direction, Pun-
      ishment and Praise
    Responsiveness to Reason
    Sense of Good and Bad
    Truth and Property

§ 10. *Philosophic Outlook*
    Time
    Space
    Language and Thought
    War
    Death
    Deity

*The foregoing areas of behavior
in ten major sectors of
child development are treated
by ages in Chapters 5 to 10 and
by gradients in Chapters 11 to 20.*

which we have encountered at the yearly age levels. The examples are not always typical, but they do illustrate the kinds of behavior and the degrees of maturity which parents and teachers have to reckon with in relatively normal children.

The maturity traits are set forth in brief, informal statements which reflect the everyday happenings of home and school life. We do not set up these traits as norms, but rather as indicators of the child's behavior equipment at a given level of maturity.

Sometimes this behavior is undesirable and preventable. If the reader understands the developmental import of the behavior he can usually work out a method of management suitable to the child's maturity. Child guidance must always be adjusted to the demands of development. Occasionally specific guidance measures are suggested. Generally the guidance will be implied in the statement of the traits and will not call for detailed formulation. For convenience, a standard set of ten rubrics will be used in presenting the illustrative maturity traits at each age.

We begin with *Motor Skills*. Basically the child is a system of muscles with which he executes motions in time and space. We are interested in the course, the form, the symmetry, and the direction of these motions. How do his motor coordinations change with age, as revealed in body posture, in handedness, in drawing, and in the use of eyes and hands?

The child is also a physiological organism which must replenish and sustain itself, which is subject to illness and outward stresses, and inward tensions. Under the rubric *Personal Hygiene* we subsume the behaviors and adjustments which relate to eating, sleeping, elimination and physical well-being.

Affective attitudes and threats to the organism are manifested in various forms of *Expressional Behavior*, and in *Fears and Dreams*.

The forces of self-conservation, however, are strong. The child builds up a sense of self, he differentiates himself from the opposite sex, he comes into increasing command of sex factors which concern his own life and his relations with others. Significant growth changes occur in the field of *Self and Sex*.

He actually works out the detailed architecture of his sense of self through social rather than private activities—through a vast web of associations with his elders, his parents, his teachers, and compeers,—the web of *Interpersonal Relations*.

Much of his activity, both personal and social, is playful, experimental, gamesome, recreational. His *Play and Pastimes* reveal his spontaneous energies and interests.

But modern culture has willed that the child from five to ten must also go to school. He has much to learn about the sciences, the arts and the amenities of civilization. The patterns of his *School Life* reveal how he reacts to the demands of the culture.

In school hours and out of school hours, he is constantly thrust into the necessity of adjusting to other persons, friends and strangers, young and old, threatening and kind. Thereby he weaves a web of personal-social relationships which express themselves in various labels and values: "thine and mine," "good and bad," "do and don't," "right and wrong," "you-are-to-blame," "I-am-to-blame," "be-a-good-boy," "be-a-nice-girl." Here is the developmental matrix of the *Ethical Sense*.

Two intermeshed worlds surround the child: the world of things and the world of persons. The environment would become overpowering and overbewildering, did not the child have an insuperable propensity to establish his own orientations. They are orientations of intellect and of attitude. They encompass the major mysteries of life and death, of nature, of mankind, and of the supernatural forces. Philosophy has been defined as the knowledge of things divine and human and the causes in which they are contained. Even a child makes his own formulations in this vast field of knowledge. His formulations undergo interesting transformations with age. We shall describe these transformations in terms of the child's *Philosophic Outlook*.

The following maturity traits are not to be regarded as rigid norms nor as models. They simply illustrate the kinds of behavior—desirable or otherwise—which tend to occur at this age. Every child has an individual pattern of growth, unique to him. The behavior traits here outlined may be used to interpret his individuality and to consider the maturity level at which he is functioning.

§ 1. MOTOR CHARACTERISTICS

Bodily Activity

FIVE is poised and controlled. He is well oriented to himself. Posturally he is less extreme and less extensor than he was at four. He is closely knit. His arms are held near his body. His stance is narrow. In kicking a ball he may throw and kick simultaneously. Eyes and head move almost simultaneously as he directs his regard to something. He is direct in his approach, facing things squarely. He goes directly to a chair and seats himself. He appears to be well oriented to the four points of the compass as he turns a quarter to left or to right or even to the back as he is seated in a chair.

Gross motor activity is well developed at five. Although he may tread with feet pronate, he can walk a straight line, descend stairs alternating his feet and skip alternately.

His alternating mechanism is put to practice in much of his behavior. He loves his tricycle and is adept at riding it. He climbs with sureness and from one object to another. He shows a marked interest in stilts and roller skates although he cannot sustain a performance for long.

FIVE's economy of movement is in contrast to FOUR's expansiveness. He appears more restrained and less active because he maintains one position for longer periods, but he changes from sitting to standing to squatting in a serial manner. He is none-the-less active. Although he plays longer in one restricted place, he is a great helper who likes to go up stairs to get something for mother, or to go back and forth from kitchen to dining room to put things on the table.

Eyes and Hands

FIVE sits with trunk quite upright, his work directly before him. He may move to right or left slightly to orient his body, and he may stand and continue. His eye-hand performance appears as capable as an adult's, although actually the finer patterns have yet to develop. His approach, grasp, and release are direct, precise and accurate in simple motor performances. He utilizes his pre-school toys more skillfully and purposefully. A familiar puzzle is done in a mercurial manner.

He is becoming more adept with his hands and likes to lace his shoes, fasten buttons that he can see, "sew" wool through holes on a card by turning it over. He likes to place his fingers on the piano keys and strike a chord. He now shows a preference for small as well as large blocks of various sizes and colors with which he builds simple structures. He also likes to copy from a model.

FIVE likes to observe too. He watches mother make something, then he tries it. He needs many models and likes to copy designs, letters and numbers. He also likes to have outline pictures to color, trying to keep within the lines. FIVE should be well provided with this type of material so that he may be better able to put it to use at six.

In spontaneous drawing he makes a single outline drawing with few details. He may attach the back and front door to the sides of a "house" or he may draw a square for a house making an indentation at the top and bottom for the two doors. He recognizes that his result is "funny."

Handedness is usually well established by five and the 5-year-old can identify the hand which he uses for writing. His initial approach is with the dominant hand and he does not transfer a pencil to the free hand. In block building he alternates the use of the hands but the dominant hand is used more frequently. This is also true when he points to pictures.

When maintained in a sedentary position he becomes restless, lifts his buttocks from the chair, turns to the side or stands, but he remains within the radius of the table and chair. Tensional outlets are brief. With his free hand he may scratch, brush, poke or touch any part of his body (on the side of that hand),—parts of his face as well as arm, leg and clothes. He may also sneeze or have to blow his nose.

§ 2. PERSONAL HYGIENE

Eating

Appetite. The shift to a better appetite noted at 4½ years of age is fairly well established by five. This does not, however, mean that all meals are uniformly better. Two meals a day are good and the third one, usually breakfast, is relatively poor. An illness or an operation does not upset this established appetite as would have been the case at an earlier age. The decrease in appetite during an illness or operation is often actually followed by a definite increase during the convalescent period.

FIVE is interested in completions, even to the extent of cleaning his plate He is slow in accomplishing this, but he is persistent. His appetite is better than his ability or interest in feeding himself; so he not only accepts help but often asks for it.

Refusals and Preferences. FIVE likes plain simple cooking. For his main meal he prefers meat, potatoes, a raw vegetable, milk, and fruit. Gravies, casseroles and even puddings may seem too complicated and artificial to him. Cooked vegetables, especially the root vegetables, are in special disfavor. Cereal is continued mainly through the will of the parent and may be accepted only if fed by the parent. The child is influenced, however, both in his preferences and in his refusals, by the example of others. He is also influenced by radio programs and may even accept turnip greens because of their vitamin content. He will accept new foods at the family table if he comes only a few times a week, at a restaurant, at a picnic, or when a guest joins the family group.

Self-Help. FIVE is expected to feed himself and on the whole he does a fairly skillful though slow job of it. Many FIVES, however, still need help, especially toward the end of the meal and with foods like cereal to which they are not partial. They eat better and faster if they eat most of their meals apart from the family table. FIVE is beginning to use a knife for spreading, but he is not yet ready to cut his meat nor will he be ready for some years to come.

Table Behavior. Manners take on little significance until the child has a good appetite and is able to feed himself completely. Therefore FIVE still has a little respite before the torrents of criticism begin. Moreover he frequently eats his main meal at night in the kitchen, apart from the family group, where he does so much better because his mother is moving about without paying too much direct attention to him. Having his meal with a sibling may help or hinder his eating. If he has been eating in his room, a promotion to the kitchen is a good stimulus. A few meals a week with the family give a further impetus, but this does not mean that he can hold up to an improved level at all meals.

If he comes to all meals, including dinner at night when father is at home, he usually wiggles in his chair. He does not get up and run around or ask to go to the bathroom as he did at four. But he usually brings his conversational ability to the table and tends to monopolize the conversation. This interferes with his eating and slows him down considerably. If it can be arranged for him to eat the main course in advance of the family meal he eats better, and can handle dessert with the family. However, FIVE likes to conform and will if reprimanded make an effort to improve his behavior, though he may need very frequent reminders. He may still wear a bib, though many now wear a napkin, tucked in at the neck.

Sleep

Nap. A fair proportion of 5-year-olds still nap occasionally. The nap seems to be an anti-fatigue adjustment. A 5-year-old may nap if he goes to morning kindergarten, or if he goes to afternoon kindergarten may nap on Saturday and Sunday only. Or he may nap on rainy days. In any case he does not usually have more than one or two naps a week. Boys are more likely to nap than girls, and a few may nap as often as five out of seven days, and for one to two hours.

The majority of 5-year-olds who do not nap usually do not take a rest period spontaneously. They may however ask to go to bed early at night. They do not resist a planned "play nap" of half an hour to one hour if provided with something interesting to do (coloring, modelling with plastecene, building structures with Tinker toys and Lincoln logs). The child rests better if his mother is resting in her room at the same time, and he especially enjoys an alarm clock set to ring when his play nap is to be ended.

Bedtime. The 7 P.M. bedtime persists with many; some delay until 7:30 or 8 o'clock. Usually the child has been read to before he starts for bed. He often prefers to have his mother precede him to turn on the lights. Getting ready for bed usually goes smoothly. Some continue to take a toy animal or doll to bed with them but many have given this up. However this does not mean that the child will not return to his pets at a later age when he needs them more.

Some who do not fall asleep quickly ask to "read" or to color for a while. Others fall asleep at once without any desire for pre-sleep activity. Still others like to lie quietly in the dark, singing to themselves or carrying on an imaginary conversation with another child. These conversations often deal with feats of prowess such as beating up another child or shooting wild animals.

A few still get up frequently, demanding a drink, something to eat, or the bathroom, but most can take care of their own needs without bothering their parents, though they report what they are doing. Usually FIVE falls asleep about half an hour after he starts to bed. A few remain awake until 9 P.M. Sleep may be delayed because of a too exciting day, the presence of company, or anticipation of the parents going out for the evening. If the child has trouble getting to sleep it sometimes helps to put him in a parent's bed, removing him later to his own bed.

Night. Some children sleep through the night but many have their sleep interrupted by need for toileting or by dreaming. This is the age when parents often waver as to whether the child should be picked up routinely to be toileted, or whether he is ready to sleep through the night. A trial of not waking him up either reveals that he no longer needs to be toileted, or that he awakens by himself, usually after midnight, and calls for his mother. Some actually toilet themselves, but feel that they must report to their mother before going back to bed. Usually there is little difficulty in getting back to bed and to sleep.

Dreams and nightmares definitely invade the sleep of many 5-year-olds. Frightening animal dreams predominate. Many children awaken screaming, have difficulty in coming out of their dream even with their mother by their side; finally with the help of shifting to another room or being toileted they wake up, realize where they are and go back to sleep again. Usually it is difficult for the child to tell you much about this type of nightmare. It is amazing to see how quickly the child generally quiets at his parent's touch or voice. The 5-year-old is beginning to talk out loud in his sleep, usually naming his mother or a sibling.

Morning. Most 5-year-olds awaken at 7 to 8 A.M. after an eleven hour sleep. They often obligingly sleep later on Sundays. The earlier-than-7 A.M. risers are often those who continue to take naps or those who are put to bed very early. At this age children may be expected to take care of themselves on waking, to close their window, put on their bathrobe and slippers, toilet themselves, and occupy themselves in bed with coloring or books until it is time to get up. A 5-year-old can often be very helpful with a younger sibling, even to the extent of changing wet pajamas. He no longer demands to go to his parents' bed in the morning for he is now quite occupied by his own activities.

Elimination

Bowel. It is customary for the 5-year-old to have one movement a day, usually after a meal. This is most commonly after lunch, and if not then, more often after supper than after breakfast. The 4-year-old tendency of interrupting a meal to have a movement is not characteristic of FIVE. But the child may, at the end of a meal, complain of a "terrible" pain, which is usually related to a need to have a bowel movement. Those children who are reported to function at "any old time" often show an increased constipation and a tendency to skip a day or two. This is more true of girls who need to be checked more carefully. They are helped by the suggestion that they must sit at the toilet long enough to function. Prune juice or some mild laxative may be needed. There is less interest in reporting on their movements than there was at four. A number are still in need of help in being wiped.

Bladder. Although FIVE takes fairly good responsibility for toileting, he urinates infrequently and is likely to put off going to the toilet when he actually needs to go. Wriggling and hopping on one foot are obvious clues to the adult. Some children are subject to fairly frequent intervals, and may need to be interrupted during a morning or afternoon play period with a bathroom reminder before it is too late. They may resist this interruption, but come more willingly at the prospect of a snack or in answer to a bell.

Certain girls need to be watched for sore, reddened genitals. This is easily controlled with a bland salve. This condition may possibly be related to masturbation, but may also be a developmental or individual characteristic.

Night accidents are infrequent but night toileting, as discussed under *Sleep,* is still relatively frequent. The child is either toileted routinely or he awakens and calls, or he may be able to go to the bathroom by himself, reporting to his parents that he has gone.

Bath and Dressing

Bath. The bath is now accomplished with a fair amount of speed and real child participation. The child cannot yet draw his own bath water, but this is in part related to his fear of the hot water tap. He definitely wants to help wash himself, especially his hands and knees. He is apt to get stranded on one knee, washing it over and over, and needs to be shifted to his other knee or to some other part of his body. Many mothers prefer to bathe the child themselves, and have it over with; others use this as a reading period, at the same time supervising the child part by part throughout his bath. A few children still cling to boat play during their bath.

Dressing and Care of Clothes. Parents commonly report that "he can but he doesn't" dress himself. Undressing is still easier than dressing. FIVE does better at dressing if his clothes are laid out singly on the floor. Otherwise he is still apt to get them on backside to. He can now handle all but back buttons. Shoelace tying is usually beyond him, and those who are able, tie too loose a bow.

A fair number of 5-year-olds handle the task of dressing without too much prodding. Others, however, are self-motivated only when they are eager to be ready for the next happening, or to surprise their parents. Some are able to choose two or three days a week when they will be responsible for dressing themselves. The other days are the mother's days when she will be completely responsible. His own days may be marked on a calendar; he is becoming interested in the calendar as a guide and record.

Children take little responsibility about their clothes at this age, either as to selecting them, laying them out, picking them up after they have been removed, or keeping them in good condition. Even those girls who are clothes conscious and proud of their appearance, do not take good care of their clothes.

Health and Somatic Complaints

On the whole the 5-year-old's health is relatively good with the exception of the communicable diseases which increase in number from the fourth year on. Whooping cough, measles, and chicken pox take the lead. Some will have only one or two colds during the winter months, which is in startling contrast to the repeated colds of the 4-year-old.

Stomach aches are fairly common and are related both to the intake of food and the need to have a bowel movement.

Stomach ache may follow the ingestion of foods the child does not like, or the too rapid taking of food. If the child is pressed to finish his meal in too much hurry, he may vomit.

Tensional Outlets

The majority of tensional outlets are related to pre-sleep activity. Thumb-sucking may still occur in a few children, but only prior to sleep. With some it occurs only once a week or once a month. Others use comfort objects such as sheets, blankets, pillows or toy animals to help them go to sleep more quickly. Many are reported to have given up these habits, or are in the process of giving them up.

FIVE is a good age to plan to terminate thumb-sucking. The parent needs to differentiate between the child who is going to be able to handle it by himself and the one who needs help. Maybe the voluntary giving up of the object related to the thumb-sucking will break up the pattern. Then the child may need help in going to sleep, such as having his mother sit beside him or having her return the sleep-inducing object if he cannot get along without it. Strapping the thumb with a band-aid, or planning for some much desired object (such as a kitten) may provide the necessary motivation. In any event, the plan should not be imposed but should be so fully discussed with the child that it becomes his own plan.

The hand to face response manifested in nose picking, nail biting, or any hand to mouth gesture, is fairly common at five. Nose sniffling may be so repetitive as to resemble a tic. Those who do not show their tensional outlets in these restricted ways do so in their interpersonal relations, especially with their mothers. They are either stubborn and resistant, or whiny and cranky. Others are still expressing 4-year-old out-of-bounds tendencies. They continue to be overactive and noisy, and may take a slight flaw in a toy as a suggestion to destroy it completely. Personality factors influence the ways in which tension is released.

§ 3. EMOTIONAL EXPRESSION

FIVE has largely overcome his 4-year-old out-of-bounds, runaway, neighborhood visiting tendencies. Home is to him often indoors and preferably within earshot of his mother. He is said to be very helpful. Though he is a great talker, he deliberates before he speaks and does not plunge in headlong as he did at four. FIVE is often seeking an answer. He is not only helpful but is often truly cooperative. He does not act before he asks permission. Though he may have been jealous of a younger sibling, he now adores this same sibling and is protective and helpful in taking care of him.

FIVE is poised. He has new inhibitory controls and anticipates immediate happenings well. Nevertheless he may be too excited by an anticipated event if he is not prepared long enough in advance. His eating and sleeping may be disturbed and he may become very shy or overactive when the actual event occurs. He has given up most of his 4-year-old brashness, and no longer shows off before company. The ringing of the telephone may induce him to answer it. When he was younger, his mother answered, while he seized the occasion to run for the cookie jar.

This inhibitory poise makes FIVE capable of a new kind of determination,—a positiveness which he uses to get his own way and to follow through his ideas. It also makes him a little dogmatic, so that he has only one way to do a thing, only one answer to a question. It is important to recognize this as a temporary and perhaps useful growth trait. If you contradict him or try to make him more broad-minded, he will contradict in turn and will argue as long as you will allow him to. You usually lose the argument, or at least you should lose. If he is pushed too far he will become angry and then cry or call names, for instance calling his mother a "naughty girl," "dirty rat," etc. If he is spoken to sharply or scolded he will usually cry. But for the most part he tries to hold his own ground and is less likely than formerly to rush off to seek comfort in one of his special comfort toys. His mother can help him to control a wayward action by interjecting a magic word such as "tent" (the word may work like magic if the child is very eager at that time to have a tent given to him).

Some FIVES do not function well unless they get off to a right start. You can often get the child to adjust to your demand if you help him to carry out your idea in his own way. That is the way in which your way and his way mix. He cannot change in midstream; he must start all over again. One 5-year-old who had started a day on the wrong foot and had kept in this groove, finally wept when the day was half spent and said, "I wish I could start Sunday all over again."

§4. FEARS AND DREAMS

Fears

FIVE is not a fearsome age, nor is it an age of over-awareness. Even though the child has been previously frightened by tales of witches, ghosts or bogey-men, he may no longer fear them because they have so little reality for him. Dogs are somewhat less feared than formerly. He may still say he is afraid of things, though his fears are actually receding in intensity.

FIVE is, however, beginning to have fears which may be more extreme at 5½ and 6 years of age, such as the fear of certain elements: thunder, hard rain and the dark.

His outstanding fear is that he will be deprived of his mother,—that she may go away and not come back, or that she may not be at home when he returns from school or that she may be gone when he awakens in the night. This may be a difficult period for the mother because it confines her to her home, even when the child is asleep. It is essential, however, to work out a satisfactory adjustment with the child so that his fear will remain under his control. He may be induced to accept the protection of some other person in his mother's absence. Or it may be that all he needs to make him feel secure is the telephone number which will reach his absent mother.

Nighttime heightens his fears. Thunder at night, sirens at night, are far more frightening than in the daytime. He is less afraid of the dark, but he still likes to have his mother precede him upstairs at bedtime. He often likes a light on in the hall or bathroom and likes to have his door a little ajar. If his mother tries to talk him out of it he may say, "But the darkness gets into my face."

Dreams

FIVE's sleep is often broken with dreams. These are usually unpleasant, and are most frequently about wolves and bears that get into bed with him. They may bite and chase him but this active aggressiveness is more common at 5½ and 6 years. Often FIVE wakes screaming because of the frightening quality of his dream. He is usually quieted fairly easily, though it may take some time to awaken him from a nightmare and also before he will go back to sleep after being awakened.

The dream may be reported at once or in the morning. Other dreams are only reported if some daytime experience helps the child to recall them. For example, one child was reading with her mother a story about a green frog, when she suddenly stopped and said, "Green, green like the woman. You know I don't think she should pop out from the floor and frighten me." Those who have nightmares are unable to report anything about their dreams. Others, judging from the elaborateness of their reporting are probably making up the dreams they report.

Wild animals and strange or bad people which frighten the child are most conspicuous in 5-year-old dreams. There are also dreams of activity in connection with the elements, flying through the air, jumping into water, being near a fire. These occur usually in a rather unpleasant, frightening connection. Everyday events and familiar persons (mother and playmates) are beginning to appear in dreams, but they are not yet taking a prominent role.

§ 5. SELF AND SEX

Self

FIVE is more self-contained than he was at four; he is more of a person. He is serious about himself and is much impressed with his own ability to take responsibilities and to imitate grown-up behavior. He is rightly spoken of as more mature. He may not seem as independent as he was, but he is more aware of the relationship of his acts to people and to the world around him. He is shy in his approach to people, but he builds up a slow steady relationship which makes FIVE one of the favorite ages of childhood for the adult. With things as with

people, FIVE likes to prepare and plan for happenings in the near future rather than to have them sprung on him.

He is secure in his relationship with his mother. She is as much himself as he is. It is essential for him to hold an even give and take with his mother. He is naturally obedient, he wants to please, he wants to help, and he asks for permission even when it is not necessary.

FIVE shows a remarkable memory for past events. He can hoard thoughts in the same way in which he hoards things. Through his questioning he builds up an impressive fund of information. And as with everything else about FIVE, there is a certain orderliness to what he thinks as well as to what he does.

FIVE lives in a here and now world, and his chief interest in the world is limited to his own immediate experiences. He likes to stay close to home base.

Sex

FIVE as a rule does not dwell upon sex questions as he did at four. His interest in sex is chiefly in the baby, in the having of a baby. This interest is manifested even in FIVE's mothering tenderness toward a younger sibling. Although he may have asked in an earlier year, "Where do babies come from?" he re-asks this question at five. All he wants to know is that the baby grows in its "mommy's tummy." He is rarely interested in how the baby started. The use of the words "seed" or "egg" reminds him of vegetables and chicken's eggs and may serve to confuse him rather than to help him. He readily accepts a statement as it is given and then repeats it with little meaning. One 5-year-old introduced his baby brother to some visitors thus: "This is my baby brother. He came from a seed."

Some FIVES still cling to the idea that

you buy a baby from a hospital. They may even solve the problem of the sex of the baby by declaring that the hospital gives out boys on certain days and girls on other days. Very few FIVES are aware of the enlarging abdomen of pregnancy, nor do they grasp the idea of the growth of the baby within the mother. A few girls are concerned about how the baby gets out and may spontaneously think that it comes out through an appendix scar if they have seen one.

As mentioned above, the real interest of the 5-year-old is in the baby rather than in its antecedents. Boys as well as girls desire to have a baby of their own. Some FIVES relate themselves back to the time when they were in their mother's stomach. They like to talk about this and to ask their mother if she remembers all about it. Or they like to relate themselves to the future when they are going to have a baby of their own. Or on noting a slight distension of the stomach in themselves, will conclude that they are going to have a baby, or maybe a doll. A child may dramatize the birth process by suddenly bringing forth a doll tucked between the legs! Another child of similar age may have a more critical sense of the realities. One 5-year-old was heard to ask another 5-year-old, "Are you old enough to have a baby?" "Goodness, no," was the reply, "I can't even tell time yet."

FIVE rarely plays the game of "show," exposing genitals or buttocks. In fact FIVE has become rather modest, especially about exposing his body to strangers. He may even display modesty before a maid or a younger sibling. He is aware of the sex organs in others when exposed and also of accessory sex characteristics such as pubic hair or breasts. Although he knows that difference in sex is indicated by the sex organs, he is still apt

to differentiate boys from girls by hair cut or by name. There is still some perplexity in the minds of some FIVES as to why a sister does not have a penis or why a father does not have breasts. Some FIVES may express a desire to become the opposite sex. Others emphasize their own sex by discarding any plaything they possess that may be related to the opposite sex. Boys, for instance, may emphatically refuse to play with such feminine toys as dolls or ironing boards.

§ 6. INTERPERSONAL RELATIONS

FIVE is that delightful stage when one takes life as it comes. On the whole he does not ask too much of life nor does he give too much. His life problems are restricted in scope and easy for him to handle. His mother finds him a joy to have around the house. He is so helpful, he is always within earshot, and he keeps his mother posted about his activities by always asking permission. He has endearing ways of showing how much he adores his mother. One 5-year-old girl who had some difficulty about her mother's departures, expressed it this way: "My stomach hurts. I begin to cry; and when you come back, oh I'm so happy!" Another FIVE who was trying to be more obedient, whispered in her mother's ear, "I've got a surprise for you. I'm going to say O.K. every time you speak to me."

Fathers also come in for their share of a 5-year-old's affection. The father, however, is rarely the preferred parent. FIVE is fond of his father, proud of him, may obey him better than the mother, but he may not take punishment as well from his father as from his mother. In the insecurity of the middle of the night he wants his mother most of all. If, however, the mother is sick, some FIVES who have been slow to build up a relationship with their fathers will now accept them. Fathers may not receive as much affection from the child as do the mothers, but on the other hand they do not receive as much disparagement! It is the mother who receives the brunt of the child's outbursts. It is the mother who is called the "bla-bla mommie"; and who is threatened with "I'm not going to play with you any more. You're a bad mommie."

FIVE is showing greater ability to play with others. He may play very well with a younger or an older sibling. He is less bossy and is now helpful and even devoted toward a younger sibling. He is protective and mothering. Oftentimes a 5-year-old boy is said to adore his younger sister. Nothing makes him more fighting mad than the threat to take away his baby sister. But life is not always smooth between siblings. Indoor play is poorer than outdoor play and needs supervision and planning. FIVE has moments of jealousy when a younger sibling is receiving all the attention, and he is capable of blaming some of his acts on a younger sibling. Because FIVE adjusts so well to a younger sib, parents sometimes overlook the fact that the younger child can be too much of a strain on a docile 5-year-old.

FIVE likes best to play with children of his own age. Some FIVES prefer their own sex, some the opposite sex, and others accept either readily. FIVE, since he is such a home body, is fairly dependent upon the children who are available in his neighborhood. Most FIVES play best out of doors. Some play best on their own home grounds, others away from home or in some neutral spot such as a park. A group of two is optimal. Whenever there are three in an unsupervised group, two usually gang up on the third. It is wise for the parent to hold to the simple rule that the child may invite only one child at a time until he is able to handle more, which is at seven or more usually at eight years of age. Sometimes FIVE responds best to an older child and may even take a minor part in neighborhood group play, accepting the role of baby in house play and leaving when he does not wish to compete. The bossy FIVE usually does best with a younger child who will accept being bossed. But even the bossy FIVE will take turns in playing other children's ways if part of the time they will concede to play his way.

Certain pairs of children from five to eight years of age prove to be incompatible for play. They seem to find no common ground except arguing and fighting. These very same pairs may become bosom friends at the age of eight or nine. Thrusting them together too often before they are socially ready does them no more good than to give them complicated reading material before they are ready for it. Some amenable FIVES need to be protected from being held too long in a social situation, because they may explode in a savage manner which might easily have been prevented if the parent had recognized the emotional fatiguability of the 5-year-old.

§ 7. PLAY AND PASTIMES

In General

When FIVE is asked, "What do you like to do best?" he is likely to answer with simply one word: "Play." And he is indeed a good player. He has his body under more smooth, skillful control and is therefore capable of play without too much adult assistance. With increasing age, differences in personality and sex become more evident in what the child chooses to play.

FIVE shows a craving for the standard kindergarten materials. He paints, draws, colors, cuts, and pastes. He specially enjoys cutting out things and is happy when provided with an old wallpaper book. Sometimes he cuts paper into shreds simply for the sake of cutting. On occasion he slips over from paper to cloth and takes gouges out of his clothes. He still needs to be watched when he is using scissors.

Blocks continue to be highly favored play material both for boys and girls. Girls build houses for their dolls and project personal situations, whereas boys build roads, tracks, bridges, tunnels, and use their houses for tanks, airplanes, army trucks and fire-engines. Houses play an important role in 5-year-old play behavior. FIVE likes to make big houses with big blocks, or tent houses of chairs draped with blankets. He wants to get into them, but he does not really play in them after he has entered.

Babies are another outstanding interest of the 5-year-old. Dolls are used as babies. And this interest is by no means restricted to girls. Boys too want to play dolls, dressing them, putting them to bed and most of all taking them for a ride in their carriages. Unhappy is the 5-year-old boy who craves a doll for Christmas and finds a stuffed animal in its place. The culture is unknowing in the ways of development or it would not act so arbitrarily. The interest in dolls is so strong that it is briefly shown at this age even by those girls who later scorn dolls.

FIVE's interest in houses is also expressed in his imaginative reenactment of domestic happenings. Boys join in this play as well as girls, but many boys prefer war games to the milder forms of house-play. Hospital-play is not as strong as it was at four, and school-play is not as strong as it will be at six.

Gross motor activity is a favorite with FIVE. He rides his tricycle with speed and adroitness. His tricycle moves freely, less hampered by the trailing equipment which he so delighted to hitch on when he was four. FIVE swings, he climbs, he skips, he roller skates and he jumps from a height. He may take to climbing trees or to jumping rope. He may attempt acrobatics, trapeze tricks, and even stilts.

Girls are likely to prefer sewing and boys carpentry. Boys already may show a well defined interest in tools. Their earlier tendency to destructiveness, their interest in taking things apart, may now be expressed in play with tools.

Reading and Numbers

There is nothing that a 5-year-old likes better than being read to, although he may spend considerable time in looking at books himself and may even pretend to read. He prefers stories about animals that act like human beings. He shows marked fondness for first grade readers which tell about occurrences in the lives of children. A few FIVES may like to listen to a reading of comic strips, regardless of whether they understand them.

FIVE is becoming more aware of the rudiments of reading and arithmetic. He is interested in copying letters and numbers. He enjoys playing simple letter and number games with his parents. Often this type of spontaneous interest is not satisfied in the home for fear that the school methods of teaching will be interfered with. The school might well recognize that home and school methods are not necessarily in conflict and that they can be used together advantageously. Any child who shows this spontaneous type of interest at home should have it satisfied.

Music, Radio and Movies

FIVE prefers his own gramophone records to the radio. He likes to play them over and over again. He likes a combination of music and words which tell a story. He may listen to the radio a little and shows a preference for the advertisements perhaps for the very reason that the adult dislikes them—he likes the catchy songs and the repetition.

Some FIVES can pick out tunes on the piano. They like to be taught how to play a few familiar melodies and they are apt to play the same song over and over again. They may sing with their records, or they may translate the music into dancing. FIVE enjoys dancing, especially at the bedtime hour.

§ 8. SCHOOL LIFE

Being such a home body, FIVE is well adjusted at home and is ready for the experience of being with children of his own age, especially in a supervised group. He usually adjusts with relative ease even though he has not had previous school experience. He may want his mother to accompany him to the threshold on the first day but may not want her to enter the schoolroom. The adjustment to one adult at a time is easier for him. Girls are more apt to want continued support of this kind for several days or a few weeks. An older child may substitute for the mother until the child is ready to go on his own. Going on a school bus sometimes solves this problem.

Girls are more apt to like school than boys. Boys complain when they are not provided with enough outdoor activity or when they do not have "large blocks." Spirited children may complain that "the teacher makes me do things," "the teacher makes me stay in line," or "I want to draw what I want to."

On the whole the health of the kindergartener is remarkably good. Some show fatigue every ten or fourteen days and a day at home with mother may be welcomed. With some children it may be advisable to plan for a four-day week with Wednesday at home allowing a two-day span, or for a four-day week with Monday or Friday at home.

Sometimes a miraculous change occurs at school and the very child who may be "bad" at home becomes "good" at school. The opposite is also possible and usually indicates that the child is not yet ready to adjust to a group situation unless he is permitted and helped to participate only on the outskirts of the group.

There is less carry-over from home to school and school to home than there was at four or will be at six. So FIVE takes fewer things to school although he may still like the security of a favorite toy which he clutches en route and then stores in his cubby. A few bring books for the teacher to read to the class. FIVE takes his handiwork home from time to time, but he is more interested in securing his teacher's immediate recognition than in taking things home for his mother's approval.

FIVE usually is not communicative about his school life. He may report that another child hit or pinched him, that the teacher made him do something. Parent and teacher profit on occasion through communicating by telephone in regard to an episode which may have occurred at home or at school.

On arrival at school, FIVE goes directly to his room and teacher. He needs some assistance with the removal of clothes and asks the teacher when he needs help. However, dressing for outdoor play or for going home is quite a different matter. Many children are not ready to take this responsibility and some need to be dressed entirely. An older child who calls for him may take over.

FIVE enjoys a routine, and adjusts well to an activity program which allows freedom of movement and yet maintains control of the sequence of separate activities. The morning may start with a free play period when he chooses blocks, carpentry, puzzles, painting, coloring, clay or house play. He changes from one activity to another. He usually completes a task although his attention may shift to watch another child at work or he may go to the teacher to tell her of a personal experience or to show her his product. Boys as well as girls play house. Daily routines such as washing, telephoning, shopping, with occasional episodes of doctoring are enacted. Boys prefer blocks; girls, houseplay.

Transitions are fairly easy for FIVE. With a word of warning from the teacher he completes his task and with some help from her puts materials away. He is then ready for the next activity, perhaps a discussion and a music period followed by a snack. Rest is often resisted if it is imposed at five; some children may not want to come to school because of it. Some, however, respond and others may follow suit. A simple song or story may accompany a short relaxation period.

The group enjoys a directed activity period of about twenty minutes, in which a simple task can be completed. This directed time may also be utilized for copying or recognizing letters, learning to print one's own name, or counting objects in the room.

Much of FIVE's reading and number work is closely associated with his play, both at home and at school. He can pick out capital letters, first at the left or right of a page and then at the beginning of a sentence in the text. Later he reads letters in combination such as "C-A-T" and asks what they spell. Signs are of particular interest to him and he may like to add a sign to his block structures. He may also add wooden letters for people such as A for Ann or S for Susan. He likes to identify repetitious words in a familiar book such as sounds the animals make or exclamatory words. At five-and-one-half some children pretend to read from a book which they have memorized; others like to underline the words they know.

FIVE enjoys counting objects; he tells how many toys he has. He can copy numbers and may write some from dictation. During the year he learns to identify a penny, nickel and dime. Attempts to add or subtract within five are made with or without using fingers or objects. Being "five" has tremendous significance to him. He is more likely to tell you that he is five years old than to tell you his name.

The directed activity period may be followed by story time which is a high light for FIVE, particularly when the story is dramatized after the reading. Stories with repetitive action and phrases are favorites, especially stories about animals, trains or fire engines.

Outdoor play usually comes at the end of the morning but is variable according to season and weather. Since FIVE is very much aware of both, it is helpful to have a large porch where most of his activities can be carried on during clement weather. Sand box, swing, large blocks and jungle gym are favorites. Sometimes an excursion is planned to a nearby farm.

The 5-year-old's morning at school is on the whole quite smooth. The here-and-nowness of FIVE requires immediate attention and thus the teacher circulates about the room ready to help, listen, or handle an emergency such as paint spilling. She provides the setting and materials for his experiences and is sought for approval and for affection.

FIVE works in short bursts of energy. He shows the same tendency when he suddenly shoves, strikes out or throws blocks or stones. He may learn to inhibit impulsive attacks by being told that "it hurts." His play is predominantly on his own even though he likes to be in a group. He goes from one activity to another usually completing each. Similarly he changes his postural orientation: he sits in a chair for one activity, stands for another, sits on the floor or on a table for another. He resents interference with his materials but he may be very obliging and provide an article on request. Some children may need to be separated from the group in play but at this age they usually can be removed to the outskirts without actual isolation.

The teacher's voice can ordinarily be heard above the chatter in which the children tell each other what they are doing, or repeat what a neighboring child has just said. Typical remarks are:

"Guess I'm through with that side"
"I'm going to do my work"
"Going to do your work, Susie?"
"I can't"
"Tommy, did you say I can't"
"Look at my house"
"Look at her house"
"Now make the grass"
"Da-da-da-da; dum-dum-dum"
"I want to save mine"

A desire for toileting is announced and a response expected from the teacher. FIVE may wait until the last minute but can care for himself. Boys may grab at their genitals and girls may wriggle or place hands on thighs. If FIVE holds off too long, particularly when outdoors, he may have an "accident." A boy may on occasion urinate out-of-doors. FIVE, however, accepts a suggestion to go to the toilet before it is time for outdoor play.

Kindergarten activity is not highly social. In free play two, three, or four children may sit at the same table to crayon or to mold clay but they work independently and readily leave for play in another part of the room. The same grouping is evident at the sand box. Housekeeping may hold a larger number together for a while. Toward the end of the year two children may be found building cooperatively on the same block structure.

§ 9. ETHICAL SENSE

FIVE's poise is sustained because his own needs and the environmental demands are rather equally balanced. FIVE is a part of his environment and his environment is a part of him. Thinking of him in these terms it becomes easier to discern the quality of his ethical sense, which is so new and so tentative that it can hardly be classed as such.

FIVE enjoys helping his mother and running errands. He likes to please, to do things in the right, accepted way. He does not usually resist a request with "I won't" as he did at four, but he may hesitate between a refusal and an acceptance. He may refuse to do things because he cannot do them, or because he is too busy to do them. Sometimes he is motivated by a simple reward. Although he likes praise, his need of it is not as great as it will be at six. His asking for permission or his telling what he is going to do indicates how much he has identified himself with his environment. The answer to his request seems often to be needed as a starter.

Making up his mind is not too difficult for he has not many alternatives to choose between, and he is apt to make a conforming choice. He can, however, change his choice, for he is susceptible to reason or to an explanation. And since he wishes to oblige, he may shift to his parents' side. A few FIVES are more rigid and by simple device can be jostled into line.

FIVE is often spoken of as being markedly good, "like an angel." His sense of good and bad, if he has any, does not differentiate right from wrong. He either takes his behavior for granted, or thinks only in terms of his practical relationships to other persons. FIVE is "good" because he loves his mother and wants to please her. FIVE does not want to do "bad" things, because such conduct annoys people and makes them uncomfortable. A few FIVES are unusually concerned about being called bad. This is worse than a spanking to them, and they may appear to be ashamed of it. But at the same time they may compulsively handle their fear of being called bad by playing "bad school." In "bad school" they jump on tables and run around the room screaming—behavior which they believe not to be acceptable in school.

If FIVE does something he should not do or did not want or mean to do, he is likely to blame the nearest person. If his mother is close by, the child may accuse her with a "Look what you made me do." A sibling, a dog or another child may be blamed when they are a part of the scene of action. There may be more validity to this accusation than one at first realizes. When a child is running down a hill and meets another child, there is no doubt that he may show an unsteadiness in his running and finally fall. The other child did not push him, but the other child's presence did remove his attention from his running. He could not do the two things at once—both look at the child and run. It is very significant that during the pre-school years serious accidents do occur when the mother is right beside the child and yet not giving her full attention to him. He becomes dependent upon her if she is there, whereas if he had been on his own he might have exercised his usual caution and not come to grief.

FIVE enjoys the possessions he has. He is not as eager for presents as he was at four, nor does he brag about his possessions as he did earlier. This does not mean that he is careful about his possessions. A few children take things home from school, such as toys or books, but readily and willingly return them. At home the 5-year-old may take things from the kitchen, or a girl may desire and take some of her mother's powder or perfume.

On the whole FIVE is relatively truthful. He believed his fanciful tales at four, but by five he knows that he is fooling, and has his tongue in his cheek. Sometimes his tales are self-protective, though oddly so. One 5-year-old who was late for dinner told his parents that "a big boy said he was going to kill me so I couldn't come home." Other fanciful tales may indicate a wish not yet fulfilled. The 5-year-old girl who reported that her teacher said she read well enough to read with the first grade, was obviously expressing an unsatisfied longing. Such a girl might well be ready for early reading.

§10. PHILOSOPHIC OUTLOOK

Death and Deity

The vast intangible creative force called God is often grasped rather well by the mind of the 4-year-old. But FIVE does not soar as high and has a tendency to bring God within the scope of his everyday world. He asks very specific questions about what He looks like, is He a man, what does He do and where does He live? He also conceives of God's world as having modern equipment and therefore asks if you can call Him up on the telephone and if He makes cars.

Some FIVES are more aware of God's presence and may even fear that He sees whatever they do. One 5-year-old thought that God pushed him whenever he fell. Others may be rather critical of God and His reported handiwork, for they feel that "God made a mistake when He made a mosquito."

Death likewise is taken in a fairly matter-of-fact way. FIVE seems to recognize dimly the finality of death and may speak of it as "the end." The dead person is to him one without living attributes: "He can't walk, he can't see, and he can't feel." He is interested in the posture of the soldier who falls dead—"Did he fall on his back or his face?" If he is told that dead people go to heaven after they die, he wonders why they don't fall out of heaven.

He has linked up the facts that when you are old you die. He is not usually concerned about his own personal relationship to death, or the possible deaths of those around him. He does, however, recognize the eventual possibility that others will die and states the fact that "When I grow up all you people will be dead." He has not as yet conceived of his own death, but readily enters into the game of playing dead when he is shot.

Time and Space

FIVE in his sense of time is concerned chiefly with the Now. It is difficult for him to conceive of himself as not having existed or as dying. Time for him is largely his own personal time.

The more common "time" words used by adults are now a part of the child's vocabulary and he handles them freely. He knows when events of the day take place in relation to each other. He can answer correctly such questions about time as the following:

How old will you be on your next birthday?
What day is today?
What day does Daddy stay at home all day?
What day comes after Sunday?
What day do you like best?

Many FIVES are very much interested in the calendar and in the clock. A few copy the numbers on the clock's face and may read them. They are especially proud of possessing an alarm clock of their own, and accept the ringing of the alarm as the time to get up, or to terminate a play nap.

FIVE'S chief spatial interest is in what is Here. He is extremely focal, is interested in the space which he immediately occupies. He has little insight into geographic relationships, but does recognize some specific landmarks. He likes to draw roads on very simple maps of his immediate neighborhood. He can now cross streets in his immediate neighborhood by himself and likes to do errands at the nearby store. His interest in more distant places depends upon his personal associations with them.

6

SIX YEARS OLD

BEHAVIOR PROFILE

"HE IS a changed child!" Many a mother has said this ruefully, when her former 5-year-old begins to lose his angelic five-year-oldness. "He is a changed child, and I do not know what has gotten into him!"

There is some mystification about this change. At five he was such a well-organized child, at home with himself and at home with the world. But as early as the age of five-and-a-half he began to be brash and combative in some of his behavior, as though he were at war with himself and with the world. At other times he was hesitant, dawdling, indecisive; and then again overdemanding and explosive, with strangely contradictory spurts of affection and of antagonism. At other times, of course, he was quite delightful and companionable. "But I can't understand him. What *has* gotten into him?"

Perhaps nothing more or less than six-year-oldness!

The sixth year (or thereabouts) brings fundamental changes, somatic and psychological. It is an age of transition. The milk teeth are shedding; the first permanent molars are emerging. Even the child's body chemistry undergoes subtle changes reflected in increased susceptibility to infectious disease. Otitis media comes to a peak; nose and throat difficulties rise in frequency. The 6-year-old is not as robust nor as staunch as he was at five. There are other important developmental changes which affect the mechanisms of vision, and indeed the whole neuro-motor system.

These changes manifest themselves in new and sometimes startling psychological traits,—traits which begin to make their appearance at five-and-a-half, as will be indicated in the listing of maturity traits. The 6-year-old proves to be not a bigger and better 5-year-old. He is a different child because he is a changing child. He is passing through a stage of transition, similar to the paradoxical stage of the 2½-year-old. He also has much of the fluidity and forthrightness of the 4-year-old. Combine the paradoxical and labile qualities of the 2½-year-old and 4-year-old and you have an indication of the maturity traits of the 6-year-old.

In describing these traits, we shall emphasize those which make the 6-year-old distinguishable from the 5-year-old. The reader will understand that the traits do not descend upon the child with a sudden onrush. The colors of a developmental spectrum shade into each other by imperceptible gradations. But to paint a vivid and usable maturity portrait, we must dip our brush where the pigment is strong. With this much apology to the 6-year-old, we shall now attempt to do him developmental justice,—remembering that such justice tends to bridge the chasm between angels and demons.

The action-system of the child is now undergoing growth changes, comparable in their way to the eruption of the sixth year molars. New propensities are erupting; new impulses, new feelings, new actions are literally coming to the surface, because of profound developments in the underlying nervous system. These manifold changes probably hark back to psychological increments which were slowly evolved through aeons of time in the remote prehistory of mankind. In the individual, the essence of the racial increments is crowded into the brief space of months and years. The 5-year-old has already come into a fundamental portion of the racial inheritance. The 6-year-old is coming into a later portion. This is "what has gotten into him!"

Psychological inheritance, however, does not come in neat packages. It comes in the form of behavior trends and dynamic forces which must be reconciled and organized within a total action-system. It takes time to pattern and to balance conflicting trends of behavior as they well up in the sixth year of life. Some conflict is a normal accompaniment of developmental progress. So we may take a constructive and optimistic view of the developmental difficulties which the 6-year-old encounters.

He tends to go to extremes,—under slight stress, whenever he attempts to use his most recently acquired powers. As an actively growing organism, he is entering new fields of action. The new possibilities of behavior seem to come in pairs. He is often under a compulsion to manifest first one extreme of two alternative behaviors and then soon after, its very opposite. The diametric opposites have almost equal sway over him, because both propensities have only recently arrived upon the scene. He is inexperienced in their management and meaning. It is hard for him to choose between such evenly competing opposites. When he is away from home, he may even be overtaxed by the simple proposition: "Will you have chocolate ice cream or vanilla ice cream?" A difficult choice,—and one which will not be decisive even after it is made; for an immature child cannot adeptly cancel out a rival alternative. He will not completely forego the vanilla after he has chosen the chocolate. Decisions which were easy or judicial at five, have become complicated with new emotional factors, for he *is* growing. The complication signifies increased maturity. The indecisiveness signifies immaturity if we allow ourselves a paradoxical distinction between maturity and immaturity.

Let a poem by Edna St. Vincent Millay bear witness to the duplexity of life situations at the age of six:

> Come along in then, little girl!
> Or else stay out!
> But in the open door she stands
> And bites her lips and twists her hands
> And stares upon me trouble-eyed:
> "Mother," she says, "I can't decide!
> I can't decide."

A 2½-year-old child displays a similar difficulty in handling opposites, —in deciding between *yes* and *no; come* and *go; fast* and *slow* and many another *do* and *don't*. The child oscillates between two alternatives, chooses the wrong; or in quick succession chooses the wrong, the right, the wrong, the right; dawdles, or reaches an impasse, stymied by the two-way possibilities. It is almost as if he were seeing two images, and were plagued with the inability to suppress one image for the sake of clear single vision. Our 6-year-old is suffering from a similar (and likewise temporary) developmental duplicitness. He is afflicted with bipolarity,—a see-saw awareness of both ends of a dilemma.

The 6-year-old manifests his bipolarities in many different ways. He flies quickly from one extreme to another. He cries, but his crying is easily diverted into laughter, and his laughter into crying. He sidles up to his mother and says, "I love you," but in another breath he may say, "I hate you, I'll hit you." He will mutter as much to a total stranger. Indeed, if we note the psychological shallowness of his brash verbalizations, his epithets (Stinker!), his profanity (Aw nuts! Dope!), we can allow with a smile of sympathetic humor that there is a certain naivete in his madness. We must discourage his irresponsibilities, and yet recognize that these warring intensities and impulses are new experiences for him. Sometimes he seems to be bent upon defining what *not* to do by doing it.

Certainly he is as inexpert in handling complex human relationships, as he once was inept in putting a spoon into his mouth. He frequently misses the mark. Watch him in his social approaches to his baby sister. He may be very good to her, and also very bad, all in the same afternoon or the same half hour. To attribute his badness to sheer perversity or even to jealousy may be erroneous. We are dealing with a general dynamic of behavior, which makes for vacillation, and lack of integration. The inconsistencies of 6-year-old conduct, his tendency to bolt in and out, his tendency to slam, his verbal aggressions, his intense concentrations, his abrupt terminations, his explosive attacks upon situations, —are all cut from the same cloth. An outstanding characteristic of the 6-year-old is his meager capacity to modulate. But we need not despair. With the help of the culture and the help of time he improves that capacity.

His difficulty in making a ready distinction between two-way possibilities is not limited to situations which are emotional or ethical in nature. In his early efforts to print letters of the alphabet he is prone to reverse them. His *B* looks backward. His tendency to reversals may be linked to his penchant for mirror symmetry. He is fond of pairs: 2 and 2 are 4 is easier than 2 and 1 are 3. He can play with one playmate more successfully than with two. In his play there is a good deal of Tit for Tat: I give you a present; you give me a present. You push me; I push you.

Life is charged with double alternatives for all of us, even after we are grown up. The 6-year-old in our complex culture happens to be in a phase of development where these alternatives crowd upon him rather thickly. He is at cross roads where he has to intermediate between contraries. When he does the wrong thing, he is called bad, but there is no use in asking him why he was bad; he has not yet made a clear distinction. He is not fully oriented. He is in new territory. He does not have command of his motor impulses nor of his interpersonal relationships.

At the age of five awareness and capabilities were in better balance. The 6-year-old is aware of more than he can well manage. He often over-differentiates (going to extremes), or he underdifferentiates. He is over-emphatic, or he hesitates and dawdles, or he attempts things which are too hard for him. He wants to be first. He always wants to win. This makes him quarrelsome and accusative on the playground. Yet he wants to be loved best. At Christmas he wants a good many presents, but doesn't know exactly what they should be. He is so active and acquisitive for new experience that his manners are likely to be hasty and sketchy,—a quick Come in, or Thank you; but no prolonged deference or formality in shaking hands! In the profound words of a poetess, herself age six:

> Mr. Hullabaloo, Mr. Hullabaloo
> He always forgot to say "How do you do?"
> Mr. Bahtot took off his haht
> And said "How do you do, Mr. Hullabaloo!"

It follows that a Birthday Party limited to 6-year-olds is not a model of decorum. Even under adult supervision with a master plan, such a foregathering tends to become a kaleidoscopic medley of high pressure activities,—short shrift amenities as the guests arrive, a pouncing seizure of presents, an excited exchange of favors, everyone expecting the first prize, bubbling bravadoes, scrambles and hullabaloo with interludes of silence induced by ice cream. At no age are children more insistently interested in parties; at no age, perhaps, are they less competent to produce a party agreeable to adult ideals of decorum. Characteristically enough the eagerness of the 6-year-old is not commensurate with his capabilities, particularly under social stress. A philosophic observer will detect evidences of constructive, adaptive behavior even in the confusions and diffusions of a high spirited party. A prudent parent will limit the complexity of the party in advance.

A primary school teacher will see in such a party a display of the same rich energies with which she deals every day as she guides her group of first-graders. A schoolroom represents the tool and the technique by which our culture attempts to pattern these abounding energies. Fortunate are those children who are entrusted to a teacher capable of interpreting their ebullitions as symptoms of a growth process which needs skillful direction. Such a teacher creates in her schoolroom a cheerful atmosphere of tolerance and security which is hospitable to a certain dramatic quality in the 6-year-old.

What do we mean by this dramatic quality? Not an artificial stage-like make-believe, but a natural tendency to express and to organize new experience through frank muscular reactions. The young body of a healthy 6-year-old is supple, sensitive, alert. He reacts with his whole action-system. He does not only smile,—he fairly dances with joy. He cries copiously when unhappy, kicks and shakes with his grief. Even during sleep he pitches his whole organism into his dreams. Hence the gross arousals of his nightmares, which come to a peak at the age of six. During the waking day he tries on and throws off moods with facility. He uses body postures, gestures and speech to give expression to emotions and ideas which are taking shape within him.

We must remember that the 6-year-old is not simply trying to perfect abilities which he had at the age of five. Nature is adding a cubit to his psychological stature. He is moving into altogether strange domains of experience. He uses his muscles, large and small, to pioneer new pathways.

Dramatic self-activation is at once a method of growth and of learning. It is a natural mechanism whereby the child organizes his feeling and thinking. But the task is too great for him alone. The school is the cultural instrument which must help him to enlarge and to refine his dramatic self-projections. Instinctively he identifies himself with all that happens about him, even with the pictures and the letters in his book and the numbers on the blackboard. Just as he must pick up a block and handle it to learn its properties, so he must project his motor and mental attitudes into life situations. Emotions are not formless forces; they are patterned experiences. The function of the school is to provide personal and cultural experiences which will simultaneously organize the growing emotions and the associated intellectual images.

Naturally this can be done effectively only through activity programs and projects which will set into operation the child's own self-activity. He learns not by rote but by participation and a creative kind of self-activation. His teacher takes him and his school mates on a trip to a dairy. The children talk it all over some time later, after an interval of assimilation. As an individual and as a tenuous member of a group the 6-year-old translates his experience by building a ground plan of the barn with building blocks. He plans with the group to re-enact part of his experience by dramatic representation. Through all these mediums of expression he clarifies meanings and relationships. There are endless opportunities for similar dramatic assimilation,—*pantomime* of simple actions (I am chopping wood); *portrayal of moods* (a lost child, a tired boy); *tableaux and self-initiated dramatic skits* (school and home life), *dramatized stories with simple plot* (Mother Goose and very simple puppet plays). The ordinary 6-year-old mind is not ready for purely formal instruction in reading, writing and arithmetic. These subjects can be vitalized only through association with creative activity and motorized life experiences. Such dramatic expression must not be confused with rehearsed theatricals or formalized kindergarten play acting. It is a developmental form of self-expression, which must be evoked impromptu and by ingenious indirection. Once a primary teacher has grasped this fundamental principle, she can establish a mutually delightful rapport between herself and her pupils.

For a disadvantaged child a well conducted school is a haven. For the average school-beginner the understanding teacher becomes a kind of auxiliary mother on whom he fixes affection. She does not displace his mother, nor does she aspire to become a substitute mother. But she strengthens his sense of security in the strange world beyond the home. He derives a new confidence in this world from her daily welcomes and assurances, and from the sheer satisfaction of his broadening experiences and from the protectiveness of a partially standardized environment.

He does not wish this environment to deviate much from a familiar set pattern. He likes some social routines. He has to assimilate so many new experiences that he prefers psychological landmarks which remain fixed. He is fond of the rituals and conventions which are reliably repeated each day. He rather likes to see his teacher in a customary location when the program of the day begins. (Sometimes he may even have a passing regret if she changes a ribbon or a coiffure!) Perhaps because he is constantly making new discoveries, he craves a few fixed points in his mental universe.

It is easy to forget that this young discoverer has to adjust to two worlds: the world of home, and the world of his school. The school provides certain simplifications and group controls which the home lacks. His emotional anchorage remains in the home, but he has to acquire a modified set of emotional moorings in the school. The two orientations are not interchangeable and not mixable. Being inexpert in emotional modulations, the school-beginner cannot always shift readily within the two worlds. An ill-timed visit at school from his mother; a mysterious conversation between his mother and his awesome new teacher may produce some jangle of images and attitudes. Often it is hard enough to make the transition when the two worlds are physically separated. He may have difficulty in the morning in leaving his true mother; he may be teased on the trip to school, because a 6-year-old freshman is an easily scareable and teasible victim for the 8-9-10-year-old upper classmen. (Hat snatching and verbal detractions.) And the new customs at school may be so rudely strange that they baffle and disorient.

Parents, teachers and school administrators may be unaware of the complex of factors both inherent and environmental which can undermine the morale of a school-beginner. Sometimes the transition to school is so blundering that it produces gastro-intestinal symptoms and severe emotional reactions. Here individual differences count. The sensitive and immature children suffer most. Difficulties of adjustment are exacerbated if the teacher has a cheerless, disciplinary personality, if the methods of instruction are over rigid with excess stress on academic proficiency, competitiveness and school marks. In some of these instances the tensions of school entrance are so abnormally weighted against the child that his mental health is overtaxed. School entrance is no simple transition and it should be tempered by flexible arrangements of attendance and program.

Many tensions, however, are normal. They are innate in the very process of child development. Paradoxically, the transitional bipolarity of six-year-oldness makes this a favorable time for achieving psychological transitions. Society has sanctioned the sixth and seventh years for a significant induction into the higher strata of culture. The induction cannot be indefinitely postponed because the child must transcend the limitations of home and also the primitive strata in his own psychological make-up. The race evolves; the child grows.

We have already alluded to certain primitive features in the maturity traits of the 6-year-old. These traits are vaguely characterized by such adjectives as impulsive, undifferentiated, volatile, dogmatic, compulsive, excitable. His spontaneous drawings are crude but realistic, and sometimes suggestive of the graphic renderings of early man, in their portrayal of action, of sky and earth, and of ornamental design. He likes to draw a house with a tree beside it. Wild animals, darkness, fire, thunder, lightning, figure in the fears and dreams of the 6-year-old. Boys and girls alike are naively proud to lose their teeth and have a ready faith in dental fairies, in elfins, and other supernatural agencies.

Although his intellectual processes are concrete and even animistic, the 6-year-old is susceptible to semi-abstract symbols, charms and conjurations. He is highly dependent upon the direction and guidance of adult authority. Witness the modern version of primitive magic in which the incantatory parent counts *1-2-3-4-5-6-7*, with the advance understanding that when the magic 7 is intoned, the required deed will be done by the obedient child. The magic works. It is not based on pure gullibility. Even in primitive times magic was close to science. The deliberate counting which can be shortened or lengthened to suit the

[97]

needs, gives the child a fulcrum and an opportunity to mobilize the adjustment which he cannot accomplish by his own unaided volition. Like any other guidance device, it should be judiciously used, but it turns a neat trick in overcoming the hobbling effect of the child's bipolarity.

In the long run both home and school will rely not upon magic but upon the utilization of the dramatic potentialities of the 6-year-old, to lead him into new ways of self-control. His dramatic self-projectiveness is one of his most significant maturity traits; and it is constantly available. By means of it he maintains his own spontaneous contacts with the culture; by means of it, also, the culture lays hold upon him and directs him into new participations and anticipations. Much environmental influence comes through automatic imitation and incidental suggestion, both of which are related to his dramatic qualities. The total process of assimilation, directed and undirected, whereby the child acquires his ways of life, is called acculturation.

Since he is given a share in the process he does not become a mere figment of the culture. Through his projections, representative and interpretive, he does not merely reduplicate portions of the culture; he reappraises and reorganizes himself in relation to the culture. He begins to see himself and his bipolar opposites in their social contexts. He thus lays the basis for self-appraisals and for evaluations which come to fuller flower in the seventh and eighth years. The social setting of the schoolroom is indispensible to this process of self-organization. His individual creative activities, his participation in group enterprises, his contribution to group planning,—all provide him with a scale of values. He finds he cannot go too far in sheer self-expression in a democratic schoolroom. He must have regard for others. It is fun to make others laugh and perhaps to lead them; but it is also fun to see what they can do. And everybody makes mistakes, himself included. So he slowly builds up that social perceptiveness of proportion and disproportion which is the essence of common sense and which is also part of the saving sense of humor.

We know of a teacher* who uses an attractive, though concealed technique for educating this invaluable sense which all first-graders should develop. When mid-morning lunch is over, her children stretch out on their rugs for a short rest, shades down. With a twinkle in her eye the teacher now opens a notebook and reads from its pages a verbatim report of what the children have said and done in their early cooperative planning of an activity project (such as the trip to the dairy). Recumbent and relaxed on their rugs the children smile as they listen, chuckling at their own remarks. The teacher, who should be a dramatist of sorts, is holding up a mirror in which the children see themselves. This is education in humor and tolerance. It is mental hygiene; it is developmental guidance. In such a genial atmosphere, personality thrives; the mind gains in pliancy and in stamina.

These inward processes of assimilation and reconstruction rise to higher levels as the child matures. We shall see some interesting growth transformations in the seventh year. But the transitional sixth year must come first.

MATURITY TRAITS

(The following maturity traits are not to be regarded as rigid norms nor as models. They simply illustrate the kinds of behavior (desirable or otherwise) which tend to occur at this age. Every child has an individual pattern of growth, unique to him. The behavior traits here outlined may be used to interpret his individuality and to consider the maturity level at which he is functioning.)

§1. MOTOR CHARACTERISTICS

Bodily Activity

The composure of FIVE is no longer characteristic of FIVE-AND-A-HALF, who is said to be restless at home. He plays indoors or outdoors and does not seem to know which place he wants to be. He occupies himself with digging, dancing and climbing. He rides his tricycle down hill. He carts things about in a wagon. Sand, water and mud play keep him oc-

* We made her acquaintance in one of the useful leaflets of a *Portfolio for Primary Teachers* issued by the Association for Childhood Education (A Good Day at School for the Sixes by Elizabeth Vernon Hubbard), Washington, D. C.

cupied. Household tasks provide him many motor activities. He likes to set the table and help his mother by getting things for her. When asked what he plays he says, "Just one thing after another."

Six is an active age. The child is in almost constant activity whether standing or sitting. He seems to be consciously balancing his own body in space. He is everywhere,—climbing trees, crawling over, under and about his large block structures or other children. He seems to be all legs and arms as he dances about the room.

He approaches activities both with more abandon and more deliberation and he may stumble and fall in his efforts to master. He may like the "cleaning up" job at school, brushing the floor, pushing furniture about albeit he is somewhat clumsy and not too thorough. He enjoys activity and does not like interference.

There is a good deal of boisterous, ramble-scramble play. He likes to wrestle with his father or a sibling, but this may end in disaster for he does not know when to stop. Indoors his ball play may become a menace as he bounces, tosses and tries to catch. He is also interested in stunts on a trapeze bar; he likes to pull himself up on a rope, and swing. Swings are favorites; he sits with more freedom and balance and he loves to swing as high as he can.

Six over-extends in much of his motor behavior. He likes to build blocks higher than his shoulder; he tries to do a running broad jump without minding if he falls. His own yard may not be as attractive as a neighbor's.

Eyes and Hands

There are also noticeable changes in the eye-hand behavior of the 5½-year-old.

He seems more aware of his hand as a tool and he experiments with it as such. He is reported to be awkward in performing fine motor tasks, yet he has a new demand for such activities. Tinker toys and tools are especially interesting to him. He may be less interested in what he accomplishes with the tools and more in manipulating them. He likes to take things apart as well as put them together. Girls especially like to dress and undress dolls at this age.

He now holds his pencil more awkwardly and he changes his grasp on it. He likes to draw, print and color as he did at five but he adheres less closely to a model. Filling in with color may occupy him for a considerable period. In coloring, he is awkward, shifts his body position as well as his prehension of the crayon and tilts his head. He may stand and lean way over the table and continue to draw or he may rest his head down on his arm. He may say that his hand "gets tired" and bring the free hand to it briefly. With his attempts at finer manipulation he is often found standing or even walking as he is working.

Six is as active in sitting as he is in the standing position. He wriggles on a chair, sits on the edge, may even fall off. There is a good deal of oral activity: tongue extension and mouthing, blowing through and biting lips. He bites, chews or taps his pencil. Pencil grasp is less awkward than at 5½ years, but his performance is laborious.

Eye and hand now function with less of the speed and close relationship that they showed at five. In building a tower of small blocks, Six makes a more deliberate regardful approach and tries to place the blocks accurately. But they may not be as accurately aligned as they were at five. At another time, Six may build with such careless abandon that the blocks fall repeatedly.

He touches, handles and explores all materials. "What do you do with this?" He wants to do everything. There is often more activity than actual accomplishment. But he cuts and pastes, making books and boxes, and moulds clay into objects.

Six can shift his eyes more facilely and he shifts his regard frequently from the task at hand. He is easily distracted by the environment and his hands may continue to work as he watches another's activity.

In carpentry he needs a good deal of assistance. The saw bends and gets jammed. He pounds and pounds in driving nails. He often fails to hit them on the head and may even break the board. He may hold the hammer near the head. He can, however, make crude structures.

§2. PERSONAL HYGIENE

Eating

Appetite. The good appetite of FIVE continues into six and may become tremendous. Some children are said to eat all day long, and are reputed to eat better between meals than at meals. Breakfast continues to be the poorest meal and may be accompanied by stomach ache, nausea and infrequently by vomiting. A liquid diet of milk and fruit juice is definitely preferred.

In contrast to his poor morning meal, the 6-year-old often feels hungry just before he goes to bed and may eat a sizable snack with real enjoyment. He may even awaken in the middle of the night and ask for food.

Six's eyes are often bigger than his stomach, and he is apt to ask for bigger helpings than he can handle. He should not be held too closely to his initial re-

quest. If he does not agree to have two helpings with the chance of refusing his planned second helping, he may be allowed to divide the food on his plate into two portions. Face-saving devices for both parent and child should be made quickly available as they are needed. Such devices gather legitimacy and meaning when one realizes that the 6-year-old is characteristically good at starting things and definitely poor at finishing.

A boost in appetite is often accomplished by some new experience, some change in routine. Thus a visit to grandmother's, or a meal at a restaurant with the family often brings about an improvement, even though it may be only temporary.

Refusals and Preferences. SIX continues to prefer plain cooking. Though he may have a fairly wide range of food likes and is willing to try new foods, his likes and dislikes are usually very positive. He may refuse meat because he once was served a piece with a little rim of fat on it, or he may refuse meat because he doesn't like to chew. He may refuse foods by spells. What's "in" is strongly in and what's "out" is completely out. This is the age when peanut butter begins its rise toward its 7-8-year-old pinnacle of preference. Many of the cooked desserts, especially rice pudding and custard, are perhaps refused for themselves alone, but often the 6-year-old goes "off desserts." If they came at the beginning of the meal he might perhaps eat them with relish. He usually prefers raw vegetables to cooked ones. Textures are extremely important: lumpy, stringy foods are commonly refused.

Self-Help. Many children return to finger feeding at six. Eating implements seem to be an unnecessary intrusion between them and the food, and they are manipulated awkwardly. Even such foods as mashed potatoes are finger fed. These children should be given more whole foods so that they may finger feed themselves. The fork is often preferred to a spoon and will be used if the food can be speared. At the opposite extreme are the fastidious children who would not think of touching their food with their fingers or of spilling a drop. These children eat with care and precision and use implements deftly.

Table Behavior. It is not an edifying experience to have a 6-year-old at the table, especially at the evening meal. He really does not belong there, and would much prefer to have a tray beside the radio while he is either listening to music or to his special program.

His motor control is very erratic in sitting as well as in standing. The minute he sits down his legs are likely to start swinging. If your leg or the table leg is within range, the force of his thrust will be duly imprinted. If he must come to the table he might be allowed to come in his stocking feet. After his initial attack upon his food he begins to dawdle and to wriggle. He reaches for a carrot and knocks over his milk. His arms jerk and he spills his food. Pretty soon he is teetering on the back legs of his chair or even on only one leg. Father is slowly losing patience and has perhaps already said too much in his attempt to hold the child in line.

When the 6-year-old does eat he stuffs his mouth too full and is apt to talk with his mouth full. If his total body is not active, he is at least likely to talk too much. If he is criticized for his behavior he is apt to find the same flaws for which he is criticized in his siblings or parents.

Leaving him alone at the table produces almost the opposite effect to the desired one. He dawdles a little more than he did. Taking the food away from him either makes him angry or produces tears. The return of the food may tip the scale in the right direction, but the best stimulus, if he is at the family table, may be to race with him, making sure that he will win.

Needless to say, not all 6-year-olds are composites of this picture, but most of them show at least some of its features. A few children actually eat better with the family group than alone, but a surprisingly large number actually request supper in bed, or a tray by the radio. They seem to sense what is best for them; for when allowed to come to the table on occasion, they handle the situation much better, showing pride in accomplishment. It is unfortunate to send a child from the table as a punishment for failure. If he insists on being with the family group regularly, he is usually quite satisfied to sit at his own little table, preferably with another sibling.

A napkin is still a cultural tool beyond his competence. The child now refuses a bib and may also refuse to have the napkin tucked in under his chin. If the napkin is beside his plate he forgets to use it and if it is on his lap it quickly falls to the floor. He may be aware of food around his mouth and may deftly remove it by a sweep of the back of his hand. Others use a napkin on being reminded, but on the whole clean hands and clean faces are still the responsibility of the adult and not of the child.

Sleep

Nap. A very few 5½-year-old children cling to a half hour nap on occasion. By six, if there still is any desire to nap it is cut into by afternoon school attendance. The rich enjoyment which a 6-year-old expresses when he takes an hour's planned "play nap" may well make us question the advisability of school attendance at that time.

Bedtime. The 5½-year-old in his presleep patterns shows a very real developmental shift in his behavior. He is definitely tired and rarely resists going to bed at his usual bedtime (7-8 P.M.) or even earlier. Some children like to get ready for bed before supper and to have a tray in bed, though they do not actually go to bed to sleep before their usual bedtime. They are more fearful at this age, want the companionship of their mother even after the lights are turned off; may ask to have an adult remain on the same floor with them, to sleep in the same room with a sibling or to have the hall light on. There is a return of interest in and of taking stuffed animals and dolls to bed with them, even to the number of two or three. They treat these toys as though they were real people keeping them company. Prayers have an unusually quieting effect upon some children and should be seriously considered especially with the fearful child.

The 6-year-old's bedtime behavior is not as fearful as that of the 5½-year-old. He goes to bed quite easily and enjoys some quiet activity or music after he is in bed. He especially likes to be read to or to look at books for half an hour. This is an excellent time to stimulate a child's interest in reading. He enjoys picking out single letters, especially capital letters, or even words in the story his parent is reading to him. After the lights are turned out he is fond of telling about the day's happenings and about things that are on

his mind. He is very spontaneous at this age: all the mother needs to do is to listen, guiding his thoughts along the channel he is taking.

Some children enjoy having father put them to bed, and respond more smoothly to him. Others, however, are overstimulated by the father. Some girls do not go to sleep until their father has kissed them goodnight. As a rule the mother is still preferred especially for the good-night chats.

Night. There is an increasing number of 6-year-olds who are said to be "wonderful sleepers." But there are still quite a few, though fewer than at five, whose sleep is disturbed by toilet needs or by "bad dreams." Strange men and women are beginning to appear in their dreams, and the dream animals which are still frequently present are becoming active, especially in biting.

When a terrifying nightmare occurs, the child may be unable to quiet until his mother gets into bed with him. Those who are able to awaken by themselves, crawl into bed with their parents, especially with their mother. Some return to their own beds after telling the dream; others after a short reassuring snuggle with their mother. Still others need to spend the rest of the night in their mother's bed, even though she may have slipped out and gone to sleep in the child's bed.

Very few children are toileted routinely at this age. Some of those who still need to get up must report to their parent after they have functioned, but an increasing number care for themselves and get back into bed by themselves.

Morning. Morning waking at 5½ years of age shows two extremes: the early wakers

(5:30-6:00 A.M.), and the late wakers (8 A.M.). The latter may even have to be awakened. By six the extremes are not quite so wide. The usual waking time is between 7 and 7:30, and the child no longer needs to be wakened. The 5½-year-old sleeps about 11½ hours; the 6-year-old 11 hours.

On rising, the 6-year-old toilets himself and usually becomes more interested in his morning play activities than in his dressing. If, however, his clothes are laid out singly on the bed for him he may carry through after a reminder to begin.

Elimination

Bowel. The general pattern of the 5-year-old persists—one movement per day, after lunch. There is a tendency to shift this function to the earlier half of the day rather than the latter half. A few shift to before breakfast or after bedtime. Two movements per day may occur but these are often two installments of one movement, since the child may not sit long enough to complete the evacuation. The parent needs to help with a little supervision to see that the child remains long enough to finish.

As a rule, functioning is rather rapid, in fact if the child has waited until the latter part of the afternoon, it may be so rapid that he makes a mad dash for the bathroom and may arrive there too late. With some children the movement seems to occur almost involuntarily before they can do anything about it. These episodes of incontinence affect the parents almost more than the child. The child may be ashamed and may crawl off into some recess, though frequently he tries to set things right by changing his pants and cleaning himself up. And the parent also is ashamed, and would never think of mentioning it to the family physician.

Ability to function easily on the school toilet usually does not come until about the age of 8 years. The 6-year-old therefore often comes to grief while loitering on his way home from the afternoon session unless a parent meets him to expedite his return home, or forestalls the episode at the noon hour. Spanking and undue "shaming" are poor measures of control.

Most children take care of their own needs without reporting before or after they have functioned. Some are more aware of the function and report, as they did earlier, on the size, shape and number of the movements; or they do the opposite and withdraw themselves completely by locking the bathroom door.

Swearing and name calling are definitely related to the bowel function at this age. "Stinker" is a term in common use and may well stem from a realistic experience. Also a 5½ to 6-year-old is apt to shout in anger to another child, "You go pooh in your pants!"

Bladder. Day or night wetting is now rare. As at five, a child may delay too long and have to make a mad dash. Frequently such episodes can be averted by reminding the child to go to the bathroom at a favorable time, e.g. before he goes out to play or before he goes on a trip. A few children suddenly wet or dampen their pants just as others suddenly have an impulsive bowel movement. They feel badly and often say, "I don't know when I do it." These lapses might be controlled by a little more planned reminding.

Night wetting is uncommon but may recur with a cold or if the sleeping temperature of the child is too warm or too cold. A fair number still need to get up for toileting, usually taking care of their own needs and going back to bed without report to their parent.

The urinary function, especially the sound of this function, may stimulate giggling and teasing between two children at this age. One child in the bathroom at a time is a simple rule and one which is easily adhered to. Peripheral and preventive control thus takes the place of direct control. In the male 6-year-old the urinary function may be used verbally in a humorous or an angry attack. He may say, "I'll pee in your eye!"

Bath and Dressing

Bath. The nightly bath is now being resisted by some children, especially boys. The child may say he is too tired to bathe, which is true in part, for he might have bathed without resistance at 5 o'clock with the plan to have supper in bed. A bath every other night may be accepted fairly readily. Some children still show no interest in washing themselves. Some try to bathe themselves completely. Others limit their efforts to legs and feet. Nearly all need help in drawing the water and with regard to finishing touches in the head and neck regions.

Often a bath goes more smoothly with father than with mother. Dawdling in the tub is the rule and it is hard to get the child out of the tub. He can be hastened by simple techniques such as pacing, counting or planning an interesting bedtime activity.

Most children of this age wash hands and face reasonably well but not spontaneously, and with some "the face is just the nose." Although beginning to be aware of dirt on another person, many SIXES are not too much concerned about dirt on themselves and they may resist washing themselves, though they will accept help. More casualness about washing up would help a good deal to make home life smoother. A mother's self-rebuke (*after a meal!*) "Oh I forgot to remind you to wash your hands!" gives the child a wonderful lift—the legitimate kind of lift one gets from knowing that others also err.

Dressing and Care of Clothes. Wanting to dress is half the battle, but many 6-year-olds have not as yet acquired this desire. That is why SIX still needs to be handled in part like a 5-year-old. Though he often will not allow his mother actually to assist him, her mere presence seems to help. It is a good time for spelling or arithmetic games or the "I see something" games. He also loves to race with a parent. If he ties his shoelaces he does it too loosely. A child may need less help on the more leisurely mornings when he does not attend school. Undressing is accomplished with considerable speed.

SIX is a clothes conscious age. Boys are interested in and proud of their knickers and ties; and girls desire pretty dresses with accessory adornment and socks to match, and often refuse to wear overalls and winter leggings. Specific styles and colors, often red, are demanded, and boys begin to talk about high boots. Six-year-olds often need help with their leggings and also with the second sleeve of the coat. Because of SIX's dressing difficulties, parents may well question the wisdom of requiring a change to play clothes after school. Why not have some in-between clothes that are both good enough for school and yet not too good for play?

Although SIX is interested in his clothes, he does not take very good care of them. As one mother expressed it, "She likes to have things right, but she doesn't do anything about it." At five-and-a-half, when the child peeled off his clothes he often threw them to (or at!) his mother. At six he flings them all about the room, often in a humorous way or to test how many places and directions he can throw. This can easily be turned into a useful game of collecting his clothes, which both mother and child enjoy, or by having a corner into which dirty clothes may be thrown. It is more fun to throw clothes into a corner than into a hamper.

"Shoe trouble" is a very real trouble at six. The 6-year-old male especially wants to take off his shoes when he is in the house, but he is apt to leave one in one room and the other in another, and all too frequently the entire household is set on a hunt the next morning so that he can go to school with his shoes on. His parents actually prefer to have him take his shoes off at the table because he kicks. Here are multiple grounds for preventive strategy. Why not do as the Dutch do, have the 6- and 7-year-old take off his shoes as he enters the house, and let him go around in his stocking feet?

Some boys are becoming interested in combing their hair. Girls may rue the day that they asked for braids, but they do not want to give them up in spite of all the discomfort that combing causes. The scalp is very sensitive at about this age, but the painfulness of the combing can be much reduced if the child may occupy herself with a book, or coloring, or piano, during the process.

Health and Somatic Complaints

It is not only the general behavior of the 6-year-old which goes awry, but the working of his physical bodily structure as well. The 5½ to 6-year-old is full of "complaints"—legitimate complaints which should be seriously listened to. At five-and-a-half his feet "hurt" him. He may walk as though he were lame. By six, his legs hurt him, occasionally his arms, and frequently the back of his neck. He says he has a "krick" in his neck. Rubbing and massage bring both comfort and alleviation of pain.

He complains of being hot, so hot that he would like to go outside without any clothes on. He perspires readily. Actually his mucous membranes seem to inflame easily. The mucous membranes of his eyes may become reddened and he may develop styes. His throat not only "hurts," but it becomes red and infected, and the infection frequently spreads to his ears and his lungs. Otitis media again reaches a peak, similar to the 2½-year-old peak. In addition to the more common communicable diseases as at five—chickenpox, measles and whooping cough,—German measles and mumps show an increase. Diphtheria and scarlet fever reach a peak similar to the pre-adolescent peak.

Allergy responses are high. These may be in the form of a return of past allergic responses or a new development of hay fever. The mucous membrane of the nose is sensitive and congests readily. A number of girls complain that their urine burns, and they obviously have reddened genitalia which need intermittent care with bland salve application. The skin may be very sensitive in the head and neck regions. Hair combing is a painful process for some girls at this age. Boys may react with half-painful convulsive laughter when washed by an adult, because of hypersensitive face and neck. If the child washes himself he is far less sensitive. Boils may develop on face, neck or arms.

The child of this age tires easily, in fact he wilts. Yet he may hate to give in by resting. Rather free use of the bed will prevent undue fatigue and even illnesses. The bed should be psychologized in the child's mind as a pleasant haven of rest and of relaxing activity.

SIX does not make transitions easily. The immediate future often looms up as something to be almost too much to cope with. He may not want to get up on school days. He may say, "I don't feel well," but makes a dramatic recovery as soon as the school bus has passed his house. Or when he is at breakfast he may complain of a stomach ache, and even vomit. Significantly enough these symptoms do not occur over the week-end. A little help, by not requiring him to eat too much at breakfast, and the added interest of having an older and admired child call especially for him or her, may well control these symptoms. A stomach ache may still as at five years of age be related to an imminent bowel movement.

The clumsy headlongedness of SIX makes him susceptible to falls. He is fairly safe in trees, but is not too well balanced on fences which he insists upon climbing. He is apt to break a fall with his arm, and thereby is liable to break his arm as he falls.

This is the age when the word "sissy" looms up as a possible reality in the minds of many fathers, in regard to their sons. The sight of blood may be upsetting to the 6-year-old and the removal of a splinter by his mother may bring an hysterical reaction. Fathers should not too readily construe this as "sissy" behavior, and should realize that it is part of the child's emotional bond with his mother. If the parent feels that the splinter must be removed at once the child may gather control by being allowed to pinch his mother as much as it hurts. But why does the splinter need to be removed at once? Sticking on a sanitary adhesive insures an oozing and healing

around the splinter which often comes out with the adhesive tape as it loosens in the bath. A child is more likely to report his scratches, slivers and blisters if he can tolerate the treatment. Serious infections usually are the result of delayed reporting and absence of care.

Tensional Outlets

Tensional manifestations rise to a peak at five-and-a-half to six years of age. They include outbursts of screaming, violent temper-tantrums and striking at the parent. The child may so completely lose control that the mother needs to intervene and take him bodily to his room, leaving him there for a brief period and then returning to help him get over his difficulty. Left alone he might go on indefinitely to a point of exhaustion. Skillful distraction helps.

Later, after the storm has passed, the mother analyzes what brought on the outburst, and how she might have avoided it. She may be able to discuss this with the child when he is in a receptive mood. By six years of age he may be snapped out of his outbursts with a humorous twist not related to himself and may shift his crying and screaming into laughter, but before this age the use of humor may well make matters worse.

The mother needs to realize that at this temporary maturity stage the child wants his way just for the sake of having his way, and that he will be more open to suggestion by six or six-and-a-half years of age. She must also realize that the child again needs to be protected from himself, just as he did at two-and-a-half years of age. Free access to candy may have to be stopped for a time, and drawers and closets may again need to be locked. A rigid schedule may have to be set up, stating how many pieces of candy are allowed, and the conditions **under** which they are allowed.

Besides violent outlets, there is also a diffusion of tensional energy into diverse channels,—leg swinging and wriggling, biting or tearing off fingernails and toenails, scratching, grimacing, grinding teeth, chewing on ties, sash ends and pigtails or pencils; picking nose and even eating nasal incrustations. These various behaviors are likely to occur when something is demanded of the child, or by the child of himself, which is not yet within his competence, or when he is waiting for something to happen, or even when he is trying to go to sleep. If pronounced, the tensional behavior may indicate that the child's task should be lightened. The disgusting aspect of nose picking can at least be alleviated by seeing that the child thoroughly cleans his nose before he starts out for school.

At night he might not fight sleep so much if he were read to or were allowed to listen to music, or to have a chat with his mother after lights are out. He may want to talk about things that are on his mind,—things that he cannot think through without his mother's help. He likes to hear about God, and to look up verses in the Bible. And finally he lets his mother go after prayers are said and he has had a long goodnight kiss.

In some children the tensional outlets are less marked,—a sigh, bringing fingers to mouth, hair to mouth or hands to hair. With some the tensional escape is verbal or expletive,—"hell," "damn," "ugh," "hum," "high hell" or "stink." Yet others manifest repetitive muscular releases, tic-like in nature: blinking, throat clearing, twitching of one side of the face, or head shaking. If such reactions occur mainly at dinner when father is at home, the child should probably have his meal on a tray

in his room. This does not imply that the father is the specific cause of these reactions. It may simply mean that the child is so immature that for the time being two is company but three is a crowd.

In a few children, especially boys, who stutter, there is a marked exacerbation at six, with a genuine difficulty in getting started to talk. By six to six-and-a-half these same children are aware that they stutter. As one boy expressed it, "No use fooling me, I know I stutter." The best handling is alleviation. Knowing how to act and what to say in new social situations reduces sensitiveness and a tendency to withdrawal.

§3. EMOTIONAL EXPRESSION

During the period from about five-and-a-half to six years, the child is in a more or less constant state of emotional tension and even ferment. His emotional reactions reflect both the state of his organism and its sensitiveness to his environment. His emotional expressions may be likened to the magnetic needle of a compass which reports an exact position. The parent needs to realize that a child of this age is very accurate in expressing the exact position and direction of the course which he is taking. It is very difficult to alter this course by external pressure. For that reason, preventive handling, or a constructive giving in, are often the only two ways of dealing effectively with the child. Fortunately by six and even more by six-and-a-half, his behavior begins to lose its rigidity. It becomes more susceptible to shifts in direction both inwardly motivated and outwardly stimulated.

Although the emotional trends of the 5½ to 6-year-old may be considered as rigid and as going in one direction, he can veer to the opposite direction and become rigid in that direction. That is why he is so often described as "sunshine and shadow," "either-or," "utterly sweet or utterly horrid." He "adores his dog but is cruel to him"; he "adores his baby sister but threatens to kill her." He may meet a new experience with shyness and then with sheer abandon. He may refuse to answer a question for lack of knowledge and yet he declares, "I know about everything." Reportedly he is "wonderful" at school and "terrible" at home, or vice versa.

Many of the difficulties of the 5½-year-old arise out of an inability to shift and to modulate his behavior. He is not so much persistent as unable to stop; so he cries continuously once he has begun. He stays with things so long that he becomes fatigued and often cannot leave them of his own accord without an emotional explosion. Children who are poor fine motor performers and who are more interested in people and in gross motor activities readily become moody, bored and restless with indoor confinement. They wander around and do not know what to do. Dawdling, which reaches a peak at this age—may be regarded as a persistence of aimlessness. When the child tries to make a difficult choice he "gets all mixed up," but finally if he does make up his mind he becomes adamant. He is completely unable to consider a compromise and neither bribes nor punishments produce their usual results. Nevertheless he does have good days as well as bad days. It is important to build up behavior on these good days when he is responsive.

The child of five-and-a-half to six years responds to impersonal handling, such as the counting technique to which he can be trained to react automatically. Also such smooth-the-way phrases as "a good thing to do," or "first do it your own way, then do it mine" may forestall the child's usual resistance. He takes criticism badly, but he thrives on praise and approval. He likes to do things on a game basis. One child expressed this mode of cooperation nicely when she said, "My mother isn't angry; we're doing things together!"

On the bad days the parent may wisely let things go, and figuratively "hit for the woods." You do not demand much from the child on these days and you utilize as much as possible the automatic releases which have taken hold on the good days.

If emotional explosions do come they come very rapidly. They come in different ways. Some children merely cry; some attack both verbally and with their hands and feet; some have an all-over temper tantrum as though their bodies were firing from all points. The children who "burst into tears" are perhaps the most sensitive. They cry because things are not going right, because their feelings are hurt, because their mother spoke sharply to them, to a maid or to one of their siblings. The children who strike out physically or verbally are more excitable and impetuous in disposition: they feel that their course of action is suddenly impeded. Their verbal missiles of attack are short and terse: "I won't," "I'll scream," "I'll hit you," "Get out of here," "Keep quiet," "I'll shoot you," "I'll get my gun." Such verbal defiance at least inhibits a physical attack.

In a temper-tantrum type of response the lower centers seem to take over completely. Parents say, "He gets so mad he's almost insane," or "He becomes positively furious!" In these rages the child may throw a vase or rip a hole in a cane seat. The swing back to equilibrium is achieved differently by different children. Some can respond to help from the parent especially if the outburst has occurred because of a misapprehension or lack of information. The majority finally respond to distraction, but a few seem to have to continue until their energy has been spent.

When a child feels sorry after a violent episode and attempts to make amends, he may well be moving away from outbursts to a higher organization, but the surest means of promoting his organization is for the parent to handle the child preventively. In all of these outbursts it is usually the little things of life that light the fuse. The child got a word wrong at school, the mother couldn't tie the child's shoe laces the minute he asked, or he stubbed his toe. The big things of life, real demands, are handled with relative ease. There is a marked decrease of these explosions by six, and still more by six-and-a-half years of age. The child is then more receptive to teaching and can at least ask for help.

The fresh, rude, "ready for a fight" attitude in the 6-year-old's voice and bearing is unduly distasteful to many parents. This attitude actually denotes a step forward, in the sense that the organism is now trying to act on its own even though it may be by defiance. The child gets a new leverage by pulling away from the parent. With hands on hips and that saucy look on her face, a 6-year-old girl defies her mother with an "I won't." Or maybe while seated at the table, she crosses her arms and looks haughtily at her mother without speaking,—but fortunately gives a clue by glancing down to the side of her plate where the mother forgot to place a spoon.

When asked a question, Six may reply, "Why do you want to know?", or when given a reason he voices his repeated phrase, "So what!" He domineers and he argues; especially does he argue when he undertakes to show his mother where she was wrong. He may become very noisy, boisterous and easily excitable. On such occasions he may quiet if you read to him or have him listen to records.

Girls especially are full of buffoonery; they giggle and grimace, and act silly, often with the intent to make others laugh. They would go on endlessly unless diverted to some new interest. When company comes, both sexes are most irrepressible. They want to be the life of the party. They monopolize the conversation, do gymnastics, act foolish, kick up their heels, laugh and interrupt without seeming to be aware that anyone else is talking. It might be better if they were given some attention and allowed to do their tricks with an audience response. Then they could be more readily transferred from the scene. Perhaps the mother has planned in advance on something for them to do or some place for them to go, or maybe one of the guests will join the child in his room to see his things and to play with him.

The excitement of a party is frequently too much for Six and he either crawls off into a corner, withdraws from the scene or becomes unrestrained in actions or talk. He may say wildly, "I'm going to eat the radiator," or "I'm going to eat the bathroom." An ideal party at six might consist of an exchange of presents, —the guests to receive as well as to bestow gifts,—with a reciprocal arrangement, or barter feast of ice cream and cake.

The 6-year-old's initial response to any personal demand made upon him is usually "No," but given time and a few detours he will come around to the idea almost as though it were his own. He may freeze into immobility if asked to "hurry up." Sometimes he is willing,—especially if asked in the proper tone of voice—but he does not carry through. Then he needs to be given three or possibly four chances. If this fails one can often get him started by counting,—a device which usually works like magic. He resents authority that is arbitrarily imposed. He also resents punishment or being reprimanded before company, and rightly so. If he rebels, as he may, about school, it would be wise to look into possible causes. Maybe he has had one unfortunate experience which he cannot get off his mind, but which could easily be made right.

Praise is an elixir to SIX, but correction is poison. However he can accept a correction if it is postponed long enough after the occurrence of the event. With some children the necessary postponement is only a few hours or less. In some households such discussions become related to a specific time of day as after lunch, at rest time or at bedtime. But with a few children, several days must elapse before discussion can take place. Too many events in the life of the child are left dangling and unresolved at this age. One parent reports that she kept a dated record of disturbing events, using the notebook to help the child to recall and finally to resolve his difficulties. This method of handling is comparable to storing away for future reference the squeaky toys which the infant once feared. Finally when he is ready, the toys are brought out again. It is wonderful for him to discover that now he can handle and enjoy these very toys.

The shift in emotions from five-and-a-half to six-and-a-half is almost as though the child were passing through an emotional spectrum from dark to light. The new sense of self which is emerging at five-and-a-half years is working pretty much in the dark. Gradually with further organization there is a real shift from the more negative emotions into a positive zone. By six, the child is becoming more happy. He laughs and squeals. He has a "twinkle in his eye" when about to tell a story; a "glow of satisfaction" after he has talked on the telephone. He seems to feel the beauty of a sunset, the grandeur of clouds, and the mysteriousness of insect sounds in the summer twilight. He is said to be angelic at times, to be more generous, to be companionable and sympathetic. Although he may have strong likes and dislikes, his preferences may show real taste.

But these new positive emotional forces are still under crude control. He trembles with excitement. He boasts that he is the best. He praises himself as he says, "I did an awfully good picture at school." He is inquisitive to the point of destructiveness. And most of all he shows pride in his acts, his accomplishments, his clothes, his family possessions and his siblings. But he may also be most jealous of the very sibling of whom he is most proud.

By the age of six-and-a-half years, joy begins to figure more strongly in his emotional life. Parents report a new kind of enthusiasm: he "loves" to do things. He "enjoys books," he "enjoys the effort of working on a thing," and most of all "he enjoys surprising his parents." Despite these positive and pleasant trends, there are recurring and less happy episodes, reminiscent of the 5½ to 6-year-old stage of immaturity. However, the overall trend toward equilibrium is so strong that after an episode, the child can plan and resolve to be "good" the rest of the day! There are also precursor signs of SEVEN, when the child looks too far within himself and begins to worry.

§4. FEARS AND DREAMS

Fears

The terrific newness and incompleteness of behavior patterns at five-and-a-half to six years of age show their reality in a marked increase of fear responses. Some of the pre-school fears such as fear of dogs may show a temporary rise, but the child may now confine his fear to *big* dogs. He may be able to touch little dogs and may be thinking ahead to the time when he can have a dog of his own. Wild animals may still be a fearful reality. The upstairs becomes inhabited with lions and tigers, but oddly enough these creatures do not invade his mother's room. That is why the 5½-year-old may go to sleep so quickly in his mother's bed. But ridding his own room and closet of wild animals by the dramatic wielding of sticks, especially by his father, makes his room safe again. Wild animals, especially bears, also inhabit woods, and the forest is accordingly to be feared. Tiny insects also are to be feared both because of their noises and their bite or sting. The reading at school of a story like Foxy-Loxy who eats you up, or a story about bees which sting, may be the true source of a child's refusal to return to school.

The elements such as thunder, rain, wind and especially fire are all fearful in their separate ways, but especially because of the sounds they make. Man-made sounds like sirens, static, telephones, noise of flushing the toilet, angry voices on the radio, all may induce fear until they are localized and identified. The child may provide his own protection by putting his hands over his ears. Helping some other person to control a fear is the surest means of resolving a fear. Even a kitten may be protected from a possible fear of thunder by a child's comforting words,

"Don't be afraid, that's only thunder." The act of comforting helps the child as well as the kitten.

The imaginative sub-human black witches and ghosts that come through a wall are also feared by the 6-year-old. He compulsively grapples with these creatures in dramatizing play with witches and ghosts in the dark, but by the fearful tones in his voice as he plays one knows that he has not yet conquered his dread. A few 6-year-olds especially if over doctrinated, are afraid of God, and think that God is watching everything that they are doing.

Human beings also are feared. The man under the bed, the man in the woods, takes on characteristics human and sub-human. There is a comparable fear of deformities. A broken leg in a cast or a spastic child fearsomely offends the 6-year-old's idea of the human normal. Some 6-year-olds, and these are readily picked out and tantalized by the very children they fear, are afraid that other children will attack them. The fear that something might happen to the mother, which began at five, persists into six, and now includes the fear that she may die.

A fear which is difficult to understand and one which often makes the child "go all to pieces" is his fear of even a slight injury to his body. A sliver, a scratch, the prick of a hypodermic, the sight of blood, all may produce a response out of all proportion to the cause. The child's control comes later when he is able to take care of his own minor injuries.

With the undoubted reorientation that the 5½ to 6-year-old child is experiencing in space, he becomes more aware of upper and nether regions. Boys particularly are frequently afraid of the cellar and occasionally of the attic. Dark is to be feared because it moves in space, and destroys all spatial relationships. The lighting of a candle in a blackout is something to be cherished because it brings back spatial relationships even though it may also produce shadows that possess a frightening form. The presence of another human being or animal is especially needed at the 5½-year-old stage when cellars and attics or being alone on the second floor are fears to be conquered. The presence of light may be enough to allay the fear, but by no means always before age six. A flashlight under the pillow, a night light in the room which produces a diffuse non-shadowy light, a light in the hall, all help to dispel these fears which are so much a part of the child's incompleteness, and a relatively normal expression of his immaturity.

There are "time fears" as well as "space fears." The fear of being late for school may appear in a few children who have over-responded to an experience of being late. A fear arising from some single experience is rather common at six, but it would not occur were the child not susceptible to that specific stimulus. The primary occasion is often unknown, because there may be a delay even of two or three months before the child expresses his fear either in words or in a dream. That is why it is well for a parent to be informed about his child's experiences both at home and at school.

It is imperative for the parent of the 6-year-old to understand the mechanism of fears. In general, fears may be thought of as "coming in" when a child becomes aware of something which he cannot comprehend or handle. His first response is one of withdrawal. This withdrawal stage may last for a split second or may persist for months. This is the child's method of protection, of waiting until he is better organized to handle the situation from which he has withdrawn. Later, when he is more ready to handle the situation he will go through a period when he approaches the situation compulsively.

All too frequently experiences come to the child prematurely. An alert, knowing, understanding environment would protect him from experiences until he was relatively ready to handle them. This does not mean that he should live an isolated sterile life. But it does mean that a 6-year-old should not see movies with airplanes crashing, that he should not be read stories about children being eaten up by bears or princesses turning to stone, that a little girl should not be left loose to pick up with a strange man. And a little boy should not have paragraph reading crammed into his brain when he has only a two-letter span.

Such protection does not preclude the fact that at a later age the child may seek the very experiences from which he now withdraws. At eight, he cannot get enough of extreme action and gore. Thereby he will resolve his former withdrawal,—by compulsive approach into the very areas from which he has earlier withdrawn. The length of a compulsion stage may well match the length of the preceding withdrawal stage. Therefore the environment should shorten the withdrawal stage if it can by a better timing of the initial experience. Sometimes the child becomes so fixed in a withdrawal stage, if the experience has been extremely premature, that the environment must actively assist in the resolution. The child cannot handle it by himself. According to the situation or the individual personality involved, the environment must either build up positive responses by minute stages, or thrust the child into a compulsive approach stage which when satisfied may lead to resolution.

Dreams

The dreams of Six, like his waking be-havior, tend toward opposite extremes: funny or ghastly, nice or bad, a jolly clown or an angry lion. Wild animals such as foxes, bears, tigers or snakes are not only in his bed but they bite him, and also chase him. Nevertheless there are usually fewer wild animal dreams than at five. Domestic animals such as the dog, cat and horse are now beginning to inhabit the child's dreams. The dog may chase him,—but these domestic ani-mals are far less frightening and usually enter into his "nice" dreams.

The commonest element dreamed about is fire. Six dreams that a house, or more specifically his own house, is on fire. He may also dream of thunder and lightning, or of war.

The near-human figured in ghosts and skeletons brings dream-fright to the child, but dream angels also sing to soothe him. Girls especially dream about bad men who appear at their windows, or who threaten to get into their rooms, or who may actually be in their rooms hidden under a piece of furniture.

Human beings are now taking more of a place in the child's dreams. He dreams of his mother, his siblings, his playmates, of himself in relation to other people. Girls may dream that their mother has been injured or killed. Six may dream that he has been abandoned by his par-ents, and is alone in the house with his dog. But when he dreams of his play-mates, he dreams of happier things, of tea parties, and play at the seashore.

Six frequently laughs in his sleep or talks out loud. He calls his mother, sib-lings, and playmates by name and is apt to give orders in his sleep: "Don't do that," or "Put it down."

Nightmares are less common than they were at five, although some children, especially boys, continue to have night-mares without being able to tell what they are about. If Six awakens, he is usually able to go to his mother's bed to seek comfort.

Within a series of dreams, some children hold on to a standard pattern, others show change from one dream to the next. Resolution is more quickly achieved when the dreams show a shift in pattern. Six may dream that the house down the street is on fire, then that the house in the middle of the block is on fire, and finally that his own house is on fire. Another Six may dream that her mother was killed, then that both she and her mother were killed, and finally that she alone was killed. Though it is difficult to find out what many nightmares are about, they probably have a stereotyped repeti-tiveness of pattern which needs to be jostled into variation to obtain a resolution.

§ 5. SELF AND SEX

Self

Six is the center of his own universe. He wants, and needs, to be first, to be loved best, to be praised, to win. "Everything for John," his mother says, is his rule. He believes that his way of doing things is right, and wants others to do his way as well. He cannot lose gracefully or accept criticism. He does not care especially about pleasing others, but may please others to please himself.

Six is his own one-sided assertive self. He operates from a self-centered bias. He is bossy, wants his own way, dominates a situation and is always ready with advice. A few Sixes may be somewhat aware of themselves as separate entities similar to others but unique in themselves. One articulate SIX was able to express this in writing the words, "I am me." Another SIX thought about the word "person": "Mommy is a person, daddy is a person, I am a person—three persons." SIX is also beginning to be interested in his own anatomical structure.

Though he may have glimmerings of a notion of himself as a person, SIX does not behave like a complete person. He is extremely possessive of his belongings, and shows a marked return to the use of the possessive pronouns "my" and "mine." This trait harks back to his 2½-year-old self. He is most secure when he is in control of a situation. Then he shows off, acts independently, boasts, changes any error into success by his qualifying remarks, and would like to play his father against his mother if he could. He often holds the sway of the dictator in the exercise of his new powers.

When the outside world impinges adversely upon his self, he is stubborn, obstinate, unreasonable, distractible. He dawdles, goes to pieces, pays poor attention or becomes over-excited especially as he relates himself to special events. Praise is the one impingement he can absorb with ease.

As a king needs his jester for a little relaxation, SIX seems to need to return, on occasion, to babyhood. Some SIXES carry on a conversation with themselves in a babyish fashion. Others talk only to a younger child or to a sibling with baby talk. Still others for a period talk baby talk at all times and to everyone, much to the exasperation of their parents. A few want to become a baby in more ways than just through speech, and may dramatically enact salient bits of a baby's life. Other children may wish to be babies, but may not dare to mention it to

anyone until finally they are able to whisper it to their mothers, adding the reason, "So I won't have to do things."

The shift from present self to a former younger self, that is, to a baby-self, is easily accomplished by the 6-year-old for he seems to have a power to pretend that he is almost anything. He may be an animal, an angel, a princess, a fireman or a parent. He is most organized when he loses himself in some make-believe role. This practicing at being somebody or something else is probably an important step on the way to a full realization of his own sense of self.

The child's own sense of self is also probably in some way strengthened through his interest in the conduct of his friends. There is a tremendous interest at this age in the conduct of friends, whether or not they do things correctly, how they behave. One SIX said of a classmate, "The naughtiest girl in the room and her two uncles dying for her in the army." SIX frequently projects his own feelings onto others and then criticizes them on this account. The adult feels that the 6-year-old is "fresh," but SIX makes this complaint against his friends. "He's so fresh," "She thinks she's everything." Or, in more detail, "She thinks she's a princess with those curls of hers bobbing up and down. But she isn't. You ought to see her drawing!"

SIX is also building up his sense of self by his embroilment with his mother and his increasing separation from her. This is expressed in his frequent resistances to his mother and also in his somewhat contradictory responses to her,—strong affection at one minute and strong antagonism the next.

The 6-year-old is beginning to experience an outside world when he attends school, and this extra-mural world may have standards and rules somewhat different from those he has met at home. In so far as the authorities of school and of home conflict, he himself experiences conflict. Even when there is no marked conflict of authority, many SIXES have difficulty in orienting themselves to two distinct worlds: that of home-mother and that of school-teacher.

SIX likes and seeks new experiences, but he tends to be undifferentiated and undiscriminating. "Everything is everywhere" to him. He has limited appreciation of scale or hierarchy, and may be angry that his mother has more possessions than he himself has.

Sex

The relative quiescence of the 5-year-old vanishes at six. His sex interests spread and penetrate many new and varied fields. SIX is interested in marriage, the origin of babies, pregnancy, birth, the opposite sex, sex role, and a new baby in the family. The facts of intercourse are still beyond his grasp. A few children at this age who are told of this aspect by older children usually come to their mother to have her confirm or deny the facts. Then the matter is usually dropped and the child shows little interest until the age of eight or older. SIX may still be looking backward to the time when he was a baby and may try to recapture that state dramatically by re-enacting some baby ways. These ways are more easy to recapture if there is a baby in the household. SIX may go so far as to put on diapers and rubber pants and then wet them. He imitates a younger sibling and especially enjoys talking his version of baby talk.

SIX giggles, sometimes uncontrollably, over bathroom words such as "wee-wee" or "pee-wee"; he giggles over panties; over

bathroom situations and exposure of a "belly-button." There is hilarious humor for boys to pretend to "tee-tee" in their mother's lap or on each other; or for girls to pretend that they are boys in an attempt to urinate standing up. Boys especially are apt to expose their genitals before girls and girls are apt to take off younger children's pants. If an older child, especially an 8-year-old, is playing with a 6-year-old, the play may elaborate into doctor play and the taking of rectal temperatures. A crayon, the eraser end of a pencil, the tip of an enema tube or the actual wooden thermometer in children's doctor kits may be used. Since this play is often stimulated by the fact that rectal temperatures have been taken during the child's illnesses, it might well be better to have temperatures taken by mouth. By four years of age a mouth temperature is safe and can be secured, especially if the child is allowed to take his teddy bear's temperature at the same time. This type of sex play can also be fairly well controlled if the rule is made that only one child at a time is allowed to go to the bathroom.

Although the distinguishing roles and organs of the two sexes are fairly well defined in the mind of the 6-year-old boy, he may still wonder why his mother has no penis. He knows that only females have babies, yet he, as a boy, may be upset because he can never have a child, or he may even be fearful that a baby is growing inside of him. A few SIXES still want to be the opposite sex. One 6-year-old girl dressed like a boy with necktie, pants and oxfords. She tucked in her hair under a cap, demanded to be called Johnny, and played with a truck.

SIX is definitely interested in marriage. One thing which was not clear in the pre-school years he now is sure of, namely, that you marry a member of the opposite sex. But this member of the opposite sex may be his mother, his aunt, a sister or a contemporary (or in the case of a girl, her father, an uncle or a brother). Often multiple marriages are planned. There is some vague idea that babies follow marriage, but there may also be some question as to whether a woman could have a baby without being married.

SIX is more interested in how the baby comes out than in how the baby starts. He may spontaneously think that the baby is born through the navel, but he accepts readily the assurance that there is a special place between the mother's legs where the baby comes out when it is time. Some children are concerned about the mother's knowing when it is time for her to go to the hospital, and also if it hurts when the baby is born. The presence of the doctor "to help" seems to alleviate any overstress on pain. It is difficult for some to picture a possible opening for the baby to come through, and if the child sees the birth of puppies he may ask, "Who is going to sew up the hole?"

The pregnancy period is not of much interest to SIX. He still is scarcely aware of the enlarging abdomen even though it may be his own mother's. It is unfortunate when SIX is told of a coming baby too long before the expected arrival. A month or two is quite long enough for him to wait.

SIX is at the beginning of interest in knowing how a baby starts. If he has been told some story such as that God makes all babies, human and animal, he will find it difficult to reconcile this fact with his knowledge of dogs having puppies, cats having kittens, and the lady next door having a baby. He now seems to grasp the idea of the baby starting from a seed and is no longer confused by his relating the seed to the ground. One SIX

even without the usual stimulus of the seed, thought that he himself came from the ground. He counted backward from his present age, finally got to one year of age, and wondered where he was before that. He asked, "Did I come from the ground?" but readily accepted the fact that he came from his mother's "stomach." Inquisitiveness in regard to the father's role ordinarily does not appear before seven or eight.

SIX wants his mother to have another baby, even though there is already one baby in the family. He usually speaks of the baby as a brother or sister. Some SIXES specify that they want a baby of their own or of the opposite sex, while others would be satisfied with either. Boys may be repudiated by a girl as possible siblings because "they fight."

§ 6. INTERPERSONAL RELATIONS

SIX is a trying age for many a parent. One of our parents reports that she dreaded to get up in the morning because it meant one continuous contest with her 6-year-old,—one long "fight, fight, fight." Another parent similarly reported that she could not be off her guard for a single second, for "If he has a thousandth of a chance he will take it."

These comments may seem extreme, but they are true to the interpersonal tensions which are so peculiar to the period from five-and-one-half to six years. No period makes a greater demand upon a sense of perspective and a sense of humor. If the parent recognizes the transitional character of this intense behavior, SIX becomes much more manageable and altogether less trying. Life is also made more complicated for him if his outbursts are taken sensitively. And the mother might wisely spare her feelings.

She had better count ten before she reacts too personally to his vehement, "I don't like you. You are mean and wicked. I want to kick you!" She feels blameless, for all she did to earn this explosion was to change the angle of the pillow on his bed! But Six has a delicate trigger psychology, which is more easily accepted than understood.

Spanking will do little good. The child will react with momentary regret or fury, but without any long term improvement in his behavior. He would feel more at one with his mother if she told him a story about another little 6-year-old who was very naughty. Maybe this other 6-year-old said he would get an axe and chop his mother up, or maybe he wished that his mother and father were killed in a fire. In any case, the story of the imaginary 6-year-old should parallel the child's own acts and experiences. What the imaginary child's mother said and did to her child becomes very important to the intently listening 6-year-old. Also he may be able to grasp some idea not only of how children act at this age but what kind of experiences pile up to make them act as they do.

The difficult, rigidly explosive behavior which the parent encounters in the 5½-year-old can best be handled by preventive means, by giving in or by suggesting the opposite of the desired behavior. Direct clashes of will between mother and child should be avoided whenever possible. Parents often use a strenuous direct approach which becomes exhausting for them. They report, "You need to clamp down, or be firm with him," "You have to pound it into him," or "He won't listen unless you're cross with him." An indirect approach or giving him several chances is far more likely to set the child on the move. Doing with him what is requested may bring out his concealed but latent cooperation. He does not like to do things as a task, but he enjoys doing things with another person, especially with his mother.

Six is sensitive to his parents' moods, emotions and tensions, even though the parents may think they have hidden their feelings from the child. Six also quickly detects any shift in facial expression and reacts badly to the raising of a voice. He cannot tolerate seeing his mother cry, becomes very sympathetic when she is sick, and may show anxiety about her well-being. Although Six is often described as being "embroiled with" his mother, he is actually extremely ambivalent in regard to her. He may say "I love you" at one minute and "I hate you, I wish you were dead" at the next. He is most loving with his mother, yet most of his tantrums are directed against her. He craves her help, especially in domestic routines, yet he often refuses to accept it.

In sharp contrast to his sensitive awareness of the other person, is the kind of behavior often described as fresh, nasty, insulting, impudent, bratty, rude and argumentative. When this side of the child's nature is shown toward grandmother, for instance, unfortunate results may ensue. Grandmothers and relatives in general often take on rights which they might more wisely not assume if they realized in advance the possible results. Six's mother in spite of his frequent embroilment with her, is actually the one person who is his real support and need, and even she may have to "make" him do things. A mere relative therefore may expect such a reply as, "I won't, and you're only my aunt and you can't make me."

Six often assumes a "know-it-all" attitude which makes him seem domineering. A little deferential response from the parent will soften his imperiousness. Parents need to beware of SIX when he is corrected or criticized for he is likely to turn on them in one way or another. A few children react with inward resentment, a few can change the subject, others may attack with words or fists.

Despite all of this furiously assertive behavior, SIX still craves affection. He wants to be assured in words of his mother's fondness for him. He may soften to the extent of sitting on his father's lap when he is being read to. Sometimes he gathers a cloak of closeness around himself and one of his parents by having a secret, even in a foreign language. The other parent is not supposed to know anything about the secret. He likes to burst into a close feeling relationship with his parent by some pleasant surprise (such as drinking his milk without protest!).

Fathers can and should play an important role in the life of the 6-year-old child. Girls are said to be "crazy about" their fathers and may demand a goodnight kiss from them. Boys are building up a father-son relationship of affection and admiration. They may demand every minute of a father's time; they respond to pep talks from him; and if he accompanies them to the doctor's office they are less likely to cry. There is something delightful and exciting in doing things with your father: gardening, painting screens, going for a train ride, playing games, or just telling him all your troubles.

There may be a startling improvement in the smoothness and ease of bedtime when father puts the child to bed, especially in the absence of the mother. Baths even may be taken with little supervision, the father being instructed to read his paper while the child undertakes to bathe himself. Going to sleep time may be shifted back a half hour when father takes over.

Even morning dressing takes on a new independence and comradeship when father is close by.

Since the response to father is so excellent, there is a danger that father will be expected to take over the lion's share. But this would be a serious mistake for the child would then begin to respond to the father as though he were the mother, with all the attendant tugs and pulls, detours and explosions. Mother, however, would benefit if the father took over two to three bedtimes a week. With such relief both mother and child would adjust better to each other; for although the child may not be able to get on with his mother, he also cannot get on without her. Growth itself brings its periods of relief, for suddenly in the midst of trying behavior, a two weeks interlude of angelic calm may descend as though from nowhere. Father tiptoes into the house at night and whispers his incredulous query: "Is he still the same?" Parents might well enjoy this lull, for it is sure to end!

SIX does not handle a younger sibling well without considerable planning and supervision on the part of the parent. A very few who have difficulty with their contemporaries play well with their younger siblings. They may be devoted to and proud of younger siblings, and eager to share a room with them at night, especially at five-and-a-half, but as a rule they play well together only occasionally. Although they may talk baby talk to a younger sibling at five-and-a-half, they become more interested in teaching him when they are six. They also like to evoke responses from him by making silly noises or by some other device. They may try to goad the younger sibling into being bad in the hopes that he will be scolded.

SIX insists upon being first in everything, and his whole day may be spoiled if a younger sibling gets downstairs in the morning before he does. He is jealous of any attention or present bestowed upon his younger sibling. If a guest unwittingly neglects him, he can be readily satisfied by a simple appeasement gift from his mother. One may need a reserve supply of such gifts on hand when there is a younger sibling in the household. A few SIXES go to the extreme of demanding a duplicate of many of the younger sibling's toys.

SIX may be bossy with a young sibling. He argues, teases, bullies, frightens, torments, makes him cry, hits him, gets angry with him, and may on occasion fight terrifically. Sometimes it is the younger sibling who irritates the 6-year-old. SIX gets along fairly well with an older sibling, but is likely to be overstimulated.

Although some SIXES play well alone, SIX generally wants other children to play with. A fair proportion play well either with children their own age or with those somewhat older. A half hour of indoor play is usually maximum. Outdoor play is better sustained. Sex lines are not sharply drawn and preferences are often dependent on neighborhood availability.

Two-somes are the rule, but small groups are forming. The make up of these groups is very shifting and group activity may go on in a manner so unorganized that any individual child may leave the group without disturbing the play. There is a great deal of exclusion of a third child by two others, and concern about whom friends are playing with: "Are you playing with So-and-So? All right then, I'm not playing with you!" SIX does not get along too well with his friends in play, even though there is considerable interest in and talk about "school friends" and "playmates." Children worry a good deal about their friends cheating or doing things the wrong way, and there is a good deal of "tattle-taling."

As to younger children, SIX is apt to handle them in the same way that he handles a younger sibling. He bosses and teases, and if not watched may lock a younger child into a small enclosed space.

SIX is usually either in high favor and sought after by the other children, or he is disliked and excluded from play. Some SIXES buzz around a girl of comparable age as though she were the queen. She in turn may dismiss one after the other in a queenly fashion. Another dominant 6-year-old may provoke crying in a whole series of children who have rebelled against playing "her way." Some SIXES are picked on, terrorized or knocked down. Older boys may lie in wait to beat up a 6-year-old. Older boys also tease SIXES to get rid of them, or they simply send them home. Some SIXES lose their appetites and others lose their tempers in response to such teasing.

SIX is often rough in his play. He threatens to go home, he quarrels, he calls names, he pushes, he (or she) pulls hair, kicks and fights when things are not going the way he wants them to. Some SIXES do not know how to play roughly, are terrorized by physical combat and should be protected accordingly by teachers as well as parents until about the age of eight years when a child is able to cope with rougher experience.

In view of SIX's multiple difficulties in interpersonal relationships, one may not expect him to be too much at ease with people or willing to meet them. The blank look, the inability to say "Hello," the unknowing impoliteness, are all a part of his callow nature. In another year he will be able to give a better account of himself,—so why make excessive demands upon him a year too soon?

§7. PLAY AND PASTIMES

In General

In his play activities, SIX spreads himself as he does in everything else. At five years the play episodes were restricted and confined; they now have spreading scope and movement. SIX's mother says, "Whatever he is doing is all over the place."

SIX continues many of his 5-year-old interests but with more intensity of feeling. His mother reports that "he *loves* to paint and color." Cutting and pasting are done as needed. He draws more actively than formerly. Boys prefer to draw airplanes, trains, train tracks and boats with occasional persons; but girls prefer to draw people and houses.

There is a very real return to an earlier interest in earth and water. Six-year-olds revel in their "muck shops" and enjoy making mud roads and houses. Boys especially like to dig. Their holes become tunnels and foxholes with boards for a roof over them. Digging may evolve into gardening and the planting of seeds. But having made the start, SIX usually finds it too difficult to continue the care of his garden.

One of the most positive new demands made by the 5½ to 6-year-old child is for a bicycle. Boys often demand an electric train. The urge for a bicycle at this age seems to be based on a need and a desire for locomotor leg exercise and body balance, rather than on mere possessiveness. Many children would be satisfied if they could borrow a small bicycle until they have learned and have had some successful experience. If this early urge were satisfied, ownership of a bicycle might be put off until the child is more ready for the responsibility.

Sex differences in choice of play are defining themselves more clearly. In gross motor and imaginative play both sexes, however, find a common meeting ground. Both sexes like to "tear around" in running games such as tag and hide-and-seek. Both like to roller skate, swing, swim, and do tricks on bars. Both indulge in ball play; but girls are apt to bounce a ball while boys attempt the rudiments of baseball. Girls delight in jumping rope.

The quick capacity of SIX to pretend greatly enriches his play life. A bed rapidly becomes a fort, a group of chairs a boat. Girls are more likely to play school, house and library but certain boys are often ready to join with them. Girls also like to dress up in costumes, including hats, slippers, lipstick and housecoats and may at times turn their play into a dramatic performance. At five-and-one-half there is a good deal of doll play which consists chiefly in the dressing and undressing of dolls. Nude dolls clutter the house and playroom. By six, doll play is at its height. There is much interest in the paraphernalia of doll play: doll clothes, suitcases, wash-baskets, swings, stoves and the like. Playing house which includes the use of dolls also is a great favorite. The mother role is definitely the favorite, and there is a marked aversion to the impersonation of baby. Some younger child, if present, is usually forced to take this inferior role.

Boys may take part in school and house play but they are more apt to play war games, cowboys, or cops and robbers. Shooting the enemy and getting under cover are two characteristic forms of play.

Boys show a marked interest in transportation and construction. Besides a very genuine interest in electric trains, they are interested in airplanes and more particularly in boats. Some girls may share with them an interest in blocks, builder blocks and work bench activity. At this age many children start the "collections" which will later use up so much time, energy and space. At present these collections are extremely miscellaneous and undifferentiated, consisting of toys, fancy paper, Xmas cards, or mere odds and ends.

If asked what he likes to do best, FIVE-AND-A-HALF will answer, "Play with *my* —doll, bicycle, blocks, train, wagon or truck." Six answers, "Play with soldiers," or "Play with dolls."

Reading and Numbers

Six is taking a more active part in reading. Through his repeated hearing of favorite books, he may "read" stories from memory as though he were really reading the printed page aloud. He is also interested in recognizing single words in familiar books and also in magazines. He enjoys printing his letters to spell real words and he also enjoys simple oral spelling as a game. Boys especially enjoy thinking about numbers, and like to read any number they see. Many of the table games that the 6-year-old plays fit in well with his intellectual interests. The favorites are anagrams, dominoes, Chinese checkers and simple card games that mainly demand matching.

Six continues to like stories about animals, but he is also branching out into an interest in nature and birds. Many SIXES enjoy poetry. The book which SIX would really prefer would be a diary about himself. Daily comics and comic books telling about animals are beginning to make a steady inroad into his life.

Music, Radio and Movies

Although some children still prefer their own phonograph records, the majority of 6-year-olds listen to the radio for at least a few programs each week. A few prefer the musical numbers, but the majority listen to a variety of talking programs (often dependent upon what their older friends have mentioned). A certain number of the less sensitive boys may listen to the hour of late afternoon programs which deal with action and shooting. When a choice needs to be made between the radio or outdoor play, the latter usually wins.

Few SIXES are ready for theater movies. They like short home movies about nature, and best of all cinema records of their own earlier years. If allowed to go to the movies they are likely to become restless, closing their eyes and stopping their ears to shut out any fighting or shooting. They may weep over sad scenes and finally have to leave the theatre. Musicals and animal pictures are the best accepted.

§8.   SCHOOL LIFE

Six shows a positive anticipation of first grade. His mother usually accompanies him on the first day but this adjustment is more assured if he has visited the teacher and has seen the room and materials previous to his induction into the group. The majority like school and want to do "real work" and to "learn." They like to do "everything"; they do "too much." Dislike of school ordinarily does not occur until the end of the year when the child for one reason or another has been unable to maintain his place in the group. Not infrequently, however, an unpleasant experience makes him refuse to go to school for one or several days. Perhaps he was frightened by a story, or was asked to put on his rubbers by himself or was asked to count and pass the crackers! He may limit his refusal to a certain day when he knows there is to be an activity he does not like. He may still wish to go to some other school, perhaps to one that he has formerly attended.

Even under the best of handling, SIX will probably be fatigued by his difficulties of adjustment and will have his share of colds. Two weeks after school starts absences become a common occurrence throughout most of the year. But some controls can be instituted to alleviate these absences. The 6-year-old is not ready for all day attendance. He still profits by an activity rest period at home when he is alone. He may adjust to an all day session by Christmas time. In some groups Monday is the poor day after a week-end at home, in others it is Friday after a week at school. Adjustments are best planned according to the group.

The interrelationship of home and school is important to the 6-year-old. He brings many things to school: stuffed animals, dolls, flowers, bugs, shells, fruit and especially books. These are brought to show his classmates, or more especially his teacher. He may also bring a treat of cookies for the whole group. He also takes things home as well, such as his drawing and his carpentry. His parents' response means a lot to him. The thrill of the year comes when he takes home the first primer he has mastered. It is to be hoped that parents will not criticize any errors at this moment of triumph.

Parents often are disappointed that SIX reports so little about his school experiences at home. SIX is most apt to bear tales about bad things other children do or to boast beyond reality of his own accomplishments. The outstanding nonconforming child is sure to be reported upon by most of the children in the group. A bedtime chatting period is an excellent opportunity for the 6-year-old to talk about himself and his school experiences.

Parent-teacher interviews by telephone or by appointment provide a means of reporting significant home or school behavior. The teacher not only gains from these interviews but the mother comes to feel that she is more a part of the school family, ready to step in and help whenever she is needed.

In characterizing first grade behavior, teachers comment as follows: "One day it is very exciting to teach first grade; the next day it is very dull." "Sometimes you have to work very hard; at other times you don't have to work at all." There are wide swings of behavior. "Things come in spells, like talking out loud all the time. You handle that specific behavior, try to counteract it as well as you can (whispering is the antidote) and suddenly the behavior has disappeared and all too soon something else takes its place."

Despite these ups and downs, these extremes, SIX wants to work. He would be continually happy if life were just one long series of beginnings. He gasps with excitement in his eagerness to tackle a new thing. It is the middle of a task which confuses him. He may want to give up, but with his teacher's help he may see the end and then he is thrilled to attack the end as a new beginning. Any help or praise from his teacher spurs him on; he is trying to conform and to please his teacher and himself. He likes an opportunity to show and talk about his finished product.

The activity program at six includes crayons, paint, clay, carpentry and large outdoor blocks, materials familiar from kindergarten days. These, however, are now approached more spontaneously and more experimentally. Products show a new creativeness, though the child may for a short period do the same picture or painting over and over again. He needs some simple direction and help to plan what he will do, and also needs guidance along the way. Direct interference, however, is not tolerated by SIXES.

Learning to utilize symbols in reading, writing and arithmetic is his new challenge. SIX especially likes group oral work since he is such an incessant talker, but he is more flexible than he was at five, and likes a variety of approaches to learning. He likes to recognize words which the teacher puts on the blackboard, and to write at his desk. (He cannot copy from the blackboard with facility as yet.) He begins to print small letters although he tends to reverse them and to revert to capital letters. Capitals are simpler to form and have less reversibility. With certain children, capitals probably should be used throughout first grade, or at least until the child shows a spontaneous desire to shift to small letters. Writing as well as reading induces the typical tensional overflow of chewing pencils, hair or fingers. SIX likes to write something for his mother or father. He may recognize his reversal of a letter but he does not always stop to correct the reversal.

The 6-year-old is learning to read combinations of words. He comes to recognize words out of their familiar setting and learns new words out of text before he approaches them in text. He makes a variety of errors: He adds words to give balance (a king and *a* queen). He reverses meaning (*Come* for *go*). He substitutes words of the same general appearance (*even* for *ever; mother* for *mouse, saw* for *was*). He adds rather than omits words (*little, very, y* at end of a word). There is also a tendency to carry down a word which he has encountered on the line above. Pronouns may be interchanged (*you* for *I*).

Many children use a marker or point with their fingers, at this age, and they may bring their heads closer as they continue to read. Mouthing of pencil, tongue, hair or fingers is frequently seen, as well as wriggling or even standing up.

SIX still likes to be read to both at home and at school and will listen to almost anything you read to him. He takes his primer home to read but may also try to read the books he had when he was younger.

SIX is learning number symbols (digits) as well as letters and they are similarly reversed. In writing numbers he may say: "I never do 2's so good." "Some people make 8's like this." "I wonder if I'm making these backward." "I'm tired. I'm hot too." The one by one counting of objects is less evident; he begins to group objects into four of this and five of that. Balanced pairs as 3+3 or 5+5 are favorites.

At this age girls are usually better in reading, writing and drawing while boys are better in number work and listening to stories.

SIX does not enter the classroom with the directness of FIVE. Some may even dawdle outside. The teacher is ready to greet the child, inspect what he has brought or give him a reassuring word when necessary. He still needs some help with rubbers and difficult articles of clothing and the teacher should be ready to supply needed help. The better coordinated children are often eager to help those who cannot manage by themselves. A few do best if they dress apart from the group.

SIX shifts from one activity to the next with comparative ease. He is willing to stop even though he is enjoying what he is doing and can leave a task incomplete and finish it the next day. If there is too much slack between activities the boys especially are apt to wrestle with each other.

Toileting is relatively easy, if the toilet adjoins the room. Six can go by himself although he may announce that he is going. He accepts the teacher's suggestion of a special time if he has not gone already. Girls and boys can use the same facilities which preferably should not have doors. Doors seem to stimulate a new awareness of functioning, expressed in giggling and peeking.

Six is oriented to the whole room and to the whole group. He is constantly on the move or manipulating things. He is impatient when his flow of movement is interfered with unless by chance you are going in his direction. He talks of his own performance and that of others. Occasionally an argument between two children may attract one child after another until the whole class is attentive, but as a rule it dissolves as another child picks up a mere thread or word of the conversation.

Characteristic verbalization during free play is illustrated by the following:

"I won't be on your side if you do."
"Oh I know that one."
"Look Rosalie, this is the first page."
"Let's change places in the desks."
"Miss H. do you know what SF means?"
"I need an eraser and I can't find it and I need one."
"Miss H. I'm going to the bathroom."
"Oh shoot the shoot pifs."
"I'll shoot the mess pot in the middle of the mess."
"You want red. I want blue."
"If he finishes it any more he'll ruin it."
"Hey, you started it." (snatches book)
"Give that right back." (snatches book)
"You know what I'm doing?"
"Fall. That's when you fall down. That's when the apples fall. That's why we call it fall."
"Hello measles, hello chicken pox."
"Hello whooping cough."

Six enjoys the feel of the group. Groupings are often of twosomes and are fre- quently shifting. The activity determines a group in part but emotional responses are now playing a stronger part. Certain children are apt to spoil group games and the proximity of the teacher may help, but often these children need to be kept apart and busy with something they enjoy doing such as digging or building

§9. ETHICAL SENSE

The growth clock appears to be set backward at the very important age of five-and-a-half to six years. In one sense this is true in reality for the child is act- ing very much like his former 2½-year- old self. Both of these ages, however, may be thought of as a back lash of reorgani- zation preparatory to new organization. Parents need to feel what is happening within the child's organism and should adapt their demands to that organism, so that he can grow into more of an entity in himself, and thereby become more of an individual capable of further adjust- ment to his ever expanding environment.

Girls as a rule, with a greater fluidity of mental structure and with a more flexible but continuing contact with their environment, do not experience the more extreme patterns of disorganization that boys exhibit. Girls are better at conform- ing. But the tendency of both sexes is to respond more slowly or to respond nega- tively to any direct demand put upon them. Given time, however, they may respond in their own way even as though from their own initiative. Many children need to be reminded of a thing two or three times to build up a stimulus strong enough to secure response. The responses may vary with the child's wishes and moods.

If the parent tries to press a command with a firm tone of voice she may anticipate an opposite response on the part of the 5½ year-old. The 6-year-old under similar pressure will defy his mother with a "No I won't," or "How are you going to make me?" If threat of physical punishment, or actual physical punishment is resorted to after such defiances, the results are usually poor. The child becomes furious, mimics his mother during the punishment and shows only a tendency to repeat the performance on future occasions. Preventive methods or the use of magic such as counting are far more effective. By six, the child responds better to some form of isolation such as play in his room or sitting on a "thinking chair" —formerly known as a "naughty chair." And how he loves to be praised! He preens himself like a peacock and his behavior is tremendously improved.

It is not easy for FIVE-AND-A-HALF to make up his mind. It is almost as though he were held in a vice made up of two opposing forces. This causes him to shift his decision back and forth. When SIX vascillates between two choices, he almost invariably ends with the "wrong" choice. That is why the parent may need to make decisions and to state clearly what is to happen and how the child is to act. When SIX finally does make up his mind, rarely can anything make him change it, even on those occasions when he has made it up with relative ease. There are very few 6-year-olds who can be reasonable about changing their minds; but there are a few others who are almost too conforming.

SIX is not only aware of "goodness" and "badness" in himself and in his acts, but he wants to be good,—especially if it does not take too much effort. He asks whether he is good, and he wants his mother to prevent his naughtiness. "Badness" separates him emotionally from his mother.

He shows his wish to be accepted by his mother when he asks, "Even though I've been bad you like me, don't you?", or when he says, "Let's be friends, mommy." He does not want to hurt people and he feels sorry and may even cry about it if he does. He is unusually aware of what in his estimate is "badness" in a younger sibling, and he may even go so far as to classify all people into "good people" and "bad people." But if he answers his own question, "Why are the German people bad?" he will reply, "Because Hitler is bad!" In his way of thinking it is parents who determine allowed things and forbidden things.

To the 6-year-old things which his parents allow are good things; things which they forbid are bad things. An expressive 5½-year-old has spontaneously dictated to her parent the following list of *Things To Do* and *Things Not To Do* which clearly defines her idea of good and bad.

Things To Do:

1. To say "I think you are eating good things today."
2. Pleasant things are lovely to do:
   a. To eat nicely.
   b. Always say "please" and "thank you."
   c. Always remember to say "Good morning, good afternoon, good evening."
3. To go on a boat when the war is over.
4. Eat dinner by ourselves without having to be reminded.
5. Keep quiet and answer people when they are talking to you.
6. Keep dresses clean.
7. Turn on the radio when the air raid is on (local station).
8. Keep watches going—winding them up.
9. Go to bed at 7:30.
10. Wake up at 7:30.
11. When people are breaking things tell them to stop.

Things Not To Do:

1. Not to say, "I am not talking to you."
2. Not to say, "Give it to me."

3. Not to say, "Give me the biggest piece of anything."
4. Spill crumbs on floor.
   a. Spill milk or water.
   b. Get food on hands or races.
5. Set fires anywhere.
6. Pulling away from someone when they are doing something nice for you.
7. Slamming doors.
8. Putting on lights in an air raid.
9. Don't telephone to anyone in an air raid.
10. Don't tear books.
11. Shouldn't keep windows open when it rains.
12. Don't tear clothes.
13. Don't break windows.
14. Don't call people when they are busy.
15. Don't break arm chairs.
16. Don't pinch people.

Some SIXES are capable of accepting responsibility for their acts. Yet they may say, "It was an accident," or "I didn't mean to do it." But the 6-year-old and more particularly the 5½-year-old, is apt to blame siblings, other children, mother, an animal, or even some inanimate object. If the misbehavior was very serious, however,—a football thrown through the living room window,—the child is often able to take full responsibility. The big things of life are easy. It is the little things that cause the most trouble. Perhaps it wasn't so difficult for George Washington to confess that he had cut down the cherry tree!

FIVE-AND-A-HALF and SIX are much better at winning than at losing, just as they love praise and cannot tolerate criticism. That is why they should not be put into positions where they are likely to lose. If they are, they may be forced into cheating in order to win. SIX loves to make up spontaneous games with rules which shift in the middle of the game. These are the kind of games he can handle. He has the controls and can shift the rules to his advantage.

Taking things belonging to others and telling tall tales are more common at SIX than the adult often wishes to believe. The distinction between mine and thine is almost as difficult for a 6-year-old to make as it was when he was two-and-a-half. "Mine" is uppermost in his mind and he easily grasps near objects that he desires, holds on to them, and adds them to his collection of just "things." Or he may have some real use for some of the objects which he takes. Girls are likely to take their mother's jewelry, slippers or a housecoat. If they ransack their mother's purse they rarely take any money, but prefer keys or lipstick. Boys prefer pipe cleaners, matches and little odds and ends from their father's desk drawer.

From school they take such innocent little items as a barret, a piece of clay, a peg, a piece of black paper or an eraser. Children who have taken things themselves are the first to criticize other children as "awful" when they take things. SIX is usually caught in the act for he takes things with others looking on. But even with the evidence before his eyes, he will flatly deny any relationship to the object in question, or will alibi with some statement such as, "Tommy gave them to me." SIX can least of all tolerate direct correction in matters of conduct. He cannot even accept it in the less personal fields of reading and arithmetic. But he will readily respond to an indirect approach if asked, "How did you break all those bottles?" or "Where did you find those matches?"

When he has told all, which is not difficult if he is not directly accused, he can plan with his parent how he can act better next time. Perhaps he needs things locked away to help him to remember; or he may need supervised experiences with fire. Or his teacher, in cooperation with his mother, should allow him to take certain things home from school. Then his mother can help him to return them when he is ready. If he takes things without permission, he is likely to destroy them. If he is made to return them, he can often best accomplish this with his mother by his side. Occasionally, at his request, it is advisable for his mother to return them for him.

A few children can handle their desire for new things by swapping. The bargain may be relatively fair—an elastic band for two pennies,—but as a rule someone gets the poor end of the bargain unless an "even swap" of similar objects is made. Six may also overdo his generosity, because of a greater interest in giving than in receiving. He needs to be protected from giving away his really valuable possessions.

Six is eager for more and more possessions. He is a great saver. He wants toys for the toys' sake almost more than for his interest in playing with them. If a guest arrives at a 6-year-old's home without a present he will probably receive criticism. Though Six likes to have quantities of possessions, he is extremely careless about them, mislays and loses them. It is the 6-year-old whom one sees downtown looking sad and bewildered while his mother demands, "Well, where did you leave it?" Six is often destructive of his possessions, and if he is held responsible for the upkeep of his room he dawdles over or kicks his toys in the process of picking them up. He usually lives in a "mess," but he responds cooperatively if his mother helps him and occasionally he likes to surprise her with a tidy room.

Money is becoming of real interest to the 6-year-old both in the form of an allowance (5c to 10c a week) and as a reward. Little chores such as emptying waste paper baskets, putting out milk bottles, drying dishes, or even eating a good meal are done more willingly when a reward is in view. Some children want only to save their money, put it in the bank; others spend for candy and cookies; others are extremely careless with it; but a few really want to put it to use and buy something special. Six may spend an hour in the ten cent store trying to decide on a purchase, and finally comes out with a roll of adhesive tape.

§ 10. PHILOSOPHIC OUTLOOK

Death and Deity

Six is often the peak period in these middle years of the child's interest in a creative power to which he can relate himself. Although he at first found it difficult to comprehend a God who saw him, but whom he did not see, he now relates God in his mind to the larger sphere of creation. He grasps the concept of God as the creator of the world, of animals and of beautiful things. He accepts these larger concepts at six, even though he will soon think them over, become skeptical, and need to have them further explained.

Six asks to go to Sunday-school. He likes to listen to Bible stories and could hear the story of the Little Lord Jesus over and over again. He especially likes to participate in a short ritualistic service with balanced candles on an altar. By his acts in his very real attempt to conform to what is demanded of him, and by his facial expression, he shows that he feels the awe of this ancient group worship. He is now developing a feeling relationship with God. Prayers become important to him. He feels confident that his prayers will be answered. If his mother would pray for a boy, he feels that she would receive one. And he hopes that if he prays, "Dear Jesus God, let me go through a red light without being killed," that this too will be granted.

God also has his counterpart in the bipolar mind of the 6-year-old. Six may be unusually susceptible to the teaching about the Devil, although such teaching is uncommon in the life of the child today. One 6-year-old recognized two forces fighting within her and acknowledged that the one who had all the bad ideas usually won. She invented a name for this opposing force by pronouncing her own name backwards. Having named it, she had more control over it. God also becomes his own counterpart when his name is used profanely. This is fairly common at six.

Death also becomes more related to Six's feeling self. He is fearful that his mother will die. He is beginning to be aware of any deaths that may occur in his immediate surroundings or to relatives and tries to penetrate the causes of these deaths. Besides dying from old age, he realizes that you can be killed. Also, he makes a slight connection between sickness, medicine, hospitals and death. There may be a preoccupation with the appurtenances of death: graves, funerals, being buried in the ground. Children discuss these matters and may express dislike of the notion that their relatives or they themselves should be buried in the ground. Six often needs to be protected from death experiences. Pictures of dead children may haunt his dreams. Seeing a dead animal is an experience he does not forget easily. He asks, "How long does it take to die?"

Six may think that there is a reversible process to death, that you return to life after you are dead. Even in his thought processes he may express to a friend, "I wish you had never been alive! And then other times I don't feel like that at all." His best acceptance of death is that someone else takes the dead person's place: puppies take the place of dogs, and children the place of their parents. If Six feels the immediate possibility that his mother might die, then he needs to think of someone, perhaps an aunt, as a possible substitute for his mother. One child became caught up in this process of dying and said, "First mother will die, then I will live with Nancy. Then Nancy will die and I will live with Hulda. Then I don't know who I would live with if Hulda should die. I think about it and it scares me."

Time and Space

Six does not live as much in the Now of time as did Five. He wants to recapture time past, and shows marked interest in hearing about his own and his mother's babyhood. He penetrates the future by the sequence of significant holidays and family birthdays. Duration of an episode in time has little meaning for him. He shows little interest in learning how to tell time beyond the hours. He answers correctly such questions as:

What time do you go to school?
What time do you come home from school?
What do you do in the fall? in the spring?
What grade are you in?

The space of the 6-year-old is definitely expanding beyond what it was when he was five. He is now interested not only in specific places but in relationships between home, neighborhood and an expanding community including school. As at four, he likes to return to his neighborhood visiting. He knows the names of some streets in his neighborhood, and the location of some major points of interest.

He may even be so aware of a special sequence of spatial relationships that he may fear he will get lost if he doesn't stay on a known specific route.

Six is learning to distinguish his own left from his own right hand, but he cannot distinguish left and right in another person. His spatial concepts like so many others are relatively undifferentiated.

7

SEVEN YEARS OLD

Teens

Aet. VII

Birth

BEHAVIOR PROFILE

THERE is a kind of quieting down at seven. Six-year-oldness tended to produce brash reactions and bursts of activity. The 7-year-old goes into lengthening periods of calmness and of self-absorption, during which he works his impressions over and over, oblivious to the outer world. It is an assimilative age, a time for salting down accumulated experience and for relating new experiences to the old.

By this token the 7-year-old is a good listener. He likes to be read to;

he likes to hear a twice-told tale. Picture him huddled or sprawled before the radio, endlessly listening. Picture his response to a sudden interruption; he resents intrusions on his ruminations; he feels ill at ease if he cannot bring them to a conclusion. All this means that he has already reached a higher level of maturity. Explosive bipolarity is giving way to inwardized consolidation. He, therefore, seems more introverted than the callow 6-year-old. Parents often say, "He is a better child now!" Basically he is, of course, the same child in a new stage of growth.

Seven is a pleasant age, if one respects the feelings of the child. His feelings need a new and even subtle regard because he is prone to lapse into musing moods during which he orders his subjective impressions. This tendency to muse is a psychological mechanism by which he absorbs, revives, and reorganizes his experiences.

As adults we scarcely appreciate how much a 7-year-old still has to learn,—not in factual knowledge, but in comprehension of the meanings of the manifold life situations which impinge upon him at home and at school. These meanings are essentially feelings. They do not emerge in definitive patterns; they must be "worked over," and practiced through mental activity. Just as a 40-week-old child exploits two cubes by tilting, tapping and combining them, so a 7-year-old manipulates his new found psychological materials through the exercise of reflective phantasy. This is a growth process. Thereby he learns to modulate the meanings of things and of persons. Thereby he overcomes the primitive impulsiveness of 6-year-old maturity and advances further into the intricate culture which continuously invests him. Never forget how vast that culture is, and how innocent of its structure is the mind of the 7-year-old! He needs his moments of reflection as well as of action. Through his inner life as well as through his outward conduct he achieves his adjustments.

This inner life is the hidden subtle aspect which demands some deference from us. We cannot do justice to the psychology of the 7-year-old unless we recognize the importance of his private mental activities. They account for his occasional brooding, his heedlessness, the minor strains of sadness and complainingness, his sulks, his mutterings, his shynesses, and a certain pensiveness which is not without charm.

He takes in rather more than he gives out. In another year he will be comparatively expansive, projecting himself into the environment. Now he mulls things over in terms of their repercussion upon his personal self. His mentation is more intensely active than appears upon the surface. He will be in a brown study and then suddenly light up with a flash of insight and dash off to proclaim or carry out the revealed idea. He is a good guesser, and he sticks to his guesses. Asked to explain his intuitional cogitation he says, " . . . You see I just notion some way in my mind."

Although given to self-absorption the 7-year-old is not an isolationist. He is becoming aware not only of himself, but of others. He is increasingly sensitive to the attitudes of others. He is beginning to see his mother in new perspective. He achieves a measure of detachment from her, by developing added attachments to other persons. Very frequently he (or she!) longs for a baby brother or sister. He shows a new interest in his father and in playmates of an older age. And usually he becomes very fond of his teacher. We can see his personal-social reactions deepening at home, on the playground, and in the schoolroom.

This socializing susceptibility is most transparently displayed at school. His joy is unalloyed when his teacher smiles upon him. He brings her a red apple. He likes to be near her, likes to touch her and to talk to her. He talks in order to establish a personal rapport, and to mobilize his abilities. At the beginning of a task he asks, "Shall I start now?" as though he could not begin without a verbal sanction. He seems very dependent upon reminders and verbal guidance. When he is older he will be more self-contained, more self-dependent, at least in the simpler school tasks.

In a genial second grade room each child is likely to have a personal relationship to the teacher. The wise teacher recognizes this relation as a developmental mechanism. She quietly circulates about the room so that she may come into personal touch with and talk individually to her children. She knows that they need speech to make social contacts and to clarify their thoughts. She uses this individualized conversation as a technique to maintain rapport, to set up challenges, and to foster self-reliance. She does not rule from a throne. By setting up sympathetic two-way relationships she exerts a powerful influence on the emotional organization of her pupils. Personality development is of great importance at this age. The second grade is peculiarly in need of sensitive and perceptive teachers.

At home as at school the child's personal-social behavior shows an increasing awareness both of self and of others. He is more companionable than he was at six and less likely to get into intense entanglements with his mother. He uses the mutual pronoun "we" in referring to himself and his mother. He likes to do things for her and for his father, if they do not hold him too long and too strictly at solitary tasks. He is better fitted for short tasks and needs the recurring support of friendly language. With such support he becomes a happy helper and errand runner during an afternoon in the garden. He likes to please.

However, he also has a deepening vein of independence. Accordingly he will on occasion resist his mother with an argumentative, "But Mommy. . . ." Sometimes he withdraws mutteringly into himself, hinting that he does not want to be a member of the family, and that the family does not like him! He can be "mad at mother" and assume a sulky mood. We may suppose that this "againstness," if not carried to extremes, is part of a normal process of developmental detachment,— of self-weaning. It is a more mature form of behavior than the verbal aggressiveness and the direct physical attacks of a year ago.

In terms of development it is entirely natural for the 7-year-old to be at times amenable and at other times assertive. Indeed he is not so stably organized that he functions at one well-sustained level. There is considerable variability from day to day and within a single day. There are mood changes from sweet-and-good to cross-and-tearful.

His self-dependence, however, is not robust enough for highly cooperative play. His group play is loosely organized and individual ends are still the most prominent. Bull-in-the-ring is a typical game which reflects his general level of cooperation. He is not a good loser. He tattle tales. If a playground situation grows too complex and things go badly, the 7-year-old runs home with a more or less righteous declaration, "I'm quitting,"—followed by muttered aspersions of "gyp," "mean" and "unfair."

Let us be duly grateful for this germinating righteousness. It is evident that the 7-year-old is developing an ethical sense. He is discriminating between good and bad in other children and even in himself. He is beginning to be conscious of the *attitudes* of his playmates as well as of their actions: "I don't want the kids to make fun of me!" He is ashamed to be seen crying. His crying is less infantile that it was at six; it comes more from the inside, often from wounded sensitiveness. Nevertheless he is learning to pull himself together and to stop crying. He tends to be a more polite and better child when away from home, which also betokens a regard for the good opinion of others.

Tantrums are vanishing. Instead, the child removes himself from the scene through fits of sullenness, or through a hasty retreat with a slam of the door. Even in these moods there can be a wrestling of the soul,— a wrestling not without ethical import. Alibiing and blaming on others are common traits. The blaming is usually ill-founded; but the alibiing may have a touching trace of conscientiousness: "I was *just* going to do it."

With this degree of self-deception we may expect a certain amount of so-called lying. But there is an increasing concern over the wrongness of lying. The concern is, actually, in excess of the child's intellectual capacity to tell the truth and should not be imposed upon by severe appeals to his honor. His sense of property is likewise immature. He will appropriate pencils, erasers, and the music teacher's pitch pipe, with a nonchalance which would be amazing did we not realize the complexity of ethical honesty. It is too early to label his shortcomings as thieving. If he fails to realize that the pitch pipe belongs to someone else, it is because he is too completely absorbed in the satisfaction of owning the pipe himself. In another year he will probably be able to project that feeling of satisfaction upon the true owner. And then he will make a culturally adequate distinction between thine and mine. He will consider the injunction Thou shalt not steal!

It takes time for these ethical feelings of meaning to grow. Again we must recall the extreme complexity of modern culture and of the process of acculturation. By dramatic projection the 6-year-old identifies himself with the culture chiefly in terms of action. The 7-year-old projects in terms of feeling as well as of action. He is coming to feel the import of actions both for himself and for others. He has some symptomatic worries. His developmental task is to adapt his emotional reactions to cultural sanctions and yet preserve his own identity. He must apprehend life emotionally as well as intellectually. His growing intelligence is manifested in insights; his growing wisdom in feelings of meaning.

At the age of seven we see new evidences of reasonableness and of critical capacity. The 7-year-old is more reflective; he takes time to think; he is interested in conclusions and logical ends. You can reason a little with him even in ethical situations which are charged with emotion. He himself uses language more freely and adaptively; not only to establish rapport, but to make running comments on the matter in hand. Often these comments are self-critical: "I can't do that." "I can't think of the next thing." "It may come out all right." "I haven't had that in school." "I think I know." "I can't figure it out." "Are you supposed to do that?" "Oh, wait a minute." "I'm stuck." "I got to think it over." "What's the matter with me! It's crooked, I can't make it straight."

And then out comes the eraser. Time and time again he expunges with rubber the valiant strokes of his pencil. We might almost call seven the eraser age. Sometimes he mutters self-disparagement as he erases and blows upon his work; but he strives none the less for improved results. That the disparagement is touched with a trace of sadness is in keeping with 7-year-old character.

Part and parcel of this maturity is the child's *perseveration*; a tendency to continue and to repeat a behavior which affords satisfaction. He listens endlessly to the radio. He draws a bomber which takes his fancy. He draws it over and over again with few variations. He perseverates at active as well as quiet games. Having started a bout of chasing or wrestling he tends to go it wilder and wilder until the game deteriorates. He is a better saturater than shifter. At card games, he likes to keep on playing till he wins.

On all these counts it is clear that the 7-year-old has progressed well beyond the impulsive and episodic tendencies of 6-year-old maturity. Although self-centered he is less completely self-absorbed. His thinking is somewhat more personal-social. It is more prolonged, more serial, more conclusive. It is also more inquiring even when he withdraws into himself to work over his experiences into feelings of meaning. He is less closely bound to the here and now.

His mental life is embracing the community and also the cosmos. He has a more intelligent awareness of the sun, moon, clouds, heat, fire, and the earth's crust. Heaven and earth are uniting. At six he portrayed the sky with a patch of blue; now his drawings fill the void; earth and sky join to make an horizon. The people who inhabit the earth take on more sociological meaning: the policeman, the grocer, the fireman. The 7-year-old has an expanding interest in the community. In all candor, it should be said that he is not too interested in the vanished culture of The American Indian, even when the course of study calls for an Indian life project!

The 7-year-old is attaining orientation in time as well as in space. He can read the clock. He can tell the season of the year and usually the calendar month. Although he can associate a specific time with a specific task, he cannot be depended upon to note the time. His characteristic self-absorption too easily interferes. So he needs warnings in advance. And if he fails, he will plead, "Oh, but you didn't remind me." He wants and expects to be reminded.

Although he is interested in fairies, in supermen, and in tales of magic, he is beginning to manifest an almost scientific interest in causes and conditions. Secretly or otherwise he entertains some skepticism of the veridicality of Santa Claus (but not to the detriment of his Christmas joys and illusions). He betrays a thoughtful interest in God and Heaven, and asks concrete questions about them. He has given up the idea that God shoves the clouds around. He is not overcome by the mysteries of death but shows a marked interest in its possible causes.

However, we would not suggest that the typical 7-year-old is a melancholy Dane who broods excessively on the paradoxes of life and death. He feels life in every limb. He draws his breath lightly as well as heavily. He likes to climb trees, to scuff, tussle and tumble, to play cops and robbers and commandos. He is careless about handkerchief, napkin and shoelaces. He has his active and silly spells as well as pensive moods.

And yet, in delineating a synthetic portrait of the 7-year-old it is necessary to re-emphasize the inner tensions which are the key to his psychology. He is preeminently in an assimilative stage, in which he develops a working balance between his inner propensities and the demands of the culture. He brings to the task a fund of native intelligence; but the task is not his alone. There are too many artificial and conflicting values in the culture. He is peculiarly in need of a discriminating guidance which does justice to the subtleties of his ruminative inner life. The 7-year-old is too readily misunderstood, too easily imposed upon.

He meets us, however, more than half way. He is susceptible to praise. He is sensitive to the point of tears to disapproval. Scolding and physical punishment are too gross for the tender tissue of his personality. His ethical sense is immature only because it is so recent. But in its processes, and even in its early patterns it suggests sensitivities which he will experience again in the years of adolescence.

MATURITY TRAITS

(The following maturity traits are not to be regarded as rigid norms nor as models. They simply illustrate the kinds of behavior—desirable or otherwise—which tend to occur at this age. Every child has an individual pattern of growth, unique to him. The behavior traits here outlined may be used to interpret his individuality and to consider the maturity level at which he is functioning.)

§ 1. MOTOR CHARACTERISTICS

Bodily Activity

SEVEN appears less brisk than SIX but he has sudden spurts of very active behavior. A few children are more tensely active than they were at six, and at the other extreme a small number are far more inactive. The tensely active may show choreiform movements of the body.

SEVEN is more cautious in his approach to new performances. He shows a new awareness of heights and is cautious in climbing and when playing in a tree house.

He repeats a performance over and over to master it. He may have "runs" on one type of activity and then suddenly drop it for another. His interest in piano or dancing lessons has a strong motor component. His motor demands may be a real need but, as with other activities, he may lose his interest suddenly.

SEVEN exhibits extremes in his outdoor play. Sometimes he is tearing about, running and tossing a hand-made paper airplane; at other times he is content to hang around, talking, swapping cards or playing house.

Boys especially are interested in acquiring ability to use a bow and arrow, and to bat a ball, both of which skills require a new orientation to the side position.

Carpentry is a favorite occupation and SEVEN likes the tug and pull as he saws a board. Sawing may be preferred to hammering.

Girls are busy with jump rope and hop scotch, but they also find house play or picking flowers enjoyable.

A favorite posture, especially of boys, is to lie prone on the floor, resting on one elbow and activating the legs while reading, writing or working.

Eyes and Hands

SEVEN's posture is more tensed and more unilateral than that of SIX. He maintains a position for a longer period. He sits with head forward and tilted toward the non-dominant side which is the more tensed and closer to the body. He frequently drops his head down on his free arm as he writes or listens; in this position he may occlude one eye.

SEVEN is fond of pencils and erasers and now discards wax for pencil crayons. His grasp, though tight, releases suddenly, and he is apt to drop his pencil repeatedly while working.

He is interested in comparative size, and the height of his capital and of his small letters is becoming more uniform although they taper uniformly as he proceeds across a page. In drawing he represents his human figures in more accurate comparative size than formerly.

Seven is less distracted by peripheral movement than is Six. He becomes absorbed with what he is doing and maintains regard within close range. He is still apt to touch anything he sees, and to manipulate it.

§ 2. PERSONAL HYGIENE

Eating

The 7-year-old eating patterns have many tag ends reminiscent of the 6-year-old patterns, but the child's relative improvement is summed up in a parent's remark: "He is less aggravating than he used to be."

Appetite. A few girls in our group still show low appetite; they enjoy their food in anticipation more than in reality. A few boys at the other extreme have tremendous appetites and are being kidded for being "fat boys." These boys are apt to voice abdominal discomfort, especially if they have eaten too fast or too much.

Refusals and Preferences. Seven expresses likes and dislikes, but not as strongly as at six. He is beginning to overcome his aversions by conscientiously eating disliked foods. This is difficult for him, but he makes the task easier for himself by dispatching the disliked food at the start or the end of the meal.

Self-Help. Seven handles his implements moderately well and is less apt to finger feed than formerly. He does find it difficult to get some foods on his spoon or fork without using his free fingers as a pusher. Some children will use a piece of toast as a pusher, others will use an actual implement called a pusher, but if given a choice, most would prefer to use their own fingers.

Table Behavior. Seven is more able to eat with the family. With his general calming down, he is now able to sit better, and may even show an interest in listening to table conversation, and in telling some of his own day's experiences. However, he is easily distracted by mention of anything that is going on outside, and frequently has to pop up from his chair to go to the window to see for himself. He often desires to bring to the table with him an object that has just engaged his interest, i.e. a gun or a comic book.

He is slow in coming to the table and usually has to be called a second time. He often chooses to eat by himself so that he can continue his reading or listening to the radio. If he is at the table with a younger sibling he may quarrel or become very silly to induce his sibling to laugh at him.

Seven does not dawdle as much as Six. He is now more adept. He is again interested in dessert and can be motivated toward this end. He is also motivated to become a member of the Clean Plate Club to which the soldiers belong. But nothing motivates him quite as strongly as a friend waiting in the back yard for him to come out and play.

Seven still needs to be reminded to wash his hands before meals, and may resist with a "Do I have to?", which he overcomes himself if given time and no further pushing. He prefers his napkin beside his plate and actually uses it as needed. He is even equal to the nicety of wiping fingers and face inside the fold of his napkin. He remembers to wipe his face but frequently merely rubs the food particles from lips to cheek.

Sleeping

Bedtime. The hour of going to bed remains between 7 and 8 P.M. Some

SEVENS are able to get ready for bed by themselves, even bathing alone, but most like an in-and-out companionship of an adult with a few helps and reminders. Those who are independent enough to get ready for bed by themselves still want to call to mother or father to come and tuck them in and say goodnight. Some like to chat for awhile after lights are out, when they divulge secrets about what happened at school, if the parent promises not to tell the teacher.

It is instructive to note the calming effect bed has on these very children who feel jittery and realize that they cannot fall asleep readily. Some sing or talk to themselves as though they were carrying on a conversation between two people. Others listen attentively to catch the conversation of the adults, and to interpret the sounds of stirrings in the house.

Some children report that thoughts go round and round in their heads as though a phonograph record were telling about monsters, robbers and burglars. Reading or being read to helps to dispel these thoughts for a while. Some see funny pictures in imagery as they fall off to sleep, and others see odd shapes in reflections, shadows or the clothes hanging over a chair, interpreting these shapes as ghosts or spies. SEVEN may still want to take a personal treasure to bed with him, whether it be a gun, a panda, or an old bathrobe.

Night. SEVEN has a certain affection for his bed and may even grow sentimental about it. He is a good sleeper. Mothers report that the 7-year-old "Sleeps like a log," or that "Not even a siren wakes him."

Although he may have disquieting thoughts before he goes to sleep, nightmares are no longer common. Night toilet-ing likewise has almost dropped out. Those who still get up, take care of themselves without waking their parents.

Morning. A common waking hour is at 7 A.M., which may fortunately stretch to 8 A.M. or later on Sunday mornings. SEVEN awakens by himself, and may even plan to waken early in order to read or "to have more time." Like SIX, he may get dressed by himself, but he still needs considerable reminding.

Elimination

Bowel. Each child is fairly consistent with his own individual rhythm of functioning. After lunch or later afternoon are common times. Only a few are able to function easily at school. Typically, the 7-year-old can consciously "wait" until he reaches home. He expresses control in elimination as well as in many other functions.

Bladder. This is the age when a long span of retention is evident. The child may even have to be reminded to go to the bathroom before he goes to school in the morning, not having gone since the night before. He may put it off so long that he has to make a mad dash. Fewer children need to get up at night, and if they do, they take care of themselves completely.

For the most part there is not much awareness of and dwelling upon elimination functioning. A few express this in "silly" humor about urinating: "The King of France wet his pants."

Bath and Dressing

Bath. Some SEVENS still hate to bathe, but as a rule there is much less resistance than there was at six. SEVEN has difficulty in getting started, which is probably why his mother usually draws the water to get him going. When he is once in the tub he

[141]

enjoys it. He can wash himself fairly completely but for some the whole process is a bit of a chore. He needs checking up after a bath. He is apt to dawdle, to dream, or imaginatively to think that a bar of soap is a boat. This type of child needs considerable reminding and some help. Getting out of the tub when all is done usually is not difficult for him.

SEVEN is reasonably good about washing face and hands before meals *if* he hears his mother when she reminds him. The mother must make sure that he has heard, and need not be disturbed if his response is, "Do I have to?" for he carries out her request in spite of this protest.

Dressing and Care of Clothes. SEVEN is not a poor dresser after he once gets started. He has a great tendency to dawdle or to be distracted by things in his room or by thoughts in his head. With one sock on he may wander about asking about telephone wires, or how many states there are in the union. Some can snap to and concentrate by imagining that they are a fireman in action. Others are motivated best by accepting the father's direct help. If motivation is not secured, parents waste much energy in nagging and emotional tension. A very few children still need to be helped throughout the dressing. Parents can usually anticipate and plan toward self-dependence in another year.

A further difficulty in dressing, besides the need to tuck in loose ends, is the tying of shoelaces. The 7-year-old can tie his shoelaces tightly, but he usually goes around with them untied. It is the old difficulty of "he can but he doesn't." Therefore it is wise to demand a little of him, but not too much. A good plan is to provide him with long enough shoelaces so that he can tie a double knot. He can be made responsible for the first tying in

the morning, and then he needs help the rest of the day, if his laces come untied or he has taken off his shoes and wants to put them back on again. As with the 6-year-old, many SEVENS would prefer to take their shoes off the minute they enter the house.

Many 7-year-olds are not much interested in clothes. They like to wear old clothes, hate to change to new clothes, and girls like to wear the same dress for a number of days in succession. Their pet aversion is an innocent little handkerchief. (But they will accept a discardable tissue.) Very few demand to choose their clothes; they generally accept what the mother has laid out for them.

The 7-year-old is apt to "hang his clothes on the floor," dropping them on the spot. With reminding he will put them on a chair, but would prefer to have his mother do so. She too may so prefer; otherwise she will have to unscramble a bunched assembly of clothes which he has deposited on the chair.

Rips in clothes are common at this age and are usually not reported unless glaringly evident. Some girls like to shine their shoes (especially if they belong to a Brownie troop).

Boys are becoming more interested in combing their own hair, and girls make a fair attempt if they do not have braids. Activity diversions similar to those used at six during hair braiding may be used at seven and later.

Health and Somatic Complaints

Life smooths out at seven; is more reasonable and more understandable to the adult. SEVEN still has a fair share of muscular pains and other difficulties such as he had at six, but these are more obviously related to specific situations and can be more readily brought under control. SEVEN may still complain of muscular pains, especially knee pains, but these are quickly alleviated with rubbing and may even disappear miraculously if the child goes to bed.

He has fewer colds than he had at six. These are less severe and less apt to develop complications. Of the communicable diseases, German measles and mumps are the most common. Chickenpox and measles also occur frequently.

SEVEN is more articulate in his complaints than he was at six, and his complaints still have validity. He frequently complains about being tired in general, especially at the close of an afternoon school session. He becomes tired rapidly when asked to do something. Stomach ache in relation to school is less frequent. It occurs more often after a heavy meal or before a bowel movement. He is more apt to complain of a headache at seven than he was at six, particularly after too much excitement.

Congestion of the mucous membrane, also noted at six, may occasion the violent rubbing of the eyes at six-and-a-half to seven years of age. Judicious eye wash or drops may alleviate the itching and reduce the rubbing, and thus prevent a possible infection of a tear duct. These symptoms may denote that too much is being demanded of the eyes. Such children should be treated more as 6-year-olds than as 7-year-olds.

A common complaint on the part of the mother is that the child is deaf. But on examination he is found to have good hearing, perhaps even better than he previously had. The apparent deafness is relative to his attention. He hears if he attends, but since he is so deeply engrossed in his activities, he does not readily shift his attention. He will respond better to the signal of a bell, a marked change in the mother's tone of voice, a whisper, a magic word or a whistle.

Tensional Outlets

Being busy with his own activities and inner thoughts, SEVEN has life under more control. He does less facial grimacing because he has "more control of his facial muscles." He returns to nose picking and nail biting especially with a cold or an illness. He may not stutter unless the stimulus is a strong one, as a house suddenly catching on fire. If he returns to sucking his thumb—and this may happen especially with a few boys—he himself wants to stop and to have help in devising ways to control this habit. A subtle cue such as the mere mention of the child's name may suffice to remind him to take thumb out of mouth. A better method may be to set up a goal or a nightly reward (as five cents) for successful control. Having the money to buy one's own aviation cap is more of a stimulus than just working toward an aviation cap.

SEVEN tends to wiggle his loose teeth and to fidget. He may still cling to some of his sleep-inducing stuffed animals or blanket, but he now can give them up rather readily under some new strong stimulus such as a favorite relative who spends the week-end at his home. Having given them up for the week-end he may well be able to give them up for good.

§3. EMOTIONAL EXPRESSION

By six-and-a-half to seven years of age the child's life takes on a more serious, a more thoughtful tone. He is more inhibited, more controlled and more aware of other people and of his relationships to them. He may have been worried about heaven and dying at six, or about his mother's welfare and the danger that she might be struck by lightning or locked up in the bathroom. By six-and-a-half, the father's health may be on the child's mind, or the children at school; but by seven, he himself is his own chief concern. He worries that second grade will be too hard for him. If he hiccoughs repeatedly he is fearful that he will die; or if he rubs his eye persistently he fears that something is going to happen to his eyeball (yet he cannot stop rubbing). He is beginning to be able to put himself in the other person's place, or more truly to put the other person's experience into himself. That is why he is so moved by sad stories, radio programs or movies. Some of his tall tales about his adventures turn out to be true happenings to another child which also have reality for him. Otherwise they would not have evoked a response so vivid.

SEVEN has an initial tendency to withdraw from situations rather than to stay and resist, as SIX does. By this withdrawal, SEVEN is protective of himself. He puts his hands over his ears to keep out loud noises. He actually does not attend enough to hear his mother when she calls him—though he may hear her if she shouts, whispers or changes her usual approach in some way. When asked questions he will often say, "I don't know" or "We haven't had that yet." When asked to do something he may say that he is too tired or that he doesn't "feel like it." He lacks confidence to the point of not wanting even to try.

Though he may attack his mother with a "You're mean," when he is scolded by her or when he gets into some difficulty with her, he is more likely to go off and sulk or to rush to his room and slam the door. If things do not go right in his play with his friends he may prefer to play by himself, or may stalk off the scene saying, "I'm quittin'." And if things are not going his way at home, he may say, "No one treats me right. I'm going to run away." He may go as far as to pack his bag and actually go out of the front door, but usually he does not get beyond the front steps or a few houses up the street. A few SEVENS who seem to be fearful of life in general are actually reluctant to grow up. They withdraw from the new demands growth puts upon them.

SEVEN still has his moments of resistance,—his "bad spells"—but these are not simply for the sake of resistance. He may say, "Just try and make me," but more often he seeks a reason, "Why do I have to?" If he has caused a scene over some demand which the parent has pushed through, he thinks it over afterwards and wonders why he was so "foolish." His anger is often directed against himself for his actions. He is apt to throw a book if he cannot read it, or to break something if he has hurt himself. He may throw stones at other children as he is leaving a scene of action, but he rarely attacks his parent any more. He has attained more effective re-stabilizing mechanisms within himself. If some form of discipline is applied he usually accepts it though grudgingly. It troubles him very deeply to be sent to his room or to have to go to bed early.

If he cries, his reasons are more subjective than formerly. He is disappointed because some gadget of his doesn't work, or because what he was doing did not come out well. He cries because he thinks people don't like him. Although he is better at losing than he formerly was, he likes to win in the end. If life is stacked too much against him, he finally bursts into tears. He also cries when he is physically hurt. Usually he tries to control his crying, especially if he is afraid someone will see him. He may even control it so completely that he merely says, "I feel like crying."

Although he cries less, he screeches more. The general noisiness and gross motor effervescence of the 6-year-old have been superseded by high pitched vocalizations, yells and occasionally unearthly screams. The 7-year-old shouts his replies to his mother; he shouts his criticisms of life in general with a "That's not fair!" He voices his exuberance in the same high-pitched manner.

SEVEN's chief interpersonal difficulties are with his siblings and with other children. He fights and contradicts, but can be motivated toward self-restraint by the prospect of a reward for better conduct. Planned separation and more opportunity for outdoor play may help him to attain his goal.

SEVEN sets up too high goals for himself. He wants to be perfect, he brings home only his "100" papers. He is deeply concerned about and even ashamed of his mistakes. He may not take correction well, and tries to cover up his errors with "That's what I meant," or "I was just going to."

Though SEVEN has difficulty in starting things, once started he is too persistent, too avid; he must finish, but he does not know when to stop. His mind "wanders on and on." If he is unskillful with his hands but facile in speech, he shows great dependence on conversation; he feels the need of someone to talk to and he talks all day long. He wakes up talking, cannot stop thinking, and persists in asking innumerable questions to support his thinking.

SEVEN is conscientious. He takes his responsibilities seriously even though at times he is not quite sure what he is responsible for. He likes to plan his day —what he is going to do; and may enjoy using a chart as a guide to his goal. He is beginning to be thoughtful, to be considerate and is anxious to please. He is less selfish; can share better. He wants and tries to be good. He wants to find his place in the family group. He expresses his awareness of himself and his family in pride. He is proud of his abilities, his being good, and of his possessions, home and family. This awareness also makes him more critical of himself. Some SEVENS can even laugh at themselves; or when they are unable to go to sleep may say, "I don't know what's the matter with me."

Although life is fairly much under SEVEN's control, he is now sensing forces outside himself such as "good luck" and "bad luck" and in general he is inclined to think that he has all the "bad luck." Magic also is looming up as a fascinating unknown. He may imagine a vehicle that transports him home from school when he is tired; he may imagine a musical instrument that plays wonderful music.

§4. FEARS AND DREAMS

Fears

SEVEN's fears focalize upon himself,— his inner self,—and his self acting on its own. He has his behavior equipment so much better in hand that he can protect himself as the 6-year-old cannot. SIX jumps right in and finds himself over his depth; SEVEN hesitates before acting. His fears and worries are to some extent useful in that they are self-protective.

Although SEVEN has some left-over fears which were not resolved at six, he now handles them differently. He may still want his parents to stay at home in the evening, but he can resign himself to their departure, once he has gotten over the first hurdle.

SEVEN is spoken of both as cowardly and brave. These words refer to the lack of or presence of an inner control. Seven is an age when the environment can capitalize on the child's bravery, but bravery also needs environmental support and cannot be left on its own until the child is off to a good start.

Many previously unresolved fears now resolve,—the fear of the dentist's chair, the fear of swimming with face under water, or the fear of having hair washed. The 7-year-old has all of these situations under better control. He knows what the dentist does and that he can lift his hand if being hurt. He can now hold his breath under water and no longer "breathes in" as he used to do. He may be able to wash his own hair and can control soap in his eyes and the temperature of the water on his scalp.

But there are a number of situations that SEVEN does not have under his control. He does not want to experience new situations by himself. Even his summer may have been miserable because he was afraid to start second grade. He is afraid of his school work because he doesn't know how to start. He is afraid of being shy, or of being laughed at. He is afraid of physical punishment. And he may even be afraid that his mother will "get down on him" as his teacher has.

Space and time are taking on new meaning for him. He may fear high places and unfamiliar visual impressions. Cellars become inhabited by strange creatures and attics by ghosts. Even his own closet may have a German spy in it. Shadows gather form and take on meaning. His clothes on the back of a chair may suddenly appear as a frightening ghost in a half light after he is in bed. He may be timid of his own shadow in his inability to interpret it and its sudden movements. Though he loves hut-play with his gang, he may be scared to death of the trap door in the hut.

SEVEN can, however, help to control his fears. He gets his sister to go down into the cellar with him and politely says "Ladies first." He flashes his flashlight on the German spy in his closet and dissolves him. He calls to his mother to analyze the ghost in his room and enjoys the realization that it was only his clothes on a chair.

The very child who is most fearful of being late for school at seven may actually never have had the experience of being late. He is usually the type of child who has his inner timing mechanism under poor control. He not only has difficulty in stopping—he goes on endlessly—but he also has difficulty in starting. It is an unsettling experience to be with a 7-year-old who is extremely afraid of being late for school. He may awake at 6 A.M. and shout to his parents, "Is it time to get up yet?" This phrase recurs at intervals. The setting of an alarm may help him temporarily to control his anxiety.

Once he is up he hurries into his clothes, rushes through breakfast and then waits. Again he plagues his parents with another oft-repeated phrase: "Is it time to go yet?" Even the assurance that his father will drive him to school may not allay his anxiety. During the last ten minutes before departure his whole body is aquiver with anxiety, he has to go to the bathroom at least three times and may even have a bowel movement. Finally he rushes off in the car, rushes across the playground and at last crosses the threshold of his room and experiences immediate calm. He gives his teacher no inkling of what he has gone through in the last two and a half hours.

This type of child under the best of handling may still express some anxiety, but he can be helped to better control. In the first place he should not be held to coming to school exactly on time, for his sense of time is still only relative and his coming to school should also include a certain relativeness. If the school cannot provide this type of handling, he should be helped to bridge the gap from home to school by one of his interests. Reading a book on electricity may turn the trick, especially during the last ten minutes before starting off for school. Then he might take the book to school, show it to his teacher, and it may be hoped that the teacher will respond with interest.

As with SIX, certain stimuli in funny books or movies may bring on fears,—such tales as opening drawers and finding skulls. This is why the child still needs considerable supervision, especially if he is the type of child who is not too self-protective and who gets into situations from which he cannot get out by himself.

Dreams

Dreams are diminishing at seven or at least are not reported as much as earlier. Nightmares and dreams about animals are also declining. Only a few children have unpleasant dreams about being chased by persons or beasts.

SEVEN dreams mostly about himself. He has wonderful dreams when he flies and floats through the air, or dives into the depths of the ocean. He may dream of embarrassing situations such as wetting the bed (which may coincide with an actual episode of wetting), or losing his pants on the way to the school bus. A clearly defined shift to the opposite sex may be experienced in a dream. A boy may dream that he is going upstairs without any clothes on and that his nipples have become extraordinarily large.

SEVEN carries on long conversations in his dreams, with spies, pilots and unfamiliar people. As he talks out loud one gathers bits of conversation which disclose that he feels himself to be definitely involved. He may say: "It's me," or "I don't think you need a bodyguard."

Certain movies and radio programs give him bad dreams. He still needs considerable supervision in making his choices of radio and movies.

§ 5. SELF AND SEX

Self

SEVEN is becoming more aware of himself. By absorbing impressions from what he sees, hears, reads, and by working things over in his own thoughts and feelings, he seems to be strengthening and building up his sense of self. At EIGHT he may take his equipment out into the outside world and try it against the environment, but at seven—for all his noisy slapdash exterior, his running through the house slamming doors and shouting—he most characteristically sits quietly by himself, reading, listening to the radio, planning about what he is going to do.

With some SEVENS, self-awareness relates strongly to the physical self. SEVEN is aware of his body and is sensitive about exposing it, especially to the opposite sex. He may refuse to go to the toilet at school if there is no door on it. He does not like to be touched. Girls are especially aware of the style in which their hair is worn, and actually may fear that their identity would be lost or at least that they might not be recognized if their braids were cut off.

Most SEVENS are concerned about their actions. They are ashamed of their mistakes and their fears, and very much ashamed to be seen crying. They are very much aware of what others might think, and are careful not to expose themselves to criticism. They cringe when they are laughed at or made fun of.

One of the ways in which SEVEN protects himself best is to withdraw from any scene of action which does not please him. His withdrawal may be combined with a distaste for physical combat. This is not the age to teach the child to "defend himself" by means of boxing lessons. By eight he may spontaneously defend himself. At seven he needs to be helped to withdraw and needs to be protected.

SEVEN is serious about himself, and about any responsibilities which may be given to him—especially if they are school or other responsibilities outside his home. He thinks and speaks seriously of such concepts as government, civilization and the like. SEVEN is not only serious but he also is cautious,—in physical activities, in social situations and in his approach to a new task. There are beginnings of slight skepticism about Santa Claus, about religion and other matters of which he has been told but which he has not experienced at first hand.

Though he withdraws successfully, he is apt to voice many complaints. He feels that people are mean and unfair. And as he thinks situations over he worries about what people think of him and fears that they do not like him, or do not think he has done well. He is particularly interested in what his mother and his friends think of him. "Of course the kids will make fun of me," he says. There is a definite minor strain in the feelings of the 7-year-old.

Boys especially may be breaking away from their mother's domination. They may refuse to wear coats, hats, rubbers.

They may ask, "Why should I?" if given a command, and may counter a direction with the response, "I don't feel like it."

SEVEN wants to make a place for himself. This place may be a physical one—his place at the table, in the family car, or a room of his own. But SEVEN is also interested in his place in the social world. He usually has strong family feelings and at the same time he may fear that he does not really belong to his family, that he has been adopted. SEVEN mulls all these things over in his mind, for even in his thoughts he withdraws. Then he may discuss the fruit of his thought with the adult in relation to such topics as: "The disadvantages of being over five and under sixteen." The particular 7-year-old in question advanced the following reasoning. "Under five people give you plenty of money, and over sixteen you have plenty of your own. But between those ages they make you work for your money and give you very little for what you do. And between those ages you are changing the fastest, so you need a great many things."

Sex

SEVEN is less likely than SIX to be involved in overt sex play. In fact, he may even withdraw from any possible exposure when he is undressing or going to the bathroom if a younger sibling of the opposite sex is near. If two girls expose themselves, one to the other, they may become interested in the details of the organs and even try to draw what they have seen. A few SEVENS, especially boys, may think that they can magically change themselves into girls by taping up their genitals. These same boys may enjoy playing dolls with a girl.

SEVEN's real interest is in *thinking about* all these things. He shows an intense longing to have a new baby in his family, and almost always he desires a baby of his own sex. One such child, reminded a year later of her 7-year-old desire which was about to be fulfilled, exclaimed, "Now whatever made me say that!" SEVEN realizes that having babies can be repeated. He may ask his mother how many more babies she has in her stomach. He is aware that older women do not still have babies. He may even draw up a plan for his mother to have a baby every five years (because this is the easiest for him to calculate) until she is sixty when he feels she won't be able to have any more.

Pregnancy is now something that he is beginning to understand. He may be the first to notice that his mother is different. He may ask, "What's the matter with you? You don't act the same." If a baby is coming in his home he is very much excited about it. If permitted the experience, he is thrilled to feel the kicking of the baby against the mother's abdominal wall. He wants to know how big the baby is, how it is fed, will it get sick if the mother becomes ill, and how long it takes before it is ready to be born.

He does not quite understand how the mother knows that the baby has started growing. He is satisfied when he learns that two seeds (or two eggs), one from the father and one from the mother come together to start the baby. He is not yet concerned about how the seed from the father got into the mother.

He is more concerned about the details of birth. In his own mind he may more or less vaguely figure out that you have to "split the mother open to take the baby out." He readily accepts the simplified statement that the baby is born between the mother's legs. He wonders whether this takes place with the mother on the floor or on a table, and whether the baby

might fall to the floor. He may even ask to be there so that he can catch the baby when it comes out. It is no wonder that he cannot understand why a baby should cost so much when it grows inside of a person.

SEVEN may himself become involved in an elementary love affair. Boy-girl pairs are fairly common, especially at school. The boys who can write and spell may even write simple notes, "Do you like me? Yes or no." With X's for kisses. If the relationship progresses to a specific "engagement" and even to a planned marriage, the boy usually adds that he plans to return to his mother's house after the marriage. The loss of a boy-friend or girl-friend is usually taken as a matter of course, but some SEVENS are more deeply affected. One 7-year-old who did not have a boy-friend wailed to her parents, "What is the matter with me? I'm not in love."

§6. INTERPERSONAL RELATIONS

SEVEN is becoming a real member of the family group, ready to take some of the household responsibilities. Many SEVENS like to help and often take on certain routine chores, especially on Saturday mornings when they like to empty wastebaskets or garbage pails, fill the potato basket, cut the lawn, make their bed, pick up their room, help with the dishes, prepare the vegetables, run errands. Sometimes this help is spotty. SEVEN also tires of one chore and wishes to shift to another. Although the 7-year-old talks about earning money, he is really as interested in doing the work as he is in receiving money for it. Money does not motivate him as much as it may at eight.

SEVEN is less resistant and stubborn than he was earlier. His mother speaks of him as being more easily controlled and influenced. He has lost his 6-year-old freshness and is even polite, sympathetic and capable of genuine affection. His chief trouble comes when he is interrupted in what he is doing whether he be playing outside or reading a book. You can plan with him, however, as to if and how he should be warned, and when and how he will be called.

SEVEN not only gets on well with his mother, for the most part, but he is becoming extremely companionable with his father. Boys especially like to go on long walks with their fathers and like to have long discussions with them about such masculine matters as sinking oil wells. Girls are more sensitive to any reprimand from their fathers and may be jealous of any attention he shows their mothers.

A few SEVENS have real difficulty in adjusting to either parent or home and wish to bolt from a trying situation. As one girl put it, "I don't want to be a member of this family. I'd like to go away!" Or the child may get the notion that he does not actually belong to this family, that his mother and father are not his real parents. Nevertheless he is proud of his home and of his family and often compares them favorably to the homes and families of his friends.

SEVEN wants to make a place for himself in the family group, especially if there is another sibling in the family. If he has been sharing a room with a sibling he may now prefer a room of his own. He is usually very fond of a younger sibling especially if the sibling is a baby. Then he assumes the part of the big brother or sister, wants to carry him, feed him his bottle or wheel him in the carriage. If his younger sibling is closer in age, he may play well with him, look after and protect him, particularly if a third child is not added to the group. But frequently he is apt to tease, poke, bicker with and fight with his younger sibling. Separation is then indicated. SEVEN is inclined toward jealousy of a sibling and worries that the sibling may put something over on him, or have more privileges. SEVEN admires an older sibling, and is often under the older sibling's influence—which may not always be for the best.

SEVEN does not demand companionship as much as he did at six. He spends considerable time by himself listening to radio programs, writing lists of things, bouncing a ball, or in other solitary activities. As a rule he plays fairly well with other children. SEVEN often has a gorgeous, silly time with playmates of his own age. Some SEVENS play better at home, others play better away from home. Indoor play is more often too stimulating and may make SEVEN act pretty wild. Usually, however, SEVEN holds up better than SIX, though he is likely to walk out on his playmates if things go too badly, or to start a fight. Some SEVENS still will not fight and may hide their fearfulness behind "big talk."

Several children are likely to gang up against some other child, and many 7-year-old boys have trouble with older boys who bully them. Group play is not well organized and is still carried out mostly for individual ends. The individual child may worry about his place in the group and fear that he cannot hold his own or that others do not like him, and he particularly does not want "the other kids to laugh at him." There is usually less direct physical and verbal attack on playmates than at six, although boys indulge in a good deal of half-friendly, half-unfriendly wrestling and scuffling.

Sex lines are not clearly drawn but some discrimination against the opposite sex is beginning to appear. Boys cannot be bothered with girls, and girls do not think boys are very well behaved. But the opposite sex is still invited to birthday parties and boy-girl friendships suggest rudimentary love affairs.

SEVEN is becoming more adept in meeting strangers. He is now able to greet them. He likes to listen to an older group's conversation and he likes to go visiting. A more inept or immature SEVEN may be very much aware of other people and yet be unable to greet them with ease, is apt to push them, rush in front of them, stumble over them, throw a ball treacherously near their noses, contacting them awkwardly in all the wrong ways. Such an awkward SEVEN is greatly benefitted if he receives more complete and personal attention from one of the visiting guests.

§7. PLAY AND PASTIMES

In General

SEVEN is inclined to be obsessive in his play interests. He is said to have a "mania" for guns, funny books and coloring. He can spend hours at whatever he is doing, whether it is playing the piano, jumping rope, reading, or working at his work bench. SEVEN has more capacity to play by himself than he did earlier, and therefore can more readily hold to a task without having to adjust to other people's ideas.

SEVEN does not branch out on many novel ventures. But he is better at planning what he is going to do. Boys now have some comprehension of a model and a blue print. They are inclined to do a little inventing of their own and they like to rig up things, utilizing cereal boxes, electrical wire equipment, and odds and ends. They like to make and to "shoot" paper airplanes as darts. Girls may be inventive in designing dresses for their paper dolls.

There is a strong return to coloring and to cutting things out. Some girls cut out paper dolls endlessly and are content with simply putting the dresses on and off after the cutting. Quantity is the rule in whatever collecting SEVEN may undertake whether it be stones or bottle tops. Outdoors, girls favor hop scotch, jump rope and roller skating; boys enjoy tops and marbles.

In his gross motor activities SEVEN is fairly cautious but not fearful. He has become an expert tree climber. Many SEVENS own bicycles and ride them well but are not yet capable of handling them responsibly off the sidewalk.

SEVEN is really learning to swim. He is a better batter at ball play than he is a catcher. The side stance of bow and arrow play, as well as the cautious release of the arrow seems to appeal to him. He has the physical stamina to hold up better during the winter season and is beginning to enjoy sliding, skating and even skiing.

His group play is similar in type to that of SIX, with less ability to pretend and more ability to provide the necessary paraphernalia. He demands more realism. For example, when library is played, he must have library slips and go through the whole formal procedure of lending out books. He equips his tent with a cot, table and chair, writing material and a gun. Guns are a prominent feature of his group games. He may become so noisy with his persistent sound of firing that his gun play may need to be restricted to out-of-doors.

SEVEN is fond of table games and of jigsaw puzzles. He can handle games better because he is not quite so intent on winning as he was earlier. He will even tackle such complicated games as Monopoly. Magic and "tricks" are greatly favored.

There are marked individual differences in play pursuits, dependent upon talents and temperament. Some boys make simple but serious beginnings in chemistry, telegraphy, and navigation.

Questioned as to their favorite play activities, SEVENS most frequently mention climbing trees, riding bicycles, playing cars. One 7-year old boy, however, succinctly said, "Color. Everything else stinks."

Reading

Many SEVENS are fair readers and enjoy reading what they can by themselves. They can get the sense of a story without knowing all of the words. Some SEVENS are even spoken of as "chain readers" for they move directly from one book to another. SEVEN enjoys fairy tales even though he might be said to prefer his funny books. Boys especially are interested in army and navy stories, and books on airplanes, electricity, earth and nature. Girls choose such books as Heidi or the A. A. Milne books. SEVEN is not read to as much as formerly, since he is less demanding, and more preoccupied with his own reading and his spontaneous listening to the radio.

Music, Radio, Movies

SEVEN often may express a strong desire to take piano lessons. The question may be asked whether this craving should be satisfied. It probably is desirable to satisfy this demand if the music teacher will allow the child to take lessons without practicing, which is often the preferred way to learn. Too many home battles are fought over piano practicing before the child is really equal to practicing by himself (nine to ten years).

The radio is now becoming part of the child's steady diet. The late afternoon programs of adventure and shooting are still favored. Some SEVENS are apt to branch out into news programs and mysteries which disturb them and also disturb their sleep. SEVEN needs to be protected from these programs since he is at times unable to judge for himself what he can take.

Interest in movies is variable with 7-year-olds. Musicals, dancing, singing and animal pictures are preferred. Love stories are very much disliked. SEVEN is likely to become overactive and to squeal during a performance. A few SEVENS like shooting pictures. Some attend weekly, but on the whole movies are not much enjoyed before eight years of age.

§8. SCHOOL LIFE

On the whole SEVEN accepts his return to school without protest but he may anticipate that second grade will be too hard. A few advance visits of the first grade group to the second grade room (i.e. a play or picnic at the end of the year) help to forestall and to alleviate such fear. SEVEN may fatigue in spells and this is noticeable at school as well as at home. He has fewer illnesses but an illness may be of longer duration.

The teacher plays an important part in SEVEN's adjustment. She becomes involved in a more personal relationship with each of her pupils and may be both liked and disliked. Boys are more apt to like their teacher and may form a close attachment to her. Girls may dislike and complain about her. SEVEN continues to bring things to the teacher but not as much as at six, nor does he bring things for the group. However, he enjoys an opportunity to display a new possession.

Home and school are more separated spheres at seven. The child may not like his mother to walk to school with him, or to visit school unless it is for a group performance when other mothers also are present. While he is with the group he may ignore her presence.

SEVEN likes to accumulate his papers in his school desk rather than take them home. If they are kept in a notebook he may wish to take this home on occasion. It would then be left at home if his mother did not remind him or put it in his hand as he leaves for school. He is apt also to leave sweaters and belongings at school unless the teacher helps him to remember them. SEVEN is not a good messenger either for teacher or for parent.

Interviews between parents and teachers may still be more useful than report cards. Two interviews a year may suffice for the majority of second-graders but in individual instances it is well for the parent and teacher to keep each other informed of any anxieties or fears in relation to the child's adjustments at school (fear of being late; fear of not completing work).

As SEVEN enters the classroom he does not always refer to his teacher; he may be noisy and talkative as he makes his entrance, manipulating objects about the room. However, he is interested in a schedule and finally settles into classroom work with absorption. He is quieter while he works than he was at six, talks more to himself. He refers to the work of his nearby neighbor, or makes an impatient demand for the teacher's assistance, often by going directly to her. He is frequently seen with head resting on his forearm while he writes and also while classroom discussions are in progress. He shows temporary fatigue with some tasks by shoving his desk, opening and closing his desk top

or getting up from his chair. These signs indicate that he is ready to change to a different activity.

"What comes next, Miss L?" is a typical remark. SEVEN makes abrupt shifts from one situation to the next. He becomes active and talkative. His voice may reach a penetrating, piercing pitch. He whistles or makes different noises and is soon joined by one child after another until the class is in an uproar. The teacher heeds this as a signal to change to a new activity.

SEVEN likes to manipulate objects, so he picks up pencils, erasers, sticks and stones and accumulates them in his desk. He may attempt to insert one object into another, and manipulates them so forcibly as to break them. It may be helpful to have an emptying of pockets at the end of a morning session, and an occasional desk cleaning day.

With SEVEN's motor manipulatory pressures, it is no wonder that carpentry is enjoyed especially by the boys. Although he builds more complicated structures than at six, he is less concerned about his product which is easily ignored or lost. He likes, however, to make a Christmas gift for one of his parents.

There is less interruption for toileting, as SEVEN has a longer retention span. The majority toilet before and after lunch and after rest period in the afternoon. A few very active boys may have a shorter span. SEVEN prefers the privacy provided by an enclosed toilet and may refuse to use the school toilet if it is without a door.

Classroom work requires the teacher nearby as she is in almost constant demand. There are many individual differences at seven. Some prefer work at their desks to work presented by the teacher on the blackboard and vice versa. (SEVEN does not combine the two easily; he cannot copy from the blackboard.) Boys like oral better than written arithmetic and girls may prefer concrete to oral or written arithmetic. Some wish widely spaced ruled paper, others prefer narrow. Some respond immediately, others need to be allowed extra time. By eight there will be more uniformity within the group, but such differences need to be respected at seven.

In reading, SEVEN recognizes familiar words accurately and rapidly. He is more mechanical in his approach to reading; he reads without stopping for the end of a sentence or a paragraph though in his efforts he is apt to repeat a phrase. He may omit or add familiar simple words (*and, he, had, but*) or a final *s* or *y*. He hesitates on new words and prefers to have them supplied so that he can maintain his speed; or he may simply guess, using a word of similar appearance, often one with the beginning and ending letter the same, though the length of the word may now be shortened (*green* for *garden*, *betful* for *beautiful*). Substitutions of meaning (*the* for *a, was* for *lived*) are prevalent. Vowel errors (*pass* for *puss, some* for *same*) are common. Speed of reading, like other behaviors, shows individual variations.

SEVEN likes to know how far to read; he likes to know how many pages in the book. If he has left a story unfinished he may want to go back to the beginning.

As he improves in the mechanics of reading he may temporarily be less concerned about meaning. He is, however, critical of his reading material and may refuse to re-read certain stories. Some SEVENS become inveterate readers with a special liking for comics. (A favorite time for such reading is in the early morning before breakfast.)

SEVEN's ability to spell usually lags behind his ability to read. He enjoys copying words but he still cannot spell them by heart. He becomes especially confused over vowels and is most apt to use the vowel *i* (*sit* for *sat*). This preference for *i* is also shown in his pronunciation (*cin* for *can; tin* for *ten*). Though he may dislike and refuse to spell whole words, he does enjoy naming the beginning and ending consonants of a word. Thus he grasps the sounds the letters make.

SEVEN likes oral arithmetic and cards with number combinations. He still reverses one or two numbers in writing (usually 2, 6, 7 or 9). He delights in writing long numbers. He likes to continue the same process on a page and he may be confused by shifting from addition to subtraction.

Pencils and erasers are almost a passion at seven. SEVEN writes to erase. He manipulates, fingers, drops his pencil and jabs it into his desk or into an object. He still reverses some letters and numbers but he usually recognizes his reversal and prefers to erase it. He may say, "Don't be surprised if you find one of my capital J's backward." His pencil grasp is tight with the index caved in and as a rule he exerts much pressure though this is variable. Several children ask to "write" rather than print; maintaining the pencil in contact with the paper may give them more security of motor control.

Pencil and paper work, although a strong interest, makes problems at this age. SEVEN may worry if he cannot finish his written work and even fears being kept after school if his paper is incomplete.

SEVEN has a new awareness of ends. "How far shall I go, Miss L?" "I can't finish," are typical remarks. He likes to complete but he wants the teacher to set his end for him, otherwise he is apt to continue too long. He likes to have his paper corrected immediately. "Did I get 100?" "Is this right?" He does not compare this with others, but in drawing he may ask the teacher to evaluate who drew the best tree or the best horse.

The thoughtful, memory-rumination of the 7-year-old is shown in the following responses to a teacher's question: *"What do you see in your mind when you think of autumn?"*

"I see the leaves going zig-zag."
"I see them going down gently."
"I see pumpkins turning yellow."
"I see milk weeds turning brown."
"I see chestnuts falling down."
"I see the birds going south."
"I see the trees with pretty near all the leaves off."

SEVEN makes a characteristic "explosive" transition from schoolroom to playground at recess time; but on the playground he may be either more, or less, active than he is in the classroom. Entanglements with classmates occur even with the teacher nearby. One child may interfere with another's block structure, one child may want to remain on the swing for the entire period, or monopolize a ball or a jump rope. When several children attempt group play they may become excited and hilarious. This usually ends with destruction of material, or personal altercations. SEVEN needs a variety of outdoor equipment and even though he is not ready for any directed group play, adult supervision is essential. During the year some become interested in group play set up by the teacher as long as they are free to join and leave the group at will.

SEVEN wants a place in the group and may be concerned that the other children or the teacher do not like him. He can be separated from the group for special help or to work or play by himself but he does not like to be singled out for reprimand or praise while he is a part of the group. Group praise, however, is a real spur. The group is slow to include a new member and may even make fun of him.

In play, four or five children may attempt to play together; to build, to shoot airplanes, to play commandoes, or simply to talk or wander about together. But there are usually several children who prefer solitary play on swing and jungle gym or play with jump-rope or ball.

§9. ETHICAL SENSE

SEVEN is becoming more responsive to the demands of his environment. For the most part he responds well to directions, especially if he has heard what was said to him. He does, however, forget readily and needs to be reminded. He often needs two chances. He may respond slowly or under protest, but this is reminiscent of the 6-year-old. If he is caught in a net of rigid perseveration he must be helped out of it to break its hold upon him.

SEVEN rarely needs punishment because he is a reasoning and by nature a responsible being. You can plan with him and thus avert disaster. Although he may still have some difficulty in making up his mind, especially when a demand is made of him, he is showing greater skill in making a decision. He now reasons with his parent, can compromise, and though he may still not wish to change his mind, he may change it when reasoned with. This reasoning with parents is often quite personal, and all of his sentences may begin with, "But mommy——."

SEVEN definitely wants to be good; although he wants to be himself, too. With some SEVENS it is not so much that they are concerned about being good as that they *just are* good. They are proud of a good day and concerned about bad days. They feel sorry for younger children who spoil things by being bad, and they instruct their younger siblings about the disadvantages of being bad. Some SEVENS have good and bad spells which seem to come in cycles. They are good for a period, and then impossible. Unfortunately this type of child may suddenly turn "bad," even when he means to be "good."

SEVEN's idea of good and bad is beginning to be slightly abstract. It is no longer concerned solely with specific actions allowed or forbidden by his parent, but involves the beginnings of a generalized notion of goodness and badness. One 7-year-old reviewed her day and asked to have listed all the things she had done *Thinking About Myself* and all that she had done *Thinking About Others.*

Thinking About Others:

1. Telling Margie about a gun for Johnny.
2. Obeying my mother—picking up the living room.
3. Went to bed willingly—fell asleep quickly.
4. Remembered to close the door to keep the bathroom warm.
5. I didn't shout in the library.
6. Came off the ice very quickly when Anne came for me.
7. Put my glasses away in their case.
8. Put my glasses on when I'm reading.
9. Dressing quickly without dawdling.
10. I look before I cross the street.
11. I don't tip my chair as much as I used to.

Thinking About Myself:

1. Eating omelette with my fingers.
2. Saying "Wah!"
3. Speaking rudely to my mother: "Yes you will!"
4. Contradicting.
5. Not washing hands before playing the piano.

SEVEN is less likely than SIX to blame others. He may even act with heroism, when no punishment is involved. Rather than blaming, he may alibi in order to cover up any of his mistakes. He says, "Well, that was what I meant," "I was just going to." He is now aware of a force outside of his own control which is influencing him and which he calls "fairness" and "luck." Whenever he gets into trouble, he is likely to say, "That's not fair." Although he may still be a poor loser, he is improving because he realizes that losing along the way does not always mean that you will lose in the end. Winning is often a question of luck to him, not too much under his control. Sometimes he thinks he has "all the bad luck." One SEVEN expressed it this way: "Why do I always have the bad luck? Why do things so often happen to me? I might as well be dead." The bad luck in question was that it was time to go to bed.

SEVEN may be very conscientious about taking things. He may have no use for a stealer or a cheater. But when he is in the schoolroom, he seems to be in the midst of so many things he wants and can add easily to his desk's store of belongings. He sometimes acquires new things by the more orthodox method of exchanging his possessions with friends. This is usually conducted on the basis of an "even swap" and does not involve real trading.

SEVEN has an increasing sense of possession and of the care of his possessions. He is better about putting things away, he helps his mother pick up his room, or he makes a mad scramble to put it in order the last minute before it is time to go off to school. The 7-year-old is becoming very much interested in making collections—of such objects as postcards or boxtops. The goal at this age seems to be mere quantity, with slight regard for formal arrangement or classification. He also likes to have a school-pouch or school-bag, and in this pouch he carries a veritable collection of pencils, erasers and rulers.

There is an increasing interest in money. He may be more anxious to earn money than to have an allowance. He is interested in buying specific things like a school magazine, a funny book, or war stamps. Sometimes he puts his money in the bank, which may be a means to saving part of the money for some specific object such as a bicycle or a typewriter. He is especially enchanted by the appearance of money in the toe of his slipper when he has left a tooth there. The money seems to him to be the proof that fairies do exist.

There is often considerably less lying at seven than in the years which precede and follow. However, SEVEN, with his rather strong ethical sense, may be very much concerned about the wrongness of lying and cheating. He is particularly concerned if this lying and cheating is done by his friends.

§ 10. PHILOSOPHIC OUTLOOK

Death and Deity

SEVEN is increasingly concerned about God's place in the world, even as he is concerned about his own place. If he is told that God lives in heaven, he wants to know where heaven is, how God got up there, does He use a ladder, does He live in a house. He wonders how God can see everything and be everywhere, and may answer his own questions in part by thinking that God must, for example, have a magic wand.

SEVEN may have lost his more personal feeling relationship to God and a certain skepticism about God comes in. As one SEVEN explained, "I have never seen God." He may still wish to go to Sunday School, though many refuse, and he is either likely to refuse to say his prayers on occasion, or to do antics as he is saying them.

His concept of death is rather similar to that held by the 6-year-old but it is more detailed, realistic and more thoughtful. He is not yet capable of accepting death as a biological process; but is still chiefly interested in it in terms of a specific human experience. He worries less about his mother's dying, and now is beginning to realize that he himself will die some day, though he usually denies that this could happen.

Chief interest in death is given to funerals and their appurtenances and to burial rites. Children talk about funerals, coffins, graves, being buried. They also take a matter of fact interest in visiting cemeteries, looking at tombstones, and noting verses, names, dates and designs on the tombstones.

Understanding of the various possible causes of death is increasing. Death is no longer entirely blamed on acts of violence or aggression. Disease, old age, over-eating are considered as other possible causes.

Time and Space

The sense of Time is becoming more practical, detailed and sequential at seven. Most SEVENS, especially boys, can tell time by the clock both by hour and minutes, and SEVEN usually demands a wrist-watch of his own. SEVEN is aware of the passage of time as one event follows another. He is interested in planning his day. He also is aware of the passage of time from month to month and may ask in September how much longer it is before Christmas. He may know the sequence of months and of seasons. He may be even able to think in terms of years. One 7-year-old who was thinking ahead to the time when she would be sixteen commented, "It's a long time to wait. Nine years. And even one year is a long time. Longer than you think."

SEVEN is especially interested in space as affording him his place in the world. Even God has his place in heaven. SEVEN is especially interested in the various objects in space—the earth's crust, stones, waterfalls and fire. He is also interested in the use of these elements—oil from the earth, power from water and heat from fire. He shows improved grasp of the points of the compass. He cannot yet distinguish right and left except in relation to his own body. He does not yet take an interest in the far places of the earth, but his interest in various parts of his community is definitely expanding.

8

EIGHT YEARS OLD

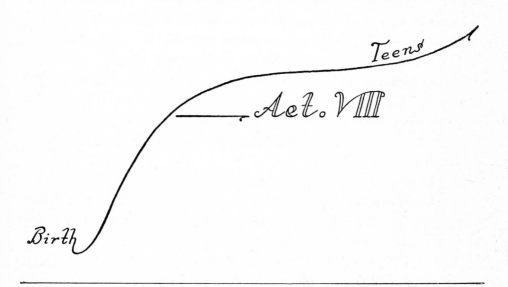

BEHAVIOR PROFILE

FOUR, you will recall, was an expansive age. FIVE was focal; SIX, dispersive; SEVEN, pensive. EIGHT again is expansive, but on a higher level of maturity. These adjectives are catchwords; but they serve to remind us of the accents of development and the spiralling trend of psychological growth. The 8-year-old is indeed an elaborated and an elaborating version of the 4-year-old. But we can understand him best by comparison with the traits of seven-year-oldness.

EIGHT is more of a person by adult standards and in terms of adult-child relationships. One converses with an 8-year-old with lessening condescension. He is growing up and both he and you are aware of it. He is governed by a growing-up impulsion which brings him into a positive outgoing contact with his environment, including his elders. He is less brooding and less inwardized than he was at seven. He is more centrifugal. He is also more rapid in his own responses, and more perceptive of the responses of others.

There are three traits which characterize the dynamics of his behavior: Speediness, Expansiveness, "Evaluativeness." The last named trait cannot be found in the dictionary, but it describes his dominant tendency to appraise what happens to him and what he causes to happen. He is spreading out into the culture, testing and applying the basic feelings of meaning which were built up in the previous year. There is a new vein of active curiosity; a mounting energy and a certain robustness which is different from the idyllic sweetness of earlier childhood. (Alice-in-Wonderland was seven. Alice-of-the Looking Glass was seven and one-half "exactually.")

Even in physical aspect the 8-year-old begins to look more mature. Subtle changes in body proportions already foretell the more marked changes which will come with pubescence. His eyes are now more ready to accommodate to both near and far distances.

EIGHT is in general healthier and less fatigable that SEVEN, more fond of rough and tumble play and boisterous games. His psycho-motor tempo is heightened. He tends to talk, to read and write and to practice his piano lesson in high gear. He bolts his food, sitting on the corner of his napkin, ready also to bolt outdoors, without pulling up his socks or tucking in his shirt. He may add a little bravado to his slap-dash demeanor to emphasize his masculine toughness.

Although we shall continue to use the pronoun "he" in a generic sense, the foregoing characterization applies more particularly to boys. At the age of eight we reach a maturity level where the two sexes are drawing somewhat apart. Boys on occasion like to herd up and to shout derision at a corresponding group of girls. The spontaneous segregation is not consistent nor prolonged, but it is symptomatic of the developmental forces which are steadily bringing boys and girls toward adolescence and adulthood.

Not without reason, therefore, does the 8-year-old listen closely when adults talk among themselves. He watches their facial expressions; he keeps looking and listening for cues and indicators in the social environment. He recognizes the gap between the world of the adult and his own world and adjusts accordingly. He is not naively docile and compliant. Somewhat consciously he shapes and establishes his own position in the circles at home and at school. He is a little sensitive about being told too directly what to do. He prefers a cue or hint. He expects and asks for praise: "This isn't good, is it?" But he does not want to be joked about his shortcomings. His sense of self is becoming a sense of status and he is constantly re-defining his status relationships with comrades, sibs and elders.

The relationships with mother and with teacher reflect the complexity of these interpersonal behavior patterns. Boys and girls alike tend to show strong admiration for their parents, expressing affection in action and words. Both sexes are susceptible to jealousy, particularly in their attachment to the mother. Mothers report that at the age of eight the child is voraciously demanding of maternal attention. "He (or she) haunts me, always wanting to walk or to play or to plan with me." This relationship reflects a growth mechanism. Earlier the child mainly wanted his mother's physical presence. Now he wants a closer communion, a psychological interchange, whereby he penetrates deeper into adult life and at the same time achieves increasing detachment from parental and domestic dominations.

At school he has already attained a large measure of detachment. He is not as dependent upon the teacher as he formerly was. The teacher is, in fact, less important and less involved in his emotional life than she was at the age of seven. She figures more as a beneficent potentate and regulator. To a considerable degree he and his schoolmates are beginning to furnish some of their own discipline, and to control their own activity through mutual criticism and assignments of responsibility. He is definitely conscious of the school group as a group to which he belongs and to which he owes something. Teacher does not have to circulate so much to lend her personal support.

However, the 8-year-old is only at the beginning of well coordinated and sustained group activity. His spontaneous club organizations are sketchy and short-lived. The concept of ballot and franchise is beyond him. He does not grasp complex rules. His ball games are far from orthodox, and often depend upon improvised spot rules. There is much bickering, dickering and disputation; but the play goes on. Let the 7-year-old secede with his "I'm quitting!" The 8-year-olds generally muddle through, albeit noisily and not altogether without murmurous disgruntlement. Their wrangling is often highly educational.

Be it noted here that we cannot profitably discuss cooperation, loyalty, sportsmanship and comparable virtues in the abstract. These virtues, to be sure, are primarily determined by general maturity factors, but they are finally manifested in specific attitudes which are patterned through numberless experiences in concrete situations at home and school and on the street. Through such acculturation the 8-year-old is steadily acquiring social aptitudes and social insights.

By the same token he is building up an ethical sense, which consists of an intricate aggregate of attitudes. When he was only a year-and-a-half-old he had certain simple feelings of shame. Now he is capable of experiencing this feeling in numerous situations. He can say contritely, "I will never do it again." He has a lively property sense, reinforced by his own urge to make collections, and by his intense interest in money. He has a growing aversion to falsehood. When he tells tall tales they usually have a grain of truth. He has a germinal sense of justice, based on a regard for "rules" and precedents. This causes him to impute unfairness in others. Frequently he criticizes his sibs severely. He can admit his wrong-doing; but he softens the admission with strong alibi-ing, which itself denotes an evaluation of ethical issues. The alibiing is not so much to shift the blame, as to indicate why under these particular circumstances he did not do what he himself would ordinarily have done! The very refinement of his explanations reveals the complexity of the anatomy of rectitude.

His feelings are easily hurt, particularly when his emotional relationships with his mother are involved. He is sensitive to criticism whether actual or implied. He looks for the approval of her smile and readily misconstrues her silences and her comments. This is because he has a well-defined image of how he wants her to react in relation to him. He includes her response as well as his own in the total relationship. Tears well up on slight provocation. His mother's passing frown may precipitate a sunshower cry. She often inadvertently treads on the tender toes of his expectations. But he is not given to prolonged moods of depression, and actively seeks reconciliation. On the playground among his equals he displays a more robust capacity to take and to give criticism. He is learning to lose. He likes to challenge himself. With his abounding energy he enjoys life despite the adult inhibitions which he is trying to interpret and to master.

Inhibitions and limitations set by schoolmates and playmates, he accepts with increasing reasonableness. He shows a significant readiness to join with three or four companions in setting up a lemonade booth or a roadside stand, with business conducted on a cash basis. There may be conflicts of managerial authority but the enterprise is carried through. Likewise, 8-year-old boys and girls are able to plan and to present with spontaneous flow fairly complete dramatic renderings, historical and otherwise.

This dramatic interest has a double significance. It evidences two of the cardinal traits of the 8-year-old: "evaluativeness" and expansiveness. His ego has a new degree of flexibility; by impersonation he can assume one role after another, *appraising* each role in terms of how he would or ought to feel under the required circumstances. A less mature mind merely mimics roles without this evaluative inflection. Because he is by nature expansive the 8-year-old likes to put on public shows, and to embark in private imaginative expeditions; he is under a compulsion to *spread himself* into the culture.

As a hungry amoeba thrusts out one pseudopod after another, the hungry 8-year-old mind actively spreads into new territory. This expansive propensity reveals itself in the contents of a boy's pocket or of a girl's satchel. It reveals itself in the collections and trophies stored in treasure box, drawer, desk and school-bag. A mail-order catalogue becomes a magic carpet. The 8-year-old delights in poring over its encyclopedic illustrations, choosing now this, now that item as an imaged extension of his personality. "If I had that, O boy, wouldn't I *do* this and that!" Thus he invades both reality and unreality. But each article has a published price; and he has a limiting money allowance. He could spend only so much, no more. This helps to organize his thinking. Everything in the world has a purchase price! If the 8-year-old also has an intense desire for unlimited money, it is not from pure avarice alone. He likes to barter. When he swaps equivalents he makes a fair trade. When he gets out of his field he can strike some very poor bargains. We have also heard of an 8-year-old girl who became something of a Lady Bountiful in sharing her mother's cosmetic supplies with neighborhood friends. All of which suggests that money, property, ownership and possessiveness are of extreme importance in the cultural organization of the childhood mind. One may well wonder whether the early property complexes are not as consequential in their dynamics as the complexes of juvenile sex life.

Psychological differentiations in the field of sex, however, are taking form during this developmental period. Boys and girls participate as equals in school and recreational activities. They share many interests; but they are also becoming vividly aware of distinctions which separate them. The expansive trends may lead to experimentations, homosexual and heterosexual. The divisive trends lead to withdrawal and to self-conscious unwillingness to touch each other even in ordinary play. The expansive trends also lead to new curiosities. There is an almost universal interest in babies. There are groping questionings about the origin of life, procreation and marriage.

Girls explore these family problems through the medium of paper dolls (with side lights from the comics). Like chess men on a chess board, the paper dolls symbolize agents and situations. Father, mother, bride, bridegroom, daughter, son, baby, visitor, etc. are represented in paper effigies which can be freely manipulated with dramatic commentary which serves to organize ideas. Sometimes the dialogue suggests more insight than the 8-year-old mind can actually claim: "My husband would not be unfaithful to me!" said one dramatic 8-year-old girl as she was creating a paper doll scene. "But he has been, already!" replied her resourceful companion.

The 8-year-old has a certain inquisitiveness about all human relationships. But his interest in marital and sexual knowledge normally does not become either overweening or excessive. Far from being erotic, it is only one manifestation of his many-sided expansiveness. He is extending himself, intellectually and emotionally, in myriad directions, even inquiring into the past history of mankind and into future fate. EIGHT is not a Here-and-Now-age. He is seeking deeper orientations in Time and Space and piercing beneath surfaces. He wishes to know more about the insides of the earth and the insides of the human body. He asks about the geography of Heaven. He is becoming interested in simple maps, Indian trails and the routes of pioneering covered wagons. He is even interested in the Pilgrim Fathers, in primitive man, and Eskimos. He is growing conscious of his own racial status and nationality. But he is by nature so cosmopolitan that this is a favorable time for strengthening sensible attitudes against racial prejudices.

He has an inherent sympathy of insight into other cultures, for he has the native honesty of childhood. This enables him to project his own life interests into the lives of children of foreign lands. He is delighted to hear that Chinese children are like him in so many ways, that they play hop scotch, marbles and hide-and-seek just as he does, that they go to school and read and write even though their word for cow has horns on it and the word for mouth looks like a mouth. He wants to know what the children of China eat for breakfast and what kind of shoes they wear. He hears that they don't have funnies to read, but he learns that they have butterfly and dragon kites to fly. He assimilates such information not as bare facts, but as human values. He evaluates as he expands his mental horizon. He is impressed with the realization that one fifth of the world's children are Chinese.

At his best, the 8-year-old is so glad to be alive, so tolerant in his sympathies, so liberal in his zeal to explore the unfamiliar, that we may regard him as a rather promising preliminary version of adult mentality. He, himself, already feels more at home with adults. He traffics and talks with them more freely. He likes to confront them with riddles which they cannot answer. When he was more childish, he wanted the adult to give the right answer at once, and precipitately supplied the answer himself. Now he enjoys his unilateral advantage. He has begun to doubt the infallibility of his parents and adults in general. He sometimes tells a tall tale with an observant, poker face in order to test the listener's capacity to detect the fraud. All this is symptomatic of an embryonic adultishness.

Intellectually he is becoming more expansive. He can express amazement and curiosity. His thinking is less animistic. He is growing aware of the impersonal forces of nature. He knows what makes a sailboat go. He can distinguish fundamental similarities and differences when comparing a baseball and an orange, an airplane and a kite, wood and glass. The origin and growth of plants from seeds begins to intrigue him. He takes a deepening interest in the life and life processes of animals. He is beginning to apprehend the momentous generality that all men are mortal. Yes, he too will die.

But this dawning recognition of death does not unduly depress him. He tends to be superlatively alive and even euphoric. His very speech inclines toward extravagance and hyperbole. And how he "loves" to talk! He comes home from school *bursting* with news. "You *never* saw anything like it!" "Oh, it was *awful*." "I *dread* it!" "He SIMPLY couldn't." "It was *big dough.*" "And *of course* she *would.*" "Oh, *grandma,* you always say *such* stupid things!"

We do not condone any disrespect for grandma. But she probably recognizes the vitality of the growth tensions to which the exuberant 8-year-old is subject. He seems to get a psychologic lift from his dramatic exaggerations. By dramatizing himself he stretches out toward maturity. He does not ever like to fail; yet he is very willing to be put on his mettle. When the assigned task proves difficult he still remains in character. We have seen him clap his brow with histrionic despair: "Hey, what's the matter with me! Am I slipping, or something." "Oh, this has got me crazy. Pretty soon I'll die of this." "I *always* get the easy ones wrong." The adult may well smile at all this. For we see ourselves in the child, in those moments when the child naively strives to be ourselves.

*   *   *

The 8-year-old burgeons in so many directions that it is impossible to sum up his diversity in a phrase. Individual differences are great, sex differences are becoming significant. Some children are not as articulate as those whom we have quoted in our characterization. Nevertheless, the articulate proclaim trends which are basic and typical for their zone of maturity. In subtle changes of physiognomy, in elongating arms and enlarging hands, the 8-year-old faintly foreshadows adolescence. He still has a rich measure of the engaging naïveté and abandon of childhood. But he is no longer a young child.

At five-and-a-half he was already breaking from old moorings. At six he was in transition capable of contacting a multitude of new facets in the widening world of nature and of man. But he could touch only the beginnings. He saw only in flashes, in opposites, he acted in impulses of avoidance and approach.

By seven, his adjustments and reactions were less piecemeal, his perceptions less sketchy. Patterns more configured began to form in his interior world. They took on a depth of meaning, imparted by memory, experience and maturation.

At eight, the child began to see conclusions, contexts and implications, where before he had seen only in part. His universe became less disconnected. He himself was less submerged by the widening world. He began to make fundamental distinctions between persons and things, between the impersonal forces of nature and the psychological forces of children and men. Above all he began to see himself more clearly as a person among persons, acting, participating, and enjoying.

This reorientation marked a tremendous advance in his life history as an individual in a democratic culture. He was now ready for the ninth year and the tenth with all their rich opportunities for further expansion and evaluation,—and consolidation.

MATURITY TRAITS

(The following maturity traits are not *to be regarded as rigid norms nor as models. They simply illustrate the kinds of behavior—desirable or otherwise—which tend to occur at this age. Every child has an individual pattern of growth, unique to him. The behavior traits here outlined may be used to interpret his individuality and to consider the maturity level at which he is functioning.)*

§ 1. MOTOR CHARACTERISTICS

Bodily Activity

The bodily movements of an 8-year-old are fluid and often graceful and poised. His walk is free. He is aware of his own posture and remembers to sit upright on occasion; he is ready to criticize others who do not. He likes to dramatize and express himself in a variety of postures and gestures. He does stunts and enjoys a game of follow the leader.

EIGHT is on the go. He runs, jumps, chases, wrestles. Hide-and-seek is a favorite pastime but he is also ready for more organized sports such as soccer and baseball. When he is a part of the activity, he is now a good spectator as well as performer.

Courage and daring are characteristics of EIGHT. If he climbs trees, walks a plank, he steels himself. He may verbalize his fear and may need some encouragement but he accomplishes the feat.

There is a new enjoyment in his skating, jump rope and swimming and he is more receptive to learning new techniques. But he is so spontaneous that he frequently goes his own way after he has tried your way.

Eyes and Hands

There is an increase of speed and smoothness in fine motor performance. Approach and grasp are rapid, smooth and even graceful; release is with sure abandon.

EIGHT can change his posture more adaptively. He bends forward, then sits upright in sitting so that his head is at various distances from his working point. There is more symmetry than at seven and he frequently rests on both elbows or extends both arms out on the table. The variability of posture and overflow shows many of the patterns seen at six and seven but there is more fluidity.

EIGHT can look before he acts but he also likes to do things speedily, so the preliminary pause is not a long one. He can sustain regard longer with blinking but if he wants to talk with someone he shifts his regard in their direction.

EIGHT is somewhat like SIX in his interest in doing many things. He has, however, some idea of a finished product. He does not have the sustaining power of NINE, and may leave many things uncompleted.

In writing, he spaces words and sentences, has a more uniform alignment and slant. His ideas may exceed his ability to write them. He is more aware of body proportions in his drawing of human figures, and particularly likes to draw them in action. He is beginning to draw in perspective.

Although EIGHT is an active doer, he is also becoming a good observer. He does not touch what he sees as often as formerly. He can be part of an activity and still watch another child's performance.

§ 2. PERSONAL HYGIENE

Eating

Appetite. Even the poorest eaters begin to pick up a good appetite by eight; they eat steadily and with interest, though not with the speed usually characteristic of this age. EIGHT typically is ravenously hungry. His mother often says, "He eats like a hog; just shovels it in." After completing one round he starts all over again and asks for "everything." He may even request a third helping. Weight curves rise rapidly and the child may suffer teasing about being too fat. This "ribbing" may produce the desired effect with some control of the food intake, but often a little adult supervision may be needed. Certain foods such as potatoes and desserts can be restricted to one helping; and milk is still relished skimmed.

Refusals and Preferences. EIGHT still has food dislikes. He cannot understand, for instance, why "they had to spoil that beautiful ham with that awful cream sauce." His appraisal of food makes rather candid use of the sense of smell. The smell of peanut butter may repel him (especially if he is allergic to it), or it may produce a beatific suffusion of affectionate delight.

Now that he is eight he is venturously ready to taste almost anything; except that he still does not like fat on his meat and if he has seen a chicken killed, he may not be able to eat chicken for some time to come. He can even inhibit his verbal expressions of dislike, and he obviously musters courage with each spoonful of a disliked food. Parents should be careful not to force foods on a child, because he still may be allergic to some at this age. Nevertheless the allergic child may most prefer the very foods to which he is allergic.

Self-Help. EIGHT is handling his implements fairly well, though some boys still hold fork and spoon pronately, which results in a pushing rather than a scooping manipulation. Fingers, however, are less requisitioned than formerly. Many EIGHTS are now able to cut their meat with a knife, but a fair number do not attain this skill before nine or ten. Carving a carrot is still easier than cutting meat.

Table Behavior. There is a definite contrast between the table manners of the 8-year-old at home and away from home. When the parent becomes too discouraged with the 8-year-old at home, he needs only to take him out to a restaurant or to invite a friend in for dinner! The extra new stimulus is often sufficient spur to reveal latent possibilities; but it does not follow that the child could easily maintain the higher level.

At home he eats best with the family group, for he does like company. Perhaps he has now graduated from a little table of his own in the dining room, to the family table. If so, it is well to have him sit next to his mother, where she can unobtrusively keep him in line with slight hints, and protect him from father's reprimands.

Bolting and speed of eating are major problems. There is something reminiscent of the ways of Henry the Eighth when an 8-year-old "goes to it," loosening belt (or skirt!) to accommodate the increased intake, and not taking pains to repress a tendency to belch. More than one parent has reported this type of behavior!

His speed in eating makes for further complications. If the meal is conducted with the formality of courses, he finds himself ready for his dessert long before the rest of the family. If the outdoors does not call, and if dessert does not immediately follow his main course, he would be happy to leave the table and to return when dessert is served. Some parents have even found that the child enjoys piano practice during the interval.

Some EIGHTS who are not as speedy are apt to play with the silver, or to mess the food around on their plates. Though EIGHT may remain pretty well settled in his chair, he may suddenly bend his body agilely to take a look under the table. When other siblings are present he may get into a dispute, but he may also be able to divert himself without interfering with the adult conversation.

EIGHT still needs to be reminded to wash his hands before a meal, and frequently responds with an, "All right, if you insist!" He uses a napkin, but still does not know what to do with it when he is not using it. He tries to hold it on his lap, but it frequently falls to the floor. Therefore many 8-year-olds solve their difficulty by sitting on it. Others still prefer to leave it beside their plate.

Sleep

Bedtime. There is a definite trend toward a later bedtime hour at eight years of age: 8 P.M. with lights out at 8:30 or occasionally at 9:00. Although EIGHT may know how to tell time, he does not utilize his ability to direct himself to bed. He needs to be reminded, and is apt to put off going upstairs as long as possible. To overcome dawdling he needs to be more specifically motivated. If he knows he cannot listen to one of his favorite radio programs unless he is ready for bed, he sees to it that he is ready. His interest in the clock and also his wish to stay up as late as possible make him susceptible to time stipulation: i.e. if he is not in bed by 8 P.M. he has to go to bed the following night as much earlier as he was tardy. He does not relish this possibility, and musters speed especially after he has once had to pay the penalty.

Generally he gets ready for bed faster when he is alone than when he is with his parent. He prefers to read, to be read to, or to listen to a bedside radio. When it is time for lights out he still prefers to have his mother tuck him in and say goodnight. This may still be a favorable time for chatting and unburdening. But it may also be the worst time for talking things over if the child is easily stirred up. This type of child fortunately does not as a rule bring up disturbing subjects on his own initiative, and he is also capable of turning off a radio program which frightens him and which might produce bad dreams.

As a rule EIGHT goes to sleep soon after lights are out if he has not been put to bed too early. But there are some children who still regularly need a quieting down time prior to sleep.

Night. Sleep is usually sound. EIGHT is often described as a "wonderful sleeper." Nightmares rarely disturb his sleep. Even toileting needs are infrequent. His total hours of sleep have dropped to an average of ten hours.

Morning. Most 8-year-olds awaken between 7 and 7:30 A.M. They are usually dressed by 8 o'clock, without much need to be reminded.

Elimination

Bowel. Very few EIGHTs have a movement following the noon meal. They seem to divide into two groups, one of which functions after breakfast, the other after supper. An increasing number of the after-breakfast group are able to function during the morning at school if they have not already done so at home. EIGHT is susceptible to the same type of rapid onset of a bowel movement that the 6-year-old experienced; this however is usually in response to a specific stimulus and is more under the child's control. A sudden shift in temperature caused by going in swimming may produce an immediate desire to have a bowel movement. This type of response may be prevented by reminding the child to go to the bathroom in advance.

Bladder. As at seven, the 8-year-old needs to be reminded to go to the bathroom, especially when he comes home from school or before he goes on a trip. Otherwise he handles his needs well by himself. In the midst of or preceding an unpleasant task either at home or at school, he may experience a genuine need of going to the bathroom. The task of drying dishes is certain to be interrupted by a trip to the bathroom, with a little dawdling thrown in.

Bath and Dressing

Bath. EIGHT may resist his bath, but he enjoys it very much after he gets under way, especially if it is prolonged into a half hour of play. When the parent suggests a bath, EIGHT may fictitiously reply, "I had a bath last night." An old-fashioned Saturday night bath would suit a number of boys, but for the most part EIGHT adjusts to at least three baths a week.

He has acquired more tolerance of warm water and enjoys seeing how hot he can stand his bath. He truly enjoys the feel of a warm bath. Although he may have bathed himself quite well at seven, he now would prefer to be bathed or at least to be read to as he bathes. He may even do spelling and oral arithmetic in the bath. He will take turns with his mother in washing himself. Boys often enjoy boat play, and may pretend that they are submarines. Now and then they may punctuate their play by drinking out of the faucet. At an earlier age they may have supped the bath water or sucked the washcloth. EIGHT is not fussy about his face, neck, ears or back because as he says, "I can't see them." He can shampoo himself. He can cut his fingernails but he still needs help with his dominant hand. Keeping fingernails cut is the best way to keep them clean.

A few 8-year-olds spontaneously wash their hands before meals, but most EIGHTS need and accept reminding with only a trace of resistance. They are apt to dash through washing and to wipe most of the dirt on the towel. Therefore a little added instruction of "Soap three times and remember your wrists" may save some laundry.

Dressing and Care of Clothes. EIGHT dresses with fair ease and speed. He may need prodding and if he is asked why he is so slow he may answer, "I think I'm just lazy." A few would still like to be helped, but they usually accept the challenge, "All children dress themselves by eight," and manage quite well, but may ask for help in the finishing touches. They still need to be tucked in, and to be reminded to button the rest of their buttons. A good zipper alleviates this problem, especially on a pants flap. Shoe laces are now easily handled and are kept tied, in fact a new problem arises in that the child wishes to remove his shoes without untying them. This is not too good for the shoes.

EIGHT is again interested in his clothes, and in buying new clothes. He may not only dictate his desires as to style and color, but may also help to select his clothes at the store. However, he is usually open to suggestions. Boys often prefer greens,—knickers, plain shirts or jerseys— all toward the cooler end of the spectrum. Girls are also shifting away from red and desire more blues and greens. Some girls refuse slacks or leggings and still others prefer them. Changing clothes is no longer a problem; in fact many children prefer daily changes of everything. Most children can now choose their own clothes each morning, with or without help. If they are still given help they are highly insulted if their clothes are laid out on the floor instead of on a chair. Some children are left too much on their own and may appear without any underwear and with two different-colored socks. Some boys like to use their clothes to show their toughness and purposely keep their socks way down because they do not want to be called sissies.

Girls are more careful of their clothes than boys. Boys are genuinely hard on their clothes, and will now report tears and holes if these make their clothes uncomfortable. When they take them off, they may still drop them on the spot or strew them about, but an increasing number now throw their clothes at a chair or even place them neatly on a chair. EIGHT is able to put his dirty clothes in a hamper, at least if reminded. He is apt to lose detachable pieces of clothing. This is in part related to his greater awareness of how he feels and how much clothing he needs. Teaching him to tie his sweater arms around his waist if he is too warm to wear it, may save him from future hunting and often from loss.

A handkerchief as well as a napkin is becoming more meaningful and acceptable. He is beginning to use a handkerchief when he coughs or sneezes as well as when he blows his nose.

Health and Somatic Complaints

EIGHT's improved school attendance record reflects his better health. If he has a cold it usually lasts no more than two days. Even though his temperature may shoot up, he tends to recover quickly. This is the first time that some children are said to have an illness "lightly." Occasionally a child may complain of a sore throat and then nothing more materializes. Hay fever and asthma may return; a number of children have not had any attacks since six years of age. EIGHT has fewer communicable diseases than do younger children, and he recovers more rapidly.

The 8-year-old is in general much less fatigable than the 7-year-old. Although he may not fatigue easily, he may have a return of stomach upsets as at six, if something bothers him. There are eye complaints as at seven, and a reporting of headaches with over-excitement.

Accidents are a major cause of death at this age:—chiefly accidents from automobiles, falls, and drowning. The 8-year-old like the 4-year-old is out of bounds. He is out for action and is ready to try anything. He has lost the caution he had at seven. He misjudges himself as being better than he really is. EIGHT is not really ready to take his bicycle out on the highway. He is apt to get hit by a passing car. When he falls he tends to land on his feet and may therefore break his leg.

Tensional Outlets

The tensional outlets which parents of 8-year-olds report are definitely minimal. The child's whole energy is positively directed toward his social and gross motor activities which he now has under far better control, or can at least tackle. A few boys pull at their pants in the genital region or scratch their buttocks, especially under rising social tension. This type of behavior is embarrassing for the parent. Looser underwear would help; but often removal of the child from the too demanding social situation is indicated.

The most common tensional outlet at eight is a need to urinate when the child is taxed with something he does not like or is unequal to. Dish wiping is almost sure to be interrupted after a bare beginning by a trip to the bathroom. A difficult school subject such as reading may produce a distended bladder in a very short time. This reaction is in the nature of "internal perspiration," emotionally induced. It is not an alibi, as shown by the copiousness of the ensuing secretion. Intense laughter may also produce an involuntary release of urine.

Thumb-sucking especially in boys has a slight exacerbation at eight. If the child did suck his thumb at six he was careful to hide it from the adult; and he definitely tried to give it up at seven with adult help. But at eight, he may be a bit blatant about it and confess no concern or shame. It tends to occur in relation to reading, radio, going to sleep or waking but not frequently enough to require specific measures. This is often the last age at which thumb-sucking recurs.

§3. EMOTIONAL EXPRESSION

EIGHT is more "outside himself" than was SEVEN. He is less sensitive, less within himself, less apt to withdraw. He is ready to tackle anything,—in fact he likes hard things. He even shows courage in his attack. He thinks he knows more than he really does and often assumes a "know it all" tone of voice. He anticipates with great eagerness and may even expend his interest in anticipation alone. His interest is short lived and he shifts rapidly from one thing to the next. This power to shift rapidly makes him more controllable, for he calms down quickly with a little help. It is even possible to control him with a look.

He is full of impatience, especially with himself, and wants to get things done at once. "I can't wait" is a repeated phrase of the 8-year-old and this may refer to a party next week, next summer's vacation or the time when he will be ready to go to college. He is constantly in and out of the house. He is so shifting, so little able to sustain his own interests, that he is ceaselessly making demands of his mother. She may say, "He haunts me." He frequently needs someone's complete attention. He needs help to hold better to a task, and he needs support through praise and encouragement. He dramatizes everything, including himself. Even his "tall" stories catch the drama of a situation, and may, let us hope, elicit the proper response from his audience. For dramatizing always needs an audience.

While demanding so much from his mother he is at the same time more resistant to her. He may resist her request or suggestion with an outright "No"; but more frequently he gives some excuse as, "I'm busy," or "Well, I'll do it later." He should be given his time for he usually does obey requests if allowed to come around on his own steam.

He bursts into tears for many reasons, especially when he is tired. He may be disappointed because something he wanted very much has been denied him; he may have had his feelings hurt, may have been criticized, or may have done something which he knew he should not have done. He cries less from inner confusion than he did earlier, but may cry over a sad dramatic episode in a movie or story.

Occasionally his temper may be aroused. He may become so furious with his mother that he may say with real venom, as his face clouds up, "You are a skunk!" He will rarely strike his mother, but may strike a sibling when he becomes angry after his mother has scolded him. It is wise later to point out this mechanism of retaliation to him, for he will understand it. Other EIGHTS may show their anger more humorously. They may tense up their faces in exasperation, project their lower jaws and draw back and flex their arms at the elbow as they clench their fists. This same dramatic pose is sure to produce a laugh from other children, especially in a schoolroom situation. EIGHT also dramatizes things verbally: "This *always* happens to me," "I *never* get a chance to do what I want," "You have asked me *eight million* questions."

Because EIGHT demands one's complete attention, it is wise for the parent to have very definite planned relief from the child of this age. School plays a large part in this relief. New experiences at school are avidly absorbed and help to widen the scope of the 8-year-old. Competition with other children is spontaneous and helps to hold EIGHT to a task. Although he may be bossy in some situations, he can also, when under supervision, utilize this same urge to direct by helping some other child who needs individual attention. His after-school-hours play still needs a certain amount of control. The introduction of an older child often provides a beneficial combination of stimulation and control.

EIGHT is not always the most delightful child to have around. He can be rude especially to his grandmother when she is a part of the household. It would be wise for grandmother to relate herself to the child only through some specific

[174]

channel such as playing games with him or reading to him. The worst time for her to intervene is when his father and mother are handling him. Then any interference from grandmother is likely to bring forth some very uncomfortable rude remarks from him. He acts quite differently and is very companionable alone with his grandmother when he goes to visit her in her own home.

EIGHT likes to argue. He is most aware of others' mistakes, especially his mother's, but he is also self-critical and may say, "Am I dopey!" He is aware that others may trick him, and he is therefore on the lookout. He expresses his silliness in nonsense rhyming, and when he is tired he may actually go on a laughing jag.

§4. FEARS AND DREAMS

Fears

Though EIGHT has a number of unresolved fears left over from the time when he was seven, and a slight return to some of his 6-year-old fears, he for the most part attacks life with courage and is out to conquer. He often will not even admit his fears to himself. But he may still be afraid of fighting, of failing, of others finding fault with him or not liking him, and he may refuse to listen to stories about snakes.

He may still have a lingering fear of the dark, and is said to be leery or shy of the dark. Yet he may now demand that the hall light be turned off, and there is nothing which gives him greater joy than to be outdoors with his parent after dark. This is an excellent time to help him to orient himself to the dark, to the coming and going of his shadow according to the direction and strength of the light if there are street lights, and to night noises. Although fire itself may not be feared,

there may be a compulsive interest in everything about fire. Books about fire may be read and re-read. Space fears at home are now under his control. He is no longer afraid of the attic; and though he may show no enthusiasm for the cellar he can handle his fear if sent on a specific errand. Girls especially may fear strange men, though these very men may be trying to be kind and helpful. They may fear that the men are going to kill them or throw them into the water.

Some children instead of having outright fears may be great worriers. In the midst of an enjoyable experience such as a trip they may worry about repeating the trip. They worry about catching a train or even about their father going into the army. These are the children who tend to cling to the past and have difficulty in coming into the future smoothly. This is their indirect method of taking the next step. Most 8-year-olds attack directly any feared experience and compulsively repeat it to resolve their fear. Or they perpetrate a fear by scaring a younger child. This may prove very unfortunate for the victim. Eight-year-olds may better frighten each other or a responsive adult. The telling of dramatic blood and thunder stories may be a useful method in some cases for satisfying this compulsive interest in the fearful.

Dreams

EIGHT is apparently not much of a dreamer. Boys may have a short return of their animal dreams about wolves, foxes and snakes, or may have dreams of a fantastic nature not necessarily unpleasant. But on the whole if EIGHT dreams, he dreams of daily happenings and pleasant things. Frightening dreams can usually be traced to some immediate influence from the radio, cinema or reading.

§5. SELF AND SEX

Self

EIGHT is coming out from his more serious, thoughtful inward self of SEVEN. Indeed, this new outer self seems to want to be constantly contacting people, going places, and doing things. It is as if the child were trying out against the world the self which he was so busy consolidating at seven. He operates best as a self within the give-and-take of relationships with another person.

EIGHT is increasingly aware of himself as a person. He is becoming an individual, a member of a social world. The adult no longer talks down to him. Rather, he talks with him. The child is becoming enough aware of his "self" to use the term. One 8-year-old, looking at her reflection in the mirror, verbalized, "I don't look like myself." The adult likewise recognizes outward signs of this more distinctive self. One mother remarked of her 8-year-old son, "Even his gestures are like him."

The child now is more conscious of himself in the ways in which he differs from other people. He is conscious of wearing glasses, of being left-handed, of not doing as well as or better than the other members of his class. But as yet he is not greatly disturbed by these discrepancies.

EIGHT loses himself in his very real ability to dramatize. He readily becomes the characters in his books, radio programs and movies. His ability improves with an audience response. His pretend cry may be so realistic as to deceive.

EIGHT may be torn between his desires to grow up and to remain as he is. Some EIGHTS "cannot wait" to grow up though some boys hate to grow up and frankly state this resistance. EIGHT's idea of growing up may be that he should be treated in a certain way. He has his idea of how he

should be spoken to. He does not like the out and out reminders which he needed at seven. Now he wants suggestive clues in words or looks that give him ideas of what is expected of him. If his mother forgets and returns to a less subtle handling he may burst into tears because she "gave it away." EIGHT also wants special privileges. He wants to stay up later or to go to grownup movies. EIGHT needs to have his new demands answered in part, even as he did at four, when on his insistence he was allowed to cross a safe street by himself, but accepted the adult's hand on a crowded thorofare.

EIGHT is interested in evaluating his own performance, his own relationship with others. At seven he was intent on living up to his own standards. Now he wishes to live up to his notion of the standard that other people have for him. Since his performance is often only mediocre, and his notion of other people's standards extremely high, there is often a discrepancy here which leads to tears and temporary unhappiness. Or he may boast and alibi to make up for the difference between what he can do and what he would like to do.

Sex

Some EIGHTS, especially boys, are still searching for some of the facts about babies in relation to their starting, to the period of pregnancy, and to their birth. Many have already thought about these matters at seven. EIGHT may still not be concerned about the father's part in the starting of a baby. Girls are more likely to be knowing, more inquisitive and more demanding of facts than are boys. Girls may think through far enough to question as to how the father put the seed into the mother's body. If a girl is not informed by her mother after she has asked such leading questions, she is apt to secure this information from her school-mates. This second-hand information is often far from clear.

An 8-year-old will usually wait for an appropriate time to ask such questions, preferably at good-night chatting time when lights are out. It is often difficult for a mother to explain in a simple un-emotional way the facts of intercourse to her daughter. But she need not be frightened, for a daughter who is ready to learn can often ask just the right questions. The daughter readily accepts the fact that the father places the male sex organ into the mother's sex organ. This may start an avalanche of questions from the child as to when, where, and between whom the sex act can occur. All of these questions can readily be answered according to the child's demands.

It is a wise mother who completes her talk with the suggestion that it is best for her daughter not to discuss these things with her schoolmates or even with her younger siblings. The mother will explain that younger children cannot understand and that other mothers want to explain such things to their own children at the proper time. When the daughter is older and comprehends these things better she may discuss them with her friends.

Boys are less apt to secure their knowl-edge of the sex act by word of mouth from their mothers. They are more apt to learn about it from observing the mating of ani-mals. However they may be slow to trans-fer their accidental knowledge about ani-mals to the human field.

Girls are becoming more aware of sani-tary napkins and ask what they are used for. They are no longer satisfied with the information that they are bandages. They may have heard of menstruation or bleed-ing and if left to their own thought de-vices they may relate this bleeding to the navel and umbilical cord. Some girls pass through this stage without sufficient awareness to ask questions. Therefore it is important for the parent to choose a suitable time at nine or ten years of age to impart this knowledge, before the child's own menstruation periods begin.

EIGHT is predominantly interested in the girl-boy relationship even though he may hold it in the margins of his mind. A few boys may still be intending to marry their mothers even though they may have received proposals from contemporary girls. They may even be mulling over in their male minds ideas about a chemical they are going to invent which will pre-vent their mother from growing old. The romantic note is creeping into the lives of 8-year-olds. Boys recognize a pretty girl, and girls chase handsome boys, much to the boys' delight. Though a boy may have two or three girls, he knows that he is going to marry only one of them. Some "engagements" last over from seven. EIGHT can now plan to live in his own new home after marriage. Some EIGHTS sit for hours over a mail-order catalogue choosing fur-niture for their far future homes. Boys of eight are often very secretive about their girl-friends especially if they have a new one, because they do not like to be teased or kidded.

There may be some overt sex play be-tween 8-year-old girls and older boys. A few girls at eight are unusually responsive to touch, and readily develop gooseflesh all over the body at the slightest stimulus. They enjoy rolling around on the floor with boys and become quite helpless be-cause of their laughter. This is the kind of girl who is easily drawn into group sex play with older children. This type of girl needs more supervision than the usual 8-year-old. If such groups form it is an indication that the children involved are not enjoying the more suitable satisfying activities characteristic of their age.

§6. INTERPERSONAL RELATIONS

EIGHT may be "easy to get on with" at home, but his best behavior is usually when he is away from home. He is less absorbed in his own activities at home and more dependent upon his mother's suggestions of what to do next. He is not the helper he was at seven. What he does now is dependent upon his mood. He prefers to do jobs he thinks of by himself. He dislikes many of his old jobs such as drying the dishes, setting the table, or picking up his room. He grumbles and grouches over them. There are, however, certain new and more responsible jobs which he attacks with real interest, and for which he readily accepts any supervision he needs. Boys like to burn trash and to do repairing jobs on electric light fixtures and other simple household equipment. Both sexes like to cook and to bake real cakes and cookies.

EIGHT needs considerable help in reorganizing his life. He is likely to spread too much in his thoughts and his activities. Then life gets too much for him and he leaves things in a "mess." His intentions are good and he may return to re-order the mess, but he needs a helping hand. He is, however, aware of orderliness, remarks about a neat kitchen, and enjoys a clean house. He may be very careful of certain things that mean a lot to him— his funny books, guns, and his desk. But otherwise he needs considerable help and planning from his parent.

He likes a reward system of some kind. A point system may suffice, but points are frequently translated into money values. Parents often are disturbed by the "money-mad" interest of the 8-year-old boy, but they should not underestimate the motivation value of this same interest. Here is an excellent opportunity to use a stimulus which at the same time also serves to give a child some idea of money values. By his poor bargaining, EIGHT shows that he relates his values chiefly to his own personal needs and desires.

A bulletin board chart of his household tasks helps the 8-year-old to accept some of his responsibilities. Then, as he says, "You won't have to yelp at me." Parents need to remember that this and other devices are means of helping the child to organize. The devices are not ends in themselves; therefore one device needs to be frequently supplanted by another.

At eight, the relationship between the mother and child is both complicated and subtle. What the mother does for the child is important as it was earlier, but more important is what she thinks and feels about him. He is extremely demanding of her—may dog her every footstep throughout the day. He demands not only her time, but her complete attention. Even so, her complete attention may not be enough to establish a smooth relationship. EIGHT makes various exactions of his mother: how she shall react, what she shall do, what she shall say. Even an extremely perceptive mother who tries to meet these exactions may find the task a hard one. It is the rare 8-year-old who can promptly forgive his mother when she makes a mistake which directly affects him.

Some EIGHTS who are not too bound up with their mother are capable of showing real devotion and may often tell her how wonderful she is. Physical affection also is expressed. The mother usually continues to be the best loved parent, although the father is coming in for an increasing share of affection, if he makes a good, adaptive response to the child.

EIGHT does fairly well with younger siblings, but he has rather lost his big brother attitude. He too readily lowers to the siblings' level of response, gets out of hand, may tease and end by fighting. When EIGHT is responsible in caring for a younger sibling he is likely to be too strict. He does best when he is helped to a good start, and is warned ahead of time how he is to act. Then he likes to hear later that he has done well, and that he has now been promoted to privileges that a younger sibling does not have. Too often an older sibling is held down to the level of a younger. Simple privileges such as a later bedtime hour even though he starts to bed with a younger sibling, give him a due sense of prestige and status. He does not have to flaunt these special privileges before his younger sibling. He even enjoys holding them a secret between himself and his parent. If the adjustment between two siblings is poor, planned separation is very helpful. Some EIGHTS protect themselves by the simple expedient of shutting a door.

EIGHT is the age when "real," "bosom" or "special" friends begin to play a part in the life of the child. School becomes important because EIGHT's friends are there. Usually these friends are of the same sex. The relationship between friends may be very close and demanding, something like the mother-child relation, and there is between friends much arguing, disputing, getting "mad on" each other. The quality of the relationship between two children, not simply what they do together, is becoming important in the eyes of the 8-year-old.

Strong friendships are more likely to occur between two children of the same age, but a fair number of EIGHTS play better with older children. EIGHT is apt to admire an older child of eleven or twelve, and this older child will often in turn protect his admirer from being bullied or mistreated. Some EIGHTS who have previously had real difficulty in approaching children, may now make crude approaches in their attempt to attract another child.

The trend is toward longer periods of relatively peaceful play with others, with only minor verbal disagreements, than formerly. However, any unsupervised play session often ends in disagreement or in the disgruntled departure of at least one participant. Nevertheless, EIGHT figures strongly in neighborhood group play, including baseball and hut play. Some EIGHTS are repeatedly picked on by the rest of the group, but others break loose from the group on their own initiative.

EIGHT marks the beginning of a definite change as to preferred sex of playmates. Boys and girls are now beginning to segregate in play. Girls as a rule are the first to separate off from the boys, and to be conscious of this separation, but theirs is usually a mere quiet drawing away. Boys, when they become conscious of a need for separation, are often very rough and boisterous about excluding girls.

EIGHT is beginning to acquire "company manners." He is better away from home, and is eager both to go visiting and sightseeing, especially to another city. He meets new people with a fair amount of ease and will even talk to strangers in a restaurant. He telephones well and is able to write down simple messages.

§7. PLAY AND PASTIMES

In General

EIGHT abhors playing alone. Whatever he does he wants to do either with adult or child, and he demands not only the presence of another person, but also that other person's complete attention and participation. Action is the key characteristic of his play. He has a new sense of the whole, a sense of interplay, active relationship, and of practical use. His drawings are now full of action. His airplanes and tanks are drawn in battle scenes, and a person pilots his airplanes and maneuvers his tanks. He puts his tools to helpful household uses by fastening hooks, nailing down train tracks or screwing in loose doorknobs. Girls mix up cooking ingredients to make cookies and cakes. Boys mix up the contents of their chemistry sets to produce new colors and smells and finally to make what they call "the magic potion."

EIGHT wants to set up his telegraph set between two rooms or two houses so that he can actually communicate with another person. He may even wish to communicate with the president of the United States about his blue-print book since he believes the government might be interested in some of his projected contraptions.

EIGHT likes to dramatize. He dramatizes air raids, accidents, fighting and bombing, with his toys. He impersonates characters in the movies he has seen or in the books he has read. He wants to perform magic tricks. Girls' dramatizing is more verbal and sedentary than that of boys. Girls are likely to arrange performances and to put on "shows." Paper dolls furnish a vehicle for this dramatic urge. They also serve as an outlet for EIGHT's powerful urge to collect. Paper dolls and their dresses can be collected in quantities. Moreover EIGHT likes to classify, to arrange and to organize. A collection of varied dolls with their numerous paper appurtenances offers a channel for such organizing activity.

Boys also succumb to a "collecting craze"—in fact with many it reaches its peak at this age. Children are not only interested in quantity when they collect their stamps or box tops;—they are becoming interested in quality and in rudimentary classification.

Gross motor activity is characteristic of EIGHT's group play. He needs some restraint, since he too readily goes out of bounds. When a group of EIGHTS are left to their own devices, they often revert to abandoned "animal spirits"—wild running, jumping, chasing, wrestling and tree climbing. They are, however, capable of organizing simple war games or hide-and-seek. EIGHT responds well to some supervised control. Both boys and girls enjoy formal baseball and soccer.

EIGHT spontaneously thinks up reasons for organizing his own clubs, such as "The Paper Salvage Club," "The Gadget Club," or "The Library Club." These represent a new interest, but are usually loosely organized and very short-lived. Hut play which may have begun at an earlier age persists longer and often has the dramatic addition of a secret pass-word.

EIGHT enjoys the different sports in season. He rows in the summer and he skiis and skates in the winter. There is nothing more typical of springtime (or of eight-year-oldness) than a group of EIGHTS wrangling over marbles. They seem to enjoy the back and forth tug of wrangling and do not wish any adult interference.

Interest in table games, especially in card games, parchesi, checkers, dominoes, reaches an almost passionate height. EIGHT scorns some of the simple earlier games, and enjoys the financial transactions in Monopoly. He is very ingenious in making up his own rules and may even invent new games. Although some EIGHTS can lose at play with fair grace, this is not always true; a good deal of bickering and some accusations of cheating occur.

Kites, marbles, and tops all appear in season, with airplanes becoming a strong rival to kites. Boys make airplane models, draw airplanes, learn to identify different kinds of planes, or indulge in imaginative airplane play. Other objects than airplanes are manufactured as they work at their work benches. Interest in erector sets and mechanical toys continues strong. Electric trains, chemistry sets, small movie projectors with real films, are enjoyed by certain boys of mechanical bent.

Reading

Those EIGHTS who are just beginning to read well, now enjoy reading spontaneously. Though EIGHT may read well, he may not spend as much time at reading by himself as he did at seven and he again likes very much to be read to. He is beginning to enjoy hearing the classics of childhood. A modern favorite relates the wonderful, magical and absurd adventures of Mary Poppins. EIGHT is also interested in books of travel, geography, and far away times and places.

Comic books are still his favorites. This interest reaches a peak at eight and nine years. EIGHT buys, collects, barters, borrows and hoards his funny books. He is more likely to borrow than to barter since he does not want to part with his own. Though he still likes the animal and slap-stick comics, he is branching out into the blood and thunder type.

EIGHT likes to look at pictorial magazines. He can pore for hours over catalogues. He plans to send for things but he is more likely to carry this through at nine. Nothing gives him more delight than to receive mail of his own, printed so that he can read it by himself.

Music, Radio, Movies

The initial 7-year-old flare of interest in music lessons may die out unless someone plays with the child or sits with him while he plays. He enjoys playing duets. Practicing cannot be forced and often it is wise to interrupt lessons for a while until he is ready to return to them at a later date (nine-ten years).

The radio has now become such an important part of his life that he will neglect play for it. This is the one activity which he enjoys alone, but he does like to have an adult listen with him and he becomes adept in choosing programs which he feels the adult would be interested in. He is beginning to choose his own programs more carefully and will even refer to the radio sheet in the newspaper. He listens to the same set programs each day, and usually knows at what time and on what station his favorite programs occur. He may still cling to the adventure programs, but he is branching out into mysteries, slapstick comedies, quiz programs and even news programs.

He is coming into his own so far as the movies are concerned. His mother reports that he "loves" the movies. Types of pictures that he previously rejected now become his favorites. He enjoys selected news reels, animal pictures, and mysteries but still does not like romantic movies. He may even follow the amusement advertisements in the daily paper to select his "kind" of movie, with his parents' help. EIGHT is indeed more aware of his likes and dislikes and realizes that they may not coincide with those of other people.

§8. SCHOOL LIFE

EIGHT enjoys school and even dislikes to stay at home, particularly if it means that he will miss a special event. Even though he may not be doing too well in his work, even though he may not be getting along too well with his teacher, his attitude is one of response toward, of attack, rather than of withdrawal. He fatigues less easily and is more ready to remain for both morning and afternoon sessions. His attendance record is remarkably good and even when he is out with a cold, his absence is of short duration. When he is absent even for a day he is thinking of the group and what the group is doing. He asks to have his school work sent home to him so that he can keep up with the group.

Some EIGHTS, especially boys, may still have difficulty in getting ready for school and in reaching school on time. It is often difficult to motivate them at home, since they are no longer fearful of being late for school. But they may be motivated by some new school responsibility which challenges them. Getting to school on time is not only the responsibility of the home at EIGHT, but also of the school.

There is now much more interplay between home and school. EIGHT brings to school things which relate to his school projects or to his personal experiences. He also likes to take his products home but is now willing to leave them with his teacher for a few days' display. Although he remembers to take them home, he may lose them in transit.

Many mothers report that for the first time they are informed about school activities. Previously they were told more about misconduct of other children or of their own child's difficulties. Finally by eight, the life in the school room is re-told at home. The mother enjoys being better informed. She now feels an easier relationship with the school, and is apt to give lavish compliments to the third grade teacher.

Actually EIGHT's teacher is not as important in his adjustment as she was in the earlier grades. She may be even taken more or less for granted. EIGHT is most interested in his school group and would like his teacher to become a part of that group. He joyously accepts her, especially when he catches her in some error and when she in turn accepts the criticism and tosses it off humorously. Learning through others' mistakes is often the surest, most rapid way for the 8-year-old.

EIGHTS enter the schoolroom with enthusiasm (unless of course it is one of those bad days!). They busy themselves by writing on the blackboard, or by inspecting a globe; they may dawdle in the dressing room; but are gradually brought together. They smile, touch, hit out at each other as they pass by.

In a classroom situation they are eager to talk and want to answer every question. They may learn to inhibit long enough for some one child to answer but if he is wrong or too slow they are sure to respond for him. When several become verbal and noisy the teacher can control them by her own silence. They do, however, enjoy taking turns and are insistent that each one has his turn. They comment on another's response or lack of response. "Oh you know that." "That's easy." "You're too slow, Mary."

Transitions are fairly smooth for EIGHT since he likes to change from one thing to another, but there is some talking and dawdling so that a little extra time needs to be allowed for him to settle down.

EIGHT can shift his eyes more easily from blackboard to desk. He can copy from the board and he also likes to write on the board while his classmates attend to his performance. At his desk he sits facing forward with head position sometimes at arm's distance from the paper and sometimes quite close; he shifts his positions frequently. He works more independently than at seven and does not need the teacher nearby. He raises his arm with an upward thrust to call the teacher's attention but he can wait at least briefly for her to come to him. The impatient EIGHT can't wait to be given directions and though he seemingly understands them, he needs to have them repeated. Often after he has worked for a while, he stops to speak to his nearby neighbor, telling him what to do, asking what page he is on, etc., but he can return to his own work for a while longer. If his interruptions become excessive he responds well to a separation to the margin of the group to do his work. It is unfortunate when this need for separation is treated with punishment as a means of shaming the child by having him sit in the hall outside of his classroom, especially when he improves so nicely after a shift to the margin of the group.

He talks about his own performance and tells another child, "I got three wrong," "My drawing isn't good. This isn't good, is it?" He may discuss who is best in art. If the class is divided into groups he is aware of the grouping and may dislike being placed in a lower group. He likes praise and seeks it.

EIGHT enjoys reading. He can tackle new words through context or by phonetics. He is more skillful and only occasionally makes errors similar to those of SIX or SEVEN. He now omits unimportant words, reverses word order in a phrase but usually maintains the meaning. He has a more uniform speed and can stop and talk about the story and pick it up again. Many now read well enough to prefer silent reading. Exciting and humorous stories are favored and he may express scorn of a story which he considers too young for him.

Writing is less laborious and there is more uniformity in slant and alignment as well as in spacing of words and sentences. There may be an occasional reversal or a substitution of a capital for a small letter in manuscript writing. Even though he is careless in writing, EIGHT likes to write neatly. "I'm doing my best writing." "Is this neat?" Doodling or drawing in notebooks or on scrap paper is a favorite practice. Despite EIGHT's facility he may not be able to write out a story to full length; he then may wish an opportunity to dictate the unfinished portion, or to continue it later.

EIGHT likes variety. He likes oral or written arithmetic; he likes to use the blackboard and to work in his workbook. He is partial to the new tables which he is learning. He likes to shift from one process to another. His shifting may even be automatic. In the midst of a multiplication example he may shift to addition or to subtraction and something may tell him his mind is playing tricks on him. He likes to take his workbook home to catch up, and is apt to go beyond his assignment. One day he may say he doesn't like arithmetic and the next he says it is easy.

EIGHTS are especially oriented to their own group, room, and teacher. They like to have their teacher a part of their activities, to have her play games with them, read with them, and sit with them at table. They like the total group inclusion in a spelling bee. They like to join other grades at an assembly but on the whole mix less with other ages than they will at nine years of age.

There is more grouping at play. All are able to join in a single group activity. Boys and girls separate on occasion: the girls for jump rope, and the boys for ball play. They can enjoy taking turns—after some struggle to secure a place—and they watch and comment on each other's performance.

§9. ETHICAL SENSE

EIGHT's behavior harks back to that of his 6-year-old self, even though he is now less rigid and is not as likely to "explode." When he is asked to do something, he delays his response. He often says, "In a minute," or "I'll do it later," or he may ask, "Why do I have to do it now?" He is likely to argue with his mother or to give excuses: "I'm too tired," "I'm busy reading," or "I had a bath last night" (when it was actually three nights ago). He may generalize on a point of view and declare, "But people think differently." Some EIGHTs, as at seven, do not hear what is asked of them because they are so engrossed in what they are doing. EIGHT may look at you as though listening, but after you have finished speaking he queries, "What did you say?" A willing, immediately responding EIGHT is somewhat exceptional. Even when he does respond it may be unwillingly as he says, "All right, if you insist," and often grouches and grumbles along the way.

EIGHT demands that the adult treat him more like a grownup. He wants his instructions to be worded just right, he likes to work from clues, or from secret codes. A look will often be enough to bring him back into line. If he is criticized he may burst into tears. But, as at six, he thrives on praise and likes to be reminded of his improvement. Physical punishment is rarely resorted to with the 8-year-old.

Small deprivations such as being deprived of a radio program, a funny book or being made to go to bed early, produce the desired effect with most EIGHTs. A few are unimpressed and may answer back, "I didn't care to hear that program anyway." If EIGHT is allowed to determine his own punishment he is often too harsh on himself and may need help to soften his punishment.

EIGHT is more capable at managing his thoughts and of thinking things through. He is fairly rapid about making up his mind about the bigger things of life, although some EIGHTs prefer to have their mothers make up their minds for them. It is usually the little things of life that set EIGHT into vacillation and deliberation. Maybe the decision involves a choice of cereal, a second helping, a glass of milk or a valentine. EIGHT does not shift from his decision as readily as he did at seven when reasoned with.

EIGHT wants to be good. He is now more aware of the two opposing forces of good and bad. He feels their operation when he is acting in one way or the other. He may be so concerned about them as absolutes that the parent may need to help him to think relatively to explain that "goodness" may be affected by intelligence or age; that one makes allowance for the "badness" of a younger child. EIGHT wants his goodness to be appreciated. He wants to please, to be thought well of, and to get a good report.

Although EIGHT is becoming more responsible for his acts and is willing to take the consequences, his first and usual impulse may be to blame others. He may be laughed out of his blaming, but he is apt to hold to the point that someone else started the trouble and this may have some truth in it. He is more apt to blame others when he is tired or upset.

EIGHT is proficient at alibiing. He especially alibis about being late. He says, "I didn't know the time," or "My friends wouldn't let me go." His time sense is often more scrupulous at seven than at eight. Therefore he often needs a little more supervision at eight. Some EIGHTS cannot tolerate making the slightest error and cover up any exposure by saying, "Oh I knew it all the time, I was just wondering how bright you were!"

The same child who earlier dictated to her mother her list of "Things to do and Things not to do" and "Thinking about myself and Thinking about others," at eight asked her mother to write down things which were "Right and Wrong." It is interesting to note that this is a single-column list. Right and Wrong are to some extent brought together into a single standard of conduct and are no longer separated in bi-polar opposition. The list follows:

Right and Wrong

1. It's not my fault that they call me a 'bad sport' when I want to play a different game after I've played one for a long time. I can't help it if there aren't enough people to start another game. Finally I get up enough strength to play some more. And finally they change to my game.

2. Question of getting to school on time: How can I tell the exact time I've got to get up and the exact time to eat breakfast so I can get to school on time. I can't help it if I'm late. It's not my fault. Probably all my guesses about time are all wrong.

3. When some of the people start up a fight, it's not my fault if I want to try and stop the fight even though Miss D. tells us to keep away from fights because the other teachers would think we'd started it. Even if we try to explain to the teachers they think we did start the fight and were just trying to get away from being punished.

4. Something hard comes up and I'm trying to do it.
I don't think it's fair for other people to come along and call me a 'sissy' because I can't do it very well. (Some of these things haven't happened yet but they might.)

5. In the coat room even though you're not supposed to talk, I can't help it sometimes because other people ask me questions and tempt me to answer them. Do you blame me?

6. Running in the halls going out to recess.
I can't help running in the halls going out to recess because I'm so eager to go out to shout and play.

7. I think I ought to have a little more freedom, more freedom about deciding things—like getting up early in the morning. (I used to plan to, then I'd be too tired when I woke up in the morning.)

8. I think I should have rewards for being good like candy and books I like very much. But I won't always have to be rewarded. Maybe when I'm about nine-and-a-half or ten I don't think I'll have to be rewarded for being good. Then I'll just be good naturally.

9. If it's a sensible reason and something I can do quite easily and something I feel I can do and want to do, and don't have to force myself to do, then I should obey.

10. I think I should do something more about getting up in the morning. I ought to be able to choose sensible clothes. And if I don't, it serves me right to have to take them off unless they are sensible clothes and the weather is right for them.

11. You shouldn't just force me to do things. I will do them if they are sensible.

12. On the playground it's not my fault if I want to slide on a wonderful sliding place in the back of the school and I'd forgotten at that minute that I wasn't supposed to play in the back. (Oh it was neat ice! and there was a little bump at the end!)

EIGHT needs considerable help in the care of his possessions. His awareness of order exceeds his ability to keep things in order. This awareness should make the adult feel that there will be better days ahead when the child will become more responsible. EIGHT would happily relinquish the care of his room to his mother.

The one sure motivation to get EIGHT to do things is the motivation of receiving money. His mother says, "He just loves money." He likes to add to his store to get the sum up to "even big dough," like fifty cents. EIGHT may spend his entire allowance (20¢-25¢) or his earnings, on funny books, but some like to save up for bigger purchases. They pore over catalogues, haunt store windows, and may indulge in a good deal of imaginative spending.

Money may also serve as a collecting medium, for EIGHT has a tremendous urge to acquire. He collects a variety of things such as stamps, postcards, souvenirs, and odds and ends. He hoards, arranges, and gloats over his accumulated belongings, but his interest in acquiring possessions is usually considerably ahead of his interest in taking good care of them.

EIGHT is not prone to take the property of others. However, with his awareness of money and what it can buy, he may be found taking some of the household supply of money. This is usually considered by parents as a far greater offense than taking pencils and erasers at an earlier age. But the child is in each case expressing a need characteristic of his age. Parents should be aware of these needs and should see that they are provided for in suitable ways. Many EIGHTS are quite generous and may use the very money they have taken to treat their friends.

EIGHT is becoming more truthful. He may tell a tall story to impress his audience. The truth he tells may even be to his own detriment, but he does not usually make damaging revelations to anyone but his mother. It is very important to him to have such a relationship of confidence that he feels free to tell her of his misdeeds, failures or omissions.

§ 10. PHILOSOPHIC OUTLOOK

Death and Deity

There is often a resurgence of an active interest in religion at eight years of age. There is no new penetration of thought into the concept of deity or death. What EIGHT has worked out in his own mind along with whatever he has been taught to believe at six and seven, he now takes for granted and accepts. He likes to go to Sunday School. He wants to be taught passages and psalms from the Bible. He likes to memorize. He may spontaneously read the Bible at home and is very much interested in Bible stories. If he has stopped saying his prayers at seven, he may now want to return to them again. He wants his mother to say them with him, and he would often prefer to sing them. EIGHT becomes an active participant without thinking too much of what it is all about.

His chief religious interest at this age seems to be in the matter of heaven. This is not so much a concern about God in heaven as it was earlier. Now God's connection with heaven appears to be taken for granted. Heaven is a place where you go after you die.

Death is something he takes pretty much for granted unless, of course, there is a death of someone who is very close to him. Most EIGHTS have accepted unemotionally the fact that all people even they themselves will one day die. The earlier interest in coffins, burial, and other appurtenances of death continues but it is much less intense.

Time and Space

EIGHT is becoming more responsible in regard to time. His increased speed in action makes him less vulnerable to the demands of time. He can now be expected to arrive at school on time. Some EIGHTS do not tell time as well as they did at seven. They may read time in reverse so that 9:20 may be read as 20 minutes of 10. Besides telling time less well, EIGHT is often careless with his wrist-watch. It may be wise for EIGHT to put his watch away for a while, if he has one.

Though he may tell time less well, he is extremely aware of punctuality, that is, of what time he should be here or there. He keeps himself posted by asking others what time it is. If he knows that he is going to arrive home late, he may be responsible enough to telephone.

He is most efficient in telling time when he wishes to tune in on his favorite radio program. He is much less efficient in telling time for bed or school and still needs a certain amount of reminding.

EIGHT is interested in time far past, in ancient times. He likes to hear and to read about things that happened when his own country was new. But his chronology is rudimentary. He may not be able to say certainly whether or not George Washington is mentioned in the Bible.

Personal space is expanding for the 8-year-old. He can now return home by bus from a more distant point and may also travel on a bus by himself on a familiar or pre-arranged route if he is met. He takes in such a wide walking area within his own neighborhood that it may be difficult to locate him. He is coming to know his own neighborhood so well that he becomes interested in new ways, especially in short cuts, and may become lost in the process.

He is eager to take trips to new cities, to visit museums, zoos and places of interest. His spatial world is expanding even further through his interest in geography. He draws maps with keen interest.

EIGHT usually has a fairly clear notion of points of the compass and of different parts of the community in relation to each other. He can now distinguish right and left on the person of others as well as on himself.

9

NINE YEARS OLD

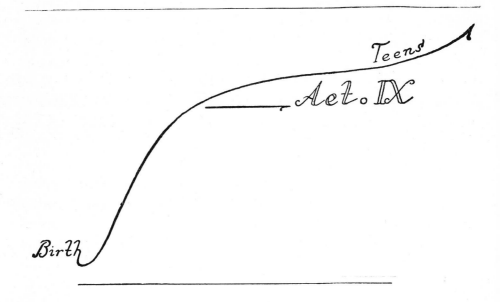

BEHAVIOR PROFILE

THE 9-year-old is no longer a mere child; nor is he yet a youth. Nine is an intermediate age, in the middle zone which lies between the kindergarten and the Junior High School teens. Significant reorientations take place during this intermediate period. The behavior trends of the eighth year come to clearer issue; the child gets a better hold upon himself; he acquires new forms of self-dependence which greatly modify his relations to his family, to school and classmates and to the culture in general. The changes come so subtly that parents and teachers often are not sufficiently aware of their import. But they are psychological transformations so consequential both for the child and for society that they deserve more recognition.

Self-motivation is the cardinal characteristic of the 9-year-old. It is the key to understanding him on his progress toward maturity. He has a growing capacity to put his mind to things, on his own initiative or on only slight cues from the environment. This typically gives him a preoccupied business-like air, both at home and at school. Indeed he is so busy that he seems to lack time for routine tasks and he does not relish interruptions. On the other hand he can interrupt himself. For example, if he is engaged at a paper task he can interrupt it and take a trip to the pencil sharpener and return to his work without loss of momentum and without a reminder. He also is able to fill idle moments with useful activity. He can work two or three hours at a stretch with his erector set. He likes to tax his skill, to put *himself* on his own mettle.

In comparison, the 8-year-old is much more dependent on environmental support,—on the pressure of the group and the stimulation of the adult. Eight expends a quantum of attention on a difficult task, but soon exhausts his energy. Nine is able to summon reserves of energy and renews his attack for repeated trials. This is due to the greater maturity of his whole behavior equipment. No wonder that he is such an excellent pupil, ready to tackle anything that lies reasonably within his powers. Nine is an optimal age for the perfecting of proficiency in the tool subjects, in the fundamental operations of arithmetic and in other skills. The 9-year-old is so interested in perfecting skills that he likes to do the same thing over and over again, whether it be the throwing of darts or dividing by one digit.

Confronted with an unfamiliar task (for example, tracing a maze with a pencil), he may say, "Hm!" with a mature inflection and reflectiveness which reminds us that he is no longer a child in his intellectual attitudes. He adds, characteristically, "Let me think about it. I always have to think first." He likes to plan in advance and to see ahead. If a task is complicated he asks to have the successive steps explained to him. Then, when he attacks the problem without immediate success, he reveals a power of self-appraisal. Perhaps he says somewhat self-deprecatingly, "I'm not so hot!" "Gee, I'm just trying to find out what's wrong here." "Sort of sloppy, isn't it?"

Presently we shall note that this power of appraisal is by no means limited to himself, but extends to other persons. He shows considerable ability in social criticism as well as self-criticism. Add to this a sizable capacity of self-motivation, and one can understand why NINE so often makes a good, solid, business-like impression!

This does not mean that he is a finished product. Although solid at the core, he has a growing margin which is neither fixed nor stable. New emotional patterns are in the making. This is shown in his complainingness, and in variability of mood,—now timid, now bold; now cheerful, now grumpy. Shyness may be associated with a new fondness for his teacher. He may "hate" to stand before the class to recite a poem. Sometimes he is said to be "in a daze," "in a fog," "in the clouds." He may need a reminder or he may excuse himself with a remark, "Oh that's my poor memory." Such benign symptoms of absent-mindedness are probably due to new mental events occurring at his growth margins!

When we say that he also is business-like we do not wish to imply that he is financially minded. He is not as money-mad as EIGHT. Frequently he is only feebly motivated by coin and by allowances. He has so many better reasons for being busy. He is fond of making inventories and check lists. He likes to classify and identify, to order his information. He is in character as a baseball fan, familiar with a surprising array of facts and figures. He has a factual interest in seriations and categories,—the insignia and ranks of army and navy officers, the distinctions between types of airplane, the flags of the United Nations, etc. If he has a passion for comics,—and he often does,—it is their informational content which makes the main appeal. He has an eye and an ear for significant details and tidbits that come via radio, movie, pictorial magazine and adult conversations.

We emphasize these intellectual traits of the 9-year-old because they color and direct the manifold patterns of his personal-social behavior. He shows a new discriminativeness in his parent-child and in his pupil-teacher relationships,—new refinements in his emotions and attitudes. The deepening of his emotional life, (for he is less shallow than he was at age eight), is, of course due to underlying growth changes in the physiology of his neuro-humoral system. Fortunately, however, feeling and insight are in better balance than they were at five-and-a-half and six years. Accordingly, your well-constituted 9-year-old tends to be a relatively well-organized young person, who is taking a measure of himself and who can take a measure of you. He neither likes nor needs to be patronized with condescension. Usually he is not over-aggressive. And his estimates of his parents and of his teachers can be penetrating and accurate, as well as candid.

In view of his immaturity he shows an impressive sense of fairness and even reasonableness in his estimates and expectations. He has overcome his more infantile alibiing. He can accept blame; and if several persons—children or adults—are involved in a difficulty he wants all blame apportioned *fairly*. He lays stress on who *started* the difficulty. He has a keen emotional and intellectual interest in punishments, privileges, rules and procedures, particularly at school and in his club life. He adjudges the fairness of discipline both by self and group standards. He is very receptive to elementary ideas of justice. The culture can sow seeds of prejudice, but he responds readily to injunctions against racial discrimination.

Naturally, there are innate differences in the depth and patterns of the ethical sense; but under favorable cultural conditions, the 9-year-old is essentially truthful and honest. He can say to himself, "I'll have to be honest," and he will go back to a store to return excess change, as well as to claim short change. Not having as yet reached perfection, he may think it is worse to lie to one's father than to someone else. But all in all, he is dependable and responsible. He likes to be trusted. He likes a little freedom, when he can be "loose on the town" for an hour or two, without over-inquisitive parental supervision. His complainingness need not be taken too seriously. As in the 7-year-old it may be a symptom that new emotional patterns are in process of growth.

Evidently he is developing a sense of individual status, which needs sympathetic understanding by his elders, above all by his own family. He likes his home; he feels a certain private loyalty to it; he glows with pride at his wonderful father. But he also feels the tensions of pulling away, of achieving a detachment which will place him more on his own. So when he is abroad he does not wish to be obtrusively called "sonny,"—and she does not wish to be identified as "my daughter"! Above all, the healthy 9-year-old does not want to be babied by a mother who unwittingly treats him as though he were still a young child in need of unremitting protection. Fathers sometimes go to the opposite extreme, and treat him as though he were a "young man." Actually he needs help at critical points; and he likes to go to his parents for such help. Skillful management suits the help to the needs; and withdraws the help when it fosters desirable independence.

Parents, therefore, should be gratified when at times the 9-year-old shows more interest in his friends than in the family excursion which has been so benevolently planned for him! Many prefer to foregather with their boon companions for one of those long clubby sessions in which talk and planning may figure more strongly than active play. There is so much that needs comfortable confabulation among friends, —a kind of exchange which even the family circle cannot afford. NINE is a great talker. Let him talk.

Let him talk with his confrères, for thereby he gets at least a rudimentary sense of brotherhood. He does a little social planning. He sharpens his perceptions of others and of himself. He shares confidences and estimates. He discusses future vocations, and frankly tells his pal: "You haven't got the makings of a doctor!" In spite of a little quarreling and disagreement he gets on well with his playmates. He builds friendships of some depth and duration. He participates actively in the formation and conduct of his still short-lived club with its passwords, codes, dress, hide-away, bulletins and tabus. He is learning to subordinate his own interests to the demands of the group. At school and else-where he is more competitive as a member of the group than as an individual.

In school the groups may include both boys and girls, but the spontaneous groupings are nearly always unilateral. Girls have their own clubs in which some time is devoted to giggling and whispering, whereas boys indulge in rough-housing and wrestling. The boys have more trouble with bullies of their own age or older. Birthday parties are, by choice, usually limited to one sex. Boys tease each other about girl friends. Girls tease each other about boy friends. Each sex cordially disdains the other.

This reciprocal disdain is part of the mechanism of development. It has much the same logic as the withdrawal tendencies which cause these same boys and girls alike to separate themselves to some degree from family ties. Attachment must be counter-balanced by detachment. To grow up, the 9-year-old must achieve a sense of his individual status, not only in relation to his parents but also to the opposite sex.

So each sex expresses a certain contempt for the other. Bragging to each other, spying on and teasing each other serve to define psychological distinctions which are in the making, both with and without the aid of the culture. "Girls don't count," says a superior-minded boy. In rejoinder a perceptive girl says, "Boys are loathsome creatures. I enjoy watching them!"

But, significantly enough, with respect to babies, such aversions do not hold. Girls may show a strong and affectionate interest in their younger sibs. And a 9-year-old boy in the capacity of big brother can take over to a remarkable extent the details of infant care when the parents are temporarily absent and entrust him with the responsibility. Such attitudes also are part and parcel of the total sex development which ultimately embraces family life.

There are varied forms of new awareness of the parental and re-productive aspects of sex. Most of the 9-year-old girls have knowledge of the process of menstruation. Many of the boys and girls have some comprehension of the father's part in procreation. They have observed the bearing of young in animals. They show both modesty and inquisitiveness with regard to the elementary physiology and anatomy of sex. The intellectual realism of this age saves it from romantic excesses. The 9-year-old boy is relatively careless as to sartorial and cosmetic appearance. The reorientations in the sphere of sex, however, are sufficiently marked to indicate that the child of yesteryears has now moved into the pre-adolescent sector of the life cycle. The girls are nearer to the age of puberty than the boys. This fact and the variations in physiological maturity within each sex account in part for the wide range of individual differences so apparent at this age.

A behavior profile can scarcely do justice to these individual differences, for a profile must be drawn with broad strokes. This compels us to disregard the finer lines and shadings, which are so important for the delineation of a specific boy or girl,—the one, for example, in your own household. He is stamped with individuality. He has gestures, ways of laughing and exclaiming; he has humor, sulks and moods, table manners, possessions, modes of speech, demeanors and enthusiasms, which make him unique. Nature will never contrive another like him, for she abhors identity, even in twins derived from a single, selfsame egg.

Nine is preeminently an age when individuality seeks to reassert and to reorganize itself. An active 9-year-old is not too dependent on praise; and may even show surprise when he gets it; but he accepts approval and benefits from it. In fact he likes timely praise, and shows much greater capacity than the 7-year-old to assimilate praise. If he is of an introverted, withdrawn nature he will, of course, need to be treated with special insight and, at times, with leniency. In case of doubt it is wise to tolerate idiosyncrasies which express forward thrusts of development. He has to find himself.

* * *

In spite of the wide diversity of individual differences we can still recognize general developmental characteristics which typify the nine-year-zone of maturity. Recall the 8-year-old. Three traits distinguish the dynamics of his behavior: speediness, expansiveness, evaluativeness. These traits continue to operate at the nine-year-level; but with important modifications and a higher degree of integration.

EIGHT seems to work very fast, because he reacts with somewhat abrupt bursts of speed. NINE still is speedy, but his speed is under better control, and therefore less noticeable. Particularly when he puts his mind to a familiar task, he works toward the end and completion of his performance; and he sustains his speed for longer intervals. But his overall modulation including middle as well as ends will be perceptibly greater in another year.

He has a greater interest in process and skill; he is more able to analyze his movements both before and during action. He also is more interested and persistent in practicing his skills,—an interest and perseverence based on the greater maturity of his neuro-motor system. Sometimes NINE is facile and modulated. Sometimes he seems to overdo something he likes; he repeats it over and over again. He may want to see the same movie again and again. He probably repeats with slight variations which help him to assimilate and refine a new experience. The extensiveness of NINE likewise shows more purpose, scope and depth. It is less sketchy, less episodic; it is more channelized, and in the end, more organized. Again a maturity difference, enriched by accumulated experience.

The expansiveness of EIGHT was much influenced by immediate environmental contingencies and fortuities. The extensiveness of NINE is engendered more from within. It is self-motivated. No one needs to tell him to make his expanding lists and inventories; nor to add new chemicals to his collection; nor to make plans for his future profession. The same inner forces impel him to spread into the remoter worlds of history and biography. This is psychic expansion,—an organizing growth process.

[195]

As we should expect, the evaluations of NINE are deeper and more discriminating than those of EIGHT. His emotivity, to use an academic word, is more sensitive, more refined. Just as the lens of his eye has greatly gained in capacity to accommodate to small distances, so his total organism has made a notable gain in capacity to feel small values and to accommodate to refined differences. We have already extolled his new powers of self-appraisal and of social judgment. They are bound up with the growth of emotivity which enables the 9-year-old to experience and to express finer shades of feeling. His voice has softened, his tensional outlets are more delicate, his disgusts more dainty. He undoubtedly feels novel emotions and novel variations of old emotions; because emotions grow and change in pattern with each passing age.

Philosophers have not solved the mystery of human conscience. But the 9-year-old might teach them something of its origins. In him, conscience is clearly in the making. His emotivity is now so mature that he detects nice shades of wrong-doing in others, and feels the blameworthiness of his own wrong-doing. He wishes to be straight with the world. He comments on an adult's unfairness: "That's a gyp." He is realistic about moral matters. He factually says to his mother, "I know you won't like this, but I'm going to tell you." In such articulate children we glimpse the very mechanisms of conscience. It is heartening and also dismaying to realize that the ethical sense is already so highly developed at this early age.

There is a certain reasonableness in the psychology of the 9-year-old. He is open to instruction; he is factual, forthright. He is not too interested in magic, he has a healthy strain of skepticism. He has put aside the Santa Claus myth, but he is not so ruthless as to destroy it for a younger sib. He believes in luck and chance; but he also believes in law; otherwise he would not be so anxious to find out how things are done, and why they are what they are. He seeks correction and explanation of his errors. For the time being he is somewhat less concerned about God, Heaven, Fate and prayers. He himself is taking himself in hand, almost in a spirit of rationalism. This is a noteworthy developmental phenomenon.

In portraying the behavior of the 9-year-old we have deliberately emphasized his positive and constructive traits, because they best represent his potentialities in terms of the future and his attainments in relation to his recent developmental past. At times, of course, he still functions like an 8-year-old. But his best traits are authentic indicators of true growth trends.

These traits are his realism, his reasonableness and his self-motivation. Functioning in favorable balance they make of him, on a juvenile scale, a business-like, fair-minded, responsible individual. He is no longer a "mere" child. He is integrating his long past,—not finally, but intermediately. He is trending toward the teens.

MATURITY TRAITS

(The following maturity traits are not *to be regarded as rigid norms or as models. They simply illustrate the kinds of behavior—desirable or otherwise—which tend to occur at this age. Every child has an individual pattern of growth, unique to him. The behavior traits here outlined may be used to interpret his individuality and to consider the maturity level at which he is functioning.)*

§ 1. MOTOR CHARACTERISTICS

Bodily Activity

NINE both works and plays hard. He is more skillful in his motor performances and he likes to display his skill. His timing is also under better control. He now shows great interest in competitive sports such as baseball.

Boys are quick to assume an active fighting posture and they strike out at each other and wrestle. They frequently "let off steam" or make a wild rush toward something.

NINE is apt to overdo. He has difficulty calming down after recess or after a strenuous game. He is apt to ride his bicycle too far or to mow the lawn until he is exhausted.

Eyes and Hands

The eyes and hands are now well differentiated. The two hands can generally be used quite independently. The fingers also show new differentiation. NINE pianos them on a table, picks and fiddles and flicks or fingers the edge of a paper he is reading.

He is now reported to be either good or poor with his hands, or to be a keen observer. Individual skills stand in bold relief at this age.

Movements expressed in so many ways at eight are now more restricted. NINE likes still life, or portrait or poster painting. He sketches lines with short strokes, adds more details to his work. There is a concentrated quality to his quick identification of an airplane in the sky.

NINE has an open-eyed stare which he maintains for several seconds without blinking. He can consciously see what he is regarding, or he may be focusing without regard. One child said she could look at something without seeing it and thoughts went jumping through her mind.

Sitting posture is now more awkward. The child slouches in his chair and gets into unusual postures. He is apt to have his head quite close to his working point at times, although he also leans way back. He thrusts an arm out forward and also back, he stamps his feet, he claps his hand on his head.

NINE can write for a prolonged time. He likes to make extended lists and to catalogue his collections.

§ 2. PERSONAL HYGIENE

Eating

Appetite. NINE has his appetite under better control than he did at eight. The good eaters have less tremendous appetites and the poorer eaters have better appetites than earlier. NINE, however, thinks more about food than formerly. He enjoys reading cook books and helping to prepare food. The minute he arrives home from school his first thought may be about something to eat.

Refusals and Preferences. NINE is rather positive in his food likes and dislikes. He states them frankly. Some NINES do eat everything, but if not, the adult is inclined to cater to their demands since these are so positive. Plain foods are still preferred. Meat gravies are now accepted. Puréed foods and fat on meat continue to be disliked. Desserts and sweets are in the ascendancy.

Self-Help. NINE is fairly deft with his implements. Although many NINES cut well with knives, a few continue to need help or tend to saw their meat in their attempt to cut it. Fingers are rarely used. NINE is aware of bad table manners even though he may not be exercising good ones. He may even be enough aware of his own bad manners to keep an eye out for his father, to see if he is going to be reprimanded or not. It is remarkable to see how much better NINE conducts a meal even in the handling of his implements when he has the added stimulus of company or of going out to dinner.

Table Behavior. The child's table behavior is evidently improving because it is less on the parent's mind. NINE may even be complimented for his manners. He chews more skillfully and is less apt to chew with his mouth open. He is also less likely to overload his fork and to bolt his food. He no longer fiddles with his food.

He may be able to combine talking, listening and eating well, but some NINES tend to talk too much at the table while others listen too concentratedly.

NINE may be expected to wash his hands spontaneously before coming to the table, although he at times gets mixed up in thinking that he has washed them when he has not. Actually he lives up to what is expected of him rather poorly, and most frequently needs to be reminded. He responds willingly. He generally places his napkin on his lap. But it still has a tendency to slide about and may fall to the floor. His eating is so much neater now that he has much less need of a napkin than when he was younger.

Sleep

Bedtime. Getting ready for bed is no longer a problem unless the child is sent to bed too early and feels that he does not have the privileges of other children. Eight o'clock is a common bedtime. NINE still needs to be reminded that it is bedtime even when his radio programs actually keep him posted on the time. He may listen to a program before he starts for bed or he may undress as he is listening if he possesses a radio of his own. Some NINES prefer to read for a while after they are in bed. The majority are asleep by 9:00 P.M. There are still a few who need to be asleep by 7:30 P.M. Such children need to be protected from the influence of their friends who do not go to sleep before 9:00 P.M. or later. Those NINES who go to sleep late may need to be protected from themselves by having their lamp or radio removed. They have a tendency to switch their radio or light on again after it is time to go to sleep.

Night. NINE is a good sleeper and on the whole a quiet one. A few awaken screaming from nightmares but are easily quieted. Although NINE often has bad dreams his sleep is not greatly disturbed by them. As at eight, his total sleep averages around ten hours.

Morning. NINE often controls his waking by setting his alarm clock. He may even set it for an early hour and then go back to sleep or he may wake up slowly after it has rung. He often plans things to do in the morning on awaking. In fact he seems to enjoy more early morning activity than bedtime activity. Seven is a common waking hour and this gives him plenty of time for reading, fooling around, dressing and even for practicing at the piano before it is time for school.

Elimination

NINE has his elimination functions under his own control. As at eight, the bowel movement is most apt to occur after breakfast or in the late afternoon or evening. One movement is the rule, but there may be two. NINE can function at school but is more apt to function at home. He rarely gets up in the night to urinate. He rarely needs to be reminded to go to the bathroom for he now possesses both an inner and outer control.

Bath and Dressing

Bath. The bath is neither resisted nor especially enjoyed. NINE does not wish to bathe more than two or three times a week. He accepts the adult's suggestion that he bathe and usually manages the tub by himself, but he still needs some supervision and likes to have an adult around. When he is once in the tub he rather enjoys soaking in quite warm water. On the whole he carries through the entire bath procedure rather well and fairly independently.

He still needs to be reminded to brush his teeth and to brush them well. He also needs to be reminded to wash his hands before meals. But he usually takes suggestions good naturedly and as though he had been planning to do all of these things by himself but had forgotten.

Dressing and Care of Clothes. NINE is better than he was about finishing the loose ends of dressing. He finishes buttoning, ties his shoe laces, and tucks in his clothes. He is not too much interested in his clothes and would prefer to have his mother lay them out for him. He is apt to throw his clothes around the room, but can be taught to put them neatly on a chair. He is not very consistent about putting his dirty clothes in the hamper unless he has a daily change. In fact he is not very proficient at judging whether clothes are dirty or not and is apt to put on yesterday's clothes because they are handy. Boys especially prefer old clothes. Most NINES are fairly good about reporting tears and holes in their clothes and may even be insistent about their being mended.

NINE is as poor at hanging up his outer garments as he is his other clothes. The minute he gets home he is inclined to dump all of his belongings including clothes on the nearest chair or to fling them about. He responds well to being reminded but he responds even better to some device such as having to pay a penny fine for each piece of clothing he has neglected to hang up. Untied shoelaces also respond well to a fine system.

Boys are becoming interested in combing their own hair. Girls likewise are interested in trying to do their own hair especially if it is not in braids.

Somatic Complaints

On the whole NINE enjoys excellent health. He continues to throw off colds rather quickly. Children who have previously had ear, lung or kidney complications may have a recurrence between the eighth and ninth year and may suffer a rather prolonged illness. A few children show marked fatigue and need to be protected from doing too much. Many complain a good deal, especially about headaches and stomach aches and these complaints often occur when the parent has requested the child to do some task which is disagreeable to him.

Tensional Outlets

There is a marked decrease in the more obvious tensional outlets at NINE. A very few children continue to suck their thumbs, but only at infrequent intervals. These children respond well to parental reminding or to the dentist's method of putting a pronged plastic in the roof of the mouth.

Boys especially seem to need to "let off steam." They often wrestle around and cannot seem to keep their hands off each other. NINE is apt to growl, mutter, sulk or find fault in relation to specific happenings.

NINE's most characteristic tension release is through fine motor movements. He fiddles, picks at his cuticle, runs his hand through his hair or shuffles his feet.

§ 3. EMOTIONAL EXPRESSION

NINE is finally becoming what his parents have been striving for. He deserves and receives outright compliments such as: "He takes more responsibility," "He is both more independent and more dependable," "He is easier to get on with," "He can be trusted," "He obeys well."

Something very real is happening to NINE in relation to his self-organization. He is coming within the realm of the more positive emotions. He may say that he hates certain subjects, but he tries to do them anyway. If, however, he is apprehensive about a certain subject such as arithmetic, it is important that he does not become more apprehensive to the point of "going to pieces," and refusing to go to school. Apprehensive children need more concrete material, so that they may succeed at one level and then gradually work up to a higher level knowing the exact process through which they must go.

NINE may be impatient and quick tempered, and may flare up, but all of these responses are very shortlived. He may cry but only if he gets mad enough or is really hurt. NINE is more likely to be upset and apprehensive about his own actions.

NINE is actually the opposite of impatient. He plans his separate activities and even his whole day. He is persistent and wants to complete what he has planned to do. He can, however, be interrupted by a request from his mother, obeys with good grace and returns to continue with his activity. His one difficulty may be that he is so absorbed that he does not hear his mother when she speaks. Some NINES are still distractible, but they can be very persistent with the few things they set their minds to. NINE like SEVEN is capable of developing passions for certain activities. As his mother says, "He could listen to the radio all day long."

NINE is ashamed of some of his past acts in fields which he now has under better control. He may show embarrassment at being criticized, at exposing his body, or when he is in a social situation with the opposite sex. Both his parents' and his siblings' acts are subject to his disgust. He has his own measuring stick by which he measures them. He wants them to act "properly."

NINE is a loyal and devoted friend. He can always be sought by his friends for protection and is upset when his friends are brow-beaten. He is prone to admire members of his own sex, either of his own age or often a few years older. This is the beginning of hero worship.

It is surprising to see how little needs to be done to tip the scales in the right direction for NINE. One experience may set off a spark that needs no replenishing. The sight of a person with bad table manners may be a powerful stimulus for NINE to improve his own ways. The redecoration and rearrangement of his room may shift him from a persistent pattern of disorder to one of pride in the care of his room. Even the present of a bone from a far off battlefield may set him on an encyclopedic search for all the knowledge he can secure about pre-historic man.

This is an age when the child becomes impressed with whatever he is told. Prejudices which often start at eight need to be explained to the 9-year-old so that he will not become caught in them.

NINE is an age when a strong feeling-tone prevails. We see here definite signs of empathy; for instance the child may say that when he sees anybody else hurt, he hurts in the same place. Some of his established emotional reactions, like other characteristics, however, are variable and he may swing quickly from one extreme to another, as for instance from marked shyness to extreme boldness. Another extreme is shown in his alternation between a "don't care" attitude, and an extreme sensitivity to criticism and desire to please.

§4. FEARS AND DREAMS

Fears

NINE says about himself, "I don't frighten very easy." Indeed he has very few fears. Some NINES, however, are still resolving tag ends of earlier fears of storms, cellars, sight of blood, or swimming with face under water. These fears have a specific personality reference by this age and have usually had a prolonged and intense course.

Though NINE has few fears, he is a great worrier. He is upset by little mistakes he makes. He may be apprehensive about crossing a street at a traffic light. He worries about failing in his studies; about doing the wrong thing in a social situation, such as extending his left hand instead of his right; or not measuring up to the other children. He needs reassurance, or praise, to be informed where he stands. Sometimes competition makes him worry more, and if it does it should be minimized or avoided.

Dreams

The sleep of the 9-year-old, though uninterrupted and quiet on the surface, is often ruffled underneath by many scary, horrid dreams. A few NINES awake screaming, sit up, or get out of bed, usually to go to their mother's bed, but for the most part they may appear to be sleep-walking. They know they have been dreaming and quiet quickly. When they do know that they have been dreaming, they may not be able to remember their dreams.

Horrid dreams are reported most commonly, and these can often be explained in the light of what has happened during the day. Reading, cinema, radio and circus performance all leave their imprint. NINE is chased by animals or people. He may be hurt, shot, or kidnapped. Murder plays a prominent role. His best friend or his mother may be killed. His mother may be running away. Fire and tornadoes may come to destroy trucks and houses.

NINE knows that there is a relationship between his daily activities and his dream life. He may know that a certain repeated rhythm will produce one of his awful dreams of standing on his head and whirling round and round. The thought of it makes him shudder. That is why he tries to protect himself from stimuli that might produce certain bad dreams. He reads scary books during the daytime only. He reads a comic book as he is listening to a scary radio program.

NINE does have some pleasant dreams but these seem to be in the minority and more difficult to remember. He often enjoys dreaming in the morning and may want to go back to sleep to continue his dreaming.

§ 5. SELF AND SEX

Self

NINE is rightly spoken of as "self-sufficient" and "on his own." His independence is something he can now manage. He can think for himself, reason by himself. You can usually depend upon him that if he says he has done something, he really has. He can be trusted.

NINE has himself under better self-control. He withdraws from his surroundings enough to gather up his sense of self and put it to good use, but he does not retreat far into himself as he did at seven. He does not feel impelled to boast and to attack to protect himself as he did at eight. Now he thinks in terms of fighting with his brain as well as with his body. For instance, he plans his time so that he can get off to school easily to protect himself from being pestered on the way.

He has a new capacity to set his mind to a task and to see it through. He is even ambitious in his demands of himself. He wants to succeed not only in a single task but also in general. Girls have a way of getting what they want without meeting resistance.

A good relationship with others is important to NINE. He is anxious to please, he wants to be liked and he loves to be chosen. He will work for a favor and he thrives on praise. But he still is sensitive to correction and may be embarrassed by it. This is the first year that he has himself well enough in hand to do things in a spirit of service. These episodes of doing "wonderful things" are infrequent, but they are stimulated by the child's feeling that so much has been done for him.

Not all NINES are as well organized as this. A number of boys at this age are wrapped up in themselves, very busy with their own activities, and very thoughtless of others; they are aggravated and can indeed be aggravating when their preoccupations are broken into. One gets on better with this type by planning ahead with him or leaving orders on a bulletin board.

Some NINES are anxious and apprehensive both about their work and about their health. They may underrate themselves as persons, lack confidence, and remark, "Oh am I stupid," or "I'm the dumbest." It is very important to make sure that NINE is not overplaced in regard to his school work for if he is, he will receive both his own condemnation and that of others.

One has to be careful, however, of taking NINE too seriously in regard to what he says. He tosses off self-critical remarks such as, "I would do that," "Oh that's my poor memory," or "Oh you know me and my dirt." He complains about many things but may forget what he was complaining about the minute after he has made the complaint. One naturally rides over much of NINE's complaining, but it is important

to judge whether or not any specific complaint has real meaning to him.

Sex

There is less interest in reproduction on the part of many NINES, if their desire for information has been satisfied at eight. Nevertheless, there may be much more continuing discussion of this subject with friends than parents realize. If sufficient information has not been given, the child usually shows his dissatisfaction. A mother can no longer stop with the explanation that a mother and a father marry and decide to have a baby. An alert 9-year-old will comment, "But you can't just decide."

Nine-year-old girls may relate themselves to their role in the process of reproduction. They may ask, "Have I got a seed inside of me?" Or if they notice that the mother is growing "fatter" they may ask, "Will I be that fat some day, too?"

Some NINES continue to think that the baby is born by Caesarian section. This is often easier for them to understand than the process of normal birth. However, birth of animals is taken quite naturally by the 9-year-old who has had familiarizing experience with animals.

NINE may be self-conscious about exposing his body. This awareness may be related only to those outside the family group, but NINE may not wish to have the parent of the opposite sex see him nude. If he is with a friend of his own sex, he may exclude a younger sibling of the opposite sex while he is changing his clothes, even though he might bathe with that same sibling on occasion.

His interest is more in the details of his own organs and functions than in those of the opposite sex. He may even seek out information, especially pictorial, in an encyclopedia or reference book. Girls have usually been told about menstruation.

Swearing is now shifting from the earlier elimination type of vocabulary to sex allusions. Rhymes that children pick up at play have more pointed sex implications. They may repeat them at home to shock mother. Neighbors may complain about the kind of language used by boys.

The girl-boy interest persists with NINE even though there is now a marked separation of the sexes in play. The sexes are rarely mixed at a birthday party, and if they are, kissing games may result. NINES tease each other about girl and boy friends and about getting married. Often two boys have one girl, or two girls have one boy. There may be some writing of terse notes: "I hate so and so," "So and so really likes you," "I love you." Boys try to kiss their girl friend, with one success as the final goal. But all this playfulness has an impersonal, matter of fact quality without any feeling of jealousy even though you share your friend with a member of your own sex. A few NINES show obvious embarrassment about the opposite sex and try to avoid situations that expose their embarrassment.

§6. INTERPERSONAL RELATIONS

Most of the child-mother embroilment of eight has quite disappeared by nine. Even episodes of "arguing back" now may be infrequent. NINE is so busy with his own life that he makes many fewer demands upon his parent. Yet when his parent makes demands upon him he usually responds willingly and may even interrupt what he is doing without any resentment. But at times, when he is very much absorbed in what he is doing, he may not hear his mother's request. Therefore it is important to secure some response from him to make sure he has heard your voice.

NINE needs a great deal of reminding. He forgets to wash his hands before meals, to brush his teeth, or to hang up his clothes. He accepts reminding willingly and usually acts on it at once.

NINE is less involved with routine chores, and accomplishes more tasks of the moment, both when asked and spontaneously. He wants to please his mother. He enjoys running errands and likes a commission to go to a place far enough away to require his taking a bus. He prepares a simple meal when someone is sick or when he wants to help his mother Some boys are even protective toward their mothers and will not allow them to do certain difficult tasks, especially when they are pregnant.

NINE does not need the assurance of a reward for his helping. He is far less motivated by money than formerly. Even with his allowance, he may forget to ask for it and may be careless with it after he has secured it. NINE really wants to perform a personal service and may prefer a pat on the back for a job well done to a material reward, or even to praise. There are some jobs for which he may be interested to receive pay, but for other jobs like caring for the baby he may refuse to accept remuneration.

The mother no longer needs to be at home when NINE comes home from school, although a few NINES still need a note telling them where their mother is. Many NINES can have a key left for them and can take over the household for a short span before their mother's return.

It usually is not difficult to discipline NINE. Often he is controlled merely by a look from his mother. At times he may need a short isolation period especially from other children. He accepts it, and soon returns a better child. NINE responds well to a warning or to an actual deprivation.

Father is not as actively demanded as he was earlier. NINE is so busy with his own activities and his friends' that he does less with his father except when they go on special trips together. NINE is often very fond of his father, enjoys discussing various things with him, and may be especially sensitive to any paternal criticism.

NINE does not as a rule present a problem with younger or older siblings. Usually he gets on well with his siblings and shows a real feeling of loyalty and will stand up for them as needed. NINE is especially good when he is made responsible for younger siblings for brief periods. He is then extremely understanding and without the strictness and sternness he exhibited at eight.

The tendency to have special friends, seen to be forming at eight, is stronger at nine. NINE chooses only a member of his own sex for a special friend. There is now overt criticism of the opposite sex. Girls may remark, "Boys stink," "too fresh," "too tough." Boys also have their say, "Can't be bothered with girls," and accept them only as a necessary evil.

Boy-girl attractions persist, but there is not much playing together. Often two boys have the same girl, or vice versa, without any feeling of jealousy. The boy's goal of conquest is to kiss the girl, and this becomes an episode to talk about.

NINES love to talk among themselves. This desire to chat even breaks into their more active types of play. Favorite topics of conversation are the bedtime hour, and radio programs.

NINE enjoys group play which shows a fair amount of organization. Informal clubs may last as long as two weeks or so. These clubs start out with a very real purpose—press club, scrapbook club, paper club or sewing club. They are more elaborately set up than at eight and may include hideouts, codes, and a secret language and club bulletins. But these clubs do not last. Many NINES enjoy the formal clubs such as Cubs and Brownies under adult leadership.

Ball play of some sort is a sure organizer of groups and may take precedence over the earlier absorbing interest in radio programs.

NINE is quite natural in his manners. He excuses himself from the table, greets a newcomer often with a handshake, and thanks his hostess very easily and feelingly for the good time he has had. Parents may now enjoy watching their children perform rather than having to coach them from the sidelines.

§7. PLAY AND PASTIMES

In General

NINE demands little of his mother's time. He is extremely busy in his chosen activities. Much of his time is spent in solitary activities such as reading and listening to the radio. NINE wants to do endlessly what he enjoys doing. Boys play football until they are black and blue, or they coast until they are soaked to the hips. Girls play dolls or paper dolls the whole day through as they re-enact an entire day's routine including scoldings, taking their dolls to the doctor, and fairly complex interpersonal situations.

Baseball is a favorite outdoor sport both for boys and girls. Bicycling, roller and ice skating, swimming, sliding, skiing and coasting are enjoyed by both sexes. NINE is setting his mind to the task of improving his skills. He worked more spontaneously at eight, but is now acting more purposefully. But he does not yet work with the ease and facility that he will show at ten. Even with his bicycling he complains that his legs get tired. Boys enjoy rough-housing. They are not as prone as formerly to play commando games. They enjoy lifting heavy objects.

The indoor life of the 9-year-old is fairly well planned. He has certain absorbing interests such as the radio, reading, or constructing with a mechano set. Some NINES enjoy making scrapbooks for hospitals. Others pore over maps and often draw them. NINE continues to enjoy card games.

Reading

NINE is a great reader. He may even appear to be living in a book world. He plans to arise early in the morning just to read. He rarely reads fairy tales now. He is too much of a realist and may say about fairy tales, "They're fantastic; they aren't true." The books he likes, he likes so much that he reads them over and over again. He is very fond of animal stories. The junior classics are now coming within his own reading scope. Repeated favorites are Tom Sawyer, Treasure Island, King Arthur and Bambi. Biographies, mysteries and the encyclopedia for reference all interest him.

Although he enjoys the classics he is still very fond of his comic books, which deal with adventure, war, and slapstick domestic humor. NINE usually has a pile of these books and enjoys trading them with his friends. With many NINES, however, the interest in comic books is beginning to wane, and can be broken into. They will accept the fact that any comic books outside of their own rooms will be confiscated. When, on the other hand, the interest becomes so absorbing that it interferes with school work, sharp measures may have to be taken, for comic books can have the attributes of a drug. This more drastic handling, however, is seldom necessary and even when indicated, the child should not be entirely forbidden comic books. NINE gets what he wants and becomes proficient at sneaking them into the house or reading them out of sight of his parents if he is not allowed to read them in his room.

Music, Radio and Movies

If a child at this age persists in his interest in taking music lessons, one may expect that he will really apply himself. Many NINES can practice by themselves, although they still need to be reminded. The child is becoming interested in correct fingering. His touch is lighter and staccato which gives him better control over the sounds he produces. He is beginning to enjoy his accomplishment of playing and fortunately his playing has improved so that his family can enjoy his music. Biographies of composers interest him.

NINE knows the time and station of radio programs by heart. The detective and mystery serials are becoming more important to him although he still may cling to a selected few of the adventure stories, and he continues to enjoy the domestic life serials, quiz and information programs and adult comic programs. A few NINES listen to the news. Happily the child is not as rigid and intent on his programs as he was earlier. He can even miss an occasional program if some more interesting activity offers. NINE is becoming more aware of the advertising on radio programs and even though he has been warned against it by his parents he may finally succumb, buy the product advertised and send in the necessary box tops for his reward.

Radio programs provide one of the

topics of conversation for the 9-year-old. NINE tells what programs he listens to and compares them with the programs reported by his friends.

There are marked individual differences among NINES as to interest in movies. Some like to see their "type" of movie off and on, and if they see one which they especially like they may want to see it over and over again. Others go to the movies weekly, are conversant about the actors and may even write to them.

§8. SCHOOL LIFE

NINE enjoys school. The morning routine of getting ready for school has smoothed out. He has better control of time and is now responsible for getting himself to school on time. He has trouble, however, in remembering to take his school material to school even though he has planned ahead and put his things in a convenient place. He still needs to be reminded. Parents should not be aggravated by this lag. They should remember how well he is getting himself ready and allotting his time. If he takes a gun or a ball to school he will readily respond to his teacher's request to leave it in the dressing room.

NINE reports more about home and outside activities at school than he reports school happenings at home. He tells a long detailed, strung-out story at school about his radio programs or some movie he has seen. He is most apt to report on his subjects at home; which subject he is best in; who is ahead of him, etc. He will also tell about a school play or some special event. He does not talk much about his teacher but may describe some of her mannerisms such as how she talks or how she does a certain thing.

Teachers report that fourth is a diffi-cult grade to teach. The teacher needs to realize that NINE is an individualist, that he has rather positive likes and dislikes. NINE wants to be independent of his teacher, but in his dealings with her he wants her to be reasonable and resents any decisions that he considers are unfair. The teacher soon recognizes that she delays in helping him until he really needs her. NINE is actually more related to his subjects than to his teacher. Dislike of a teacher may be linked to a dislike of a subject especially if the child has more than one teacher. He may even blame the teacher for a lowered grade.

Because of these more emotional responses it is very important to be sure that he can handle the more self-demanding tasks of fourth grade. NINE is afraid of failing and is also ashamed of having failed. Need for repetition of a grade or going at a slower pace are best taken care of within the first three grades when the child does not become as emotionally involved and usually improves by the removal of too high demands. He is happier with the group which will allow him to operate at his optimal level rather than his minimal level. Parents are the ones who feel the emotional pangs of failure within the first three grades and wrongly ascribe their own emotions to the child.

The change from third to fourth grade is a crucial one. Many who have been developing on the slower side with some support to hold a place (such as a "reading" or "arithmetic disability") may now have a real spurt of improvement. Some who have previously done well may now need individual help.

In the classroom NINE appears to be more orderly and performs with greater dispatch. Each child has his own individual manner of entering the room. One child tosses his book on his desk, another slams it down and a third places it carefully. A few may need a word from the teacher to stir them on their way, but once the class is started they take out a book, make a comment or two about the task, and set to work. NINE has a greater capacity for working independently both of children and of teacher. He is challenged by a task. He sits with trunk bent forward, resting on his elbows, hands propping his chin as he brings his face near the book on his desk. At times he throws himself way back, extends his whole body and holds the book at full arms' length. He flings his arm forward or backward to call the teacher's attention, usually without calling her name, and awaits his turn. He may look at his neighbor's work but prefers the teacher's assistance. He has less need than EIGHT to verbalize and also can talk more quietly. The classroom is therefore quieter. When he drops his desk top down with a bang, he may give his neighbor a glance as though expecting him to complain. On occasion he sits with wide open eyes, stares forward, apparently fixating without regard and seems to be in a daze. At the end of a period there is a general stir; some children rush to leave their papers on the teacher's desk, while others remain at work until they have finished. On some occasions the whole class becomes so interested that it remains overtime to continue with a discussion or lesson.

NINE is interested in achieving in his school subjects, and likes to be graded in them. He is anxious for good marks and works for them. He can be discouraged by failure. There is considerable competition with others and he may show resentment if surpassed by one who is close to him in achievement, or he may be impatient with a duller classmate. When failing he usually needs individual atten-tion rather than isolation. He also often competes better as a member of a group than as an individual.

NINE has a better critical evaluation of his own abilities. He can describe his preferred method of working. He knows he can do a problem better if he writes it down; that he can do arithmetic combinations better with flash cards than orally. Some say they cannot maintain meaning when they read aloud. Some tasks are better performed at home than at school.

Complaining comments may precede any task but soon fade out. NINE has a certain amount of self-discipline. Faced with an unpleasant task, if told how much he is required to do and about how long it will take, he proceeds without further ado. He is speedy in his work and if he is given a goal he rushes to get there.

"I haven't a good memory" is one of NINE's favorite complaints. Immediate recall is not always easy for him. He may remember better if he writes an item down or if it is written down for him. Once his mind is made up, however, he is not easily influenced to change it. He can evaluate his performance: "This one I'm not too sure. This one I am sure."

In reading he may prefer to read silently and may dislike to read orally before the group though he still needs to be checked by oral reading. He tackles any word and is not too concerned if he does not know the meaning unless it is important to the story. Reading is now associated with several subjects. Those who have been slow in learning to read can now join the group in their favored subject. NINE especially likes to read for facts and information.

Handwriting is now put to practical use. Perhaps he keeps a diary. He writes lists, cataloguing his collections. He likes to order things by mail. "Business" letters hold more interest than do social ones. One 9-year-old made out a form letter which she used to acknowledge her Christmas gifts. NINE likes to copy. This is his way of supporting his "poor memory." When he looks up a subject to write about he is truly a plagiarist.

Penmanship, particularly in girls is smaller, neater and done with less pressure. Boys usually still write with heavy strokes. Most use finger movement with tension of the forearm. The 9-year-old ordinarily sustains his writing long enough to complete a given task. However, some children may continue to avoid writing any more than is necessary. NINE is also critical of his writing: "Sort of sloppy isn't it?" "That's my most careless thing." He may even copy his own paper to make it more legible.

Arithmetic is perhaps the most talked of subject in fourth grade. It is "loved" or "hated," but despite the latter emotional response NINE may do well in this subject. He may fluctuate in his like and dislike from day to day according to his accomplishment and grasp. He now knows many number combinations by heart and is aware of the ones which cause him difficulty. He writes these down and wants to master them by having someone call them off to him. He usually prefers written to oral work. Though he likes to prove his long division, he does not yet check his own error spontaneously. He wants to know how he made his error and enjoys analyzing his process with his teacher to determine how he made his mistake. The teacher in turn needs to know how his mind works and to think less about correct or incorrect answers. He may be close or far from the correct answer.

NINE often has more spontaneous interest in problem solving than his school work affords. He becomes interested in the prices of things and figures out many practical problems related to numbers which he encounters in reading or conversation.

Although individual differences appear to be strong, NINE uses the pronoun "we" to identify himself with the classroom group. A comment such as "I wish we could do reading workbooks all day" brings an echo in unison from the rest of the class. At times the whole class will muster a sudden spurt in order to finish a task.

Friendships are being formed. NINE chooses a best friend to work or play with. He protects and defends him on occasion. There may be a definite shift in twosomes. Some who have played together off and on during the earlier grades may form completely new friendships. Also two children who have had difficulties getting along together now suddenly become friends. Boys form stronger twosomes and also act as a group more than girls. Girls are more varied in their groups and two-, three- and four-somes often exist. Boys and girls now play separately for the most part, and there is exclusion of the opposite sex in play. The adult is rarely included or referred to in their play. However, they do enjoy a group game supervised by an adult.

§9. ETHICAL SENSE

NINE is, as a rule, responsive to any demand put upon him if he has heard it. His hearing may be related to his absorption in what he is doing, but it also may be related to his interest in and willingness to do the task required. His response often has the quality of a rapid flash. If he acts upon it immediately he "clicks" in the demanded direction. But if he delays he is apt to forget and then needs to be reminded. He takes reminding with good grace. NINE's intentions are often higher than his acts. He really wants to be helpful, to relieve his mother, but he lacks spontaneity in doing things. He is, however, feeling the demands of his age which bring him more privileges and more responsibilities. Although there are fewer battles over chores at nine, if too much is demanded of NINE (especially a boy) he resents it and speaks out his mind. Most NINES are so busy that they have little time for chores. Fortunately NINE responds well to immediate little demands and these usually take the place of chores.

The drag and uncertainty in making up his mind which he experienced earlier are no longer evident. NINE makes up his mind rapidly, definitely, and often to his parent's satisfaction. His decisions often are easily made and almost automatic. He also shows a considerable degree of fore-thought for he can set his mind to a task and can thus carry it through to completion.

NINE accepts blame fairly well when it is due him, but he becomes very much upset if blamed for something he has not done. At times he becomes involved in some group activity which he did not start, but circumstantial evidence points to him as the responsible party. Evidence should then be sifted by an adult so that each child may take a just share of blame, and not leave him "holding the bag." Fairness is NINE's credo. He can always be appealed to through fairness. He may even be so realistic about it that he will not accept praise that he thinks is not his due even though he likes praise very much. One 9-year-old refused an award in a public speaking contest because he felt it should go to his mother, since she had helped him to learn the poem he recited.

The rudiments of a conscience are developing in NINE. This does not, however, mean that NINE never blames or alibis.

He might even blame his difficulties on his piano lessons. If he is in a tight spot he is capable of making quite plausible excuses. He would often alibi if permitted but he can be held to the evidence of the truth.

NINE has less need to want to be good than he did when younger, for now he is good more naturally. He may be more concerned about the things he has not done than the things he has done. He thinks in terms of right and wrong. He says he is ashamed that he is failing in school or that he does not eat well. He may even say that he "feels guilty" because he has neglected to return some thing.

His are becoming the errors of omission as well as of commission. If he has committed some wrong he feels the need to confess to his mother. He does not come straight to the point but approaches her considerately. He watches his mother's face. He does not want to offend her, so he breaks things to her easily. But if he does not confess, his conscience, young as it is, may bother him.

NINE is relatively easy to discipline. He does have to be reminded a good deal. Hanging up his outside clothes and his pajamas, and tying his shoelaces should no longer require reminders. A fine for each forgetting brings him into line with amazing speed. Isolation is needed at times, and denials of favored activities such as movies produce the desired result. Often a mere threat of denial or some very small denial is sufficient. One does not have to be drastic with NINE. Most NINES accept punishment with good grace though a few become extremely resentful and express their feeling with, "That's a gyp." A few NINES, who are obviously riding for a fall and cannot be helped to bypass their difficulty, respond well to a re-trial. In the midst of their tears they are eager to start all over again and do it right on the second trial.

NINE is beginning to be neater about his room. He may even be particular about his own things and spends hours sorting out his numerous possessions. He responds well to his mother's remindings and can carry through a task on his own.

The words "honest" and "truth" are now becoming a part of NINE's vocabulary. Even when he exaggerates on occasion he rapidly sets things right by saying, "Oh Mom, you know it isn't real." NINE rarely takes things not belonging to him and if he does he wants to return them and set things right. He is now developing a sense of ethical standards and means to live up to them.

Most NINES are no longer intrigued by money as they were at eight. Some handle money very well, even budget it, lend it, and carry around a fair sum in their wallets. Some do work in return for their allowance, others have a basic allowance and supplement it with pay for tasks. Yet it is surprising to see how many NINES forget to ask for their allowance and leave it lying around after they have received it. Many would prefer to receive money as they need it, for their needs are as a rule small and immediate.

§10. PHILOSOPHIC OUTLOOK

Death and Deity

NINE, the realist, often shows a marked lack of interest in God and religion. He also no longer believes in Santa Claus and does not enjoy fairy tales. He may refuse to go to Sunday School and to say his prayers. Church schools may anticipate a marked reduction in the attendance of 9- and 10-year-olds. With some the social aspect of Sunday School still holds interest. And with others a true religious feeling persists and grows. NINE may even

pray spontaneously if he is in great need. He may have the rudiments of faith and an ethical feeling that it is important for him to do certain things.

Although a few NINES may be concerned about the soul and its separation from the body, death is usually thought of more closely in connection with the process of dying. NINE is interested in how you "stop breathing" and have no pulse, and in the fact that you are "not living." NINE may say, "Oh I wish I'd never been born" or "I wish I were dead" but he does not mean these remarks seriously. As with so many of NINE's complaints one has a justified tendency to treat them lightly, because for the most part they are very transient.

Time and Space

NINE is more controlled by time than controlling time. His day is filled to the brim with things to do. He is going here and there and has difficulty in finding time to do extra things which may be requested of him. Everything he does is important and therefore anything is difficult to give up.

NINE does control time, however, in that he plans his day and knows what follows what. In his race with time he may set his alarm clock for early morning rising either to gain time for reading or to enjoy the leisure of an extra hour's sleep.

His handling of space involves the same type of restriction and specificity as his response to time. He goes to a special place by himself: to the doctor's office, to the dentist's office or for his music lesson. He handles this well even though his destination can only be reached by some public conveyance. But one does not divert him by demanding an extra errand on such an occasion. One thing at a time fully accomplished is NINE's set goal.

10

TEN YEARS OLD

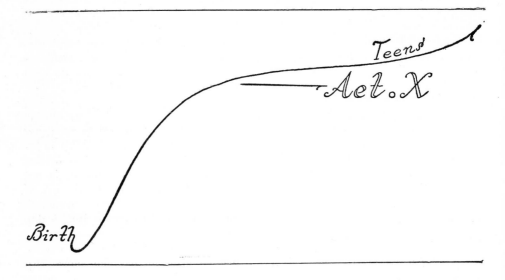

BEHAVIOR PROFILE

TEN, like five, is a nodal age. Both ages bring to partial fulfillment the trends of immediately preceding development; but ten much more than the age of five suggests a latent future. A typical 5-year-old is so self-contained and self-adjusted that he might almost seem to be a finished product. The environment scarcely has any separate existence for him; it is virtually an extension or an appurtenance of his well ballasted self. A typical 10-year-old, likewise, is in good equilibrium, but he is so adaptively and diversely in touch with the adult environment that he seems rather to be an adult in the making. Indeed his individuality is now so well defined and his insights are so much more mature that he can be readily regarded as a pre-adult or at least as a pre-adolescent.

FIVE is a neutral as well as nodal age. Not so TEN. At ten years, sex differences are pronounced. The psychology of a 10-year-old girl is significantly distinguishable from that of a 10-year-old boy of equivalent breeding and experience. The girl has more poise, more folk wisdom, and more interest in matters pertaining to marriage and family. This difference appears to be fundamental. Under current cultural conditions other sex differences become obvious; but they need not be taken into account in a general behavior profile.

The distinctive characteristics of the ten-year level are best interpreted in terms of the maturity traits of the 9-year-old. NINE, as we have seen, is earnestly engaged in mastering skills; he works with channelized intentness and is not too easily diverted from one activity to another. He is in a more or less constant state of urgency, as though in contest with Time. In comparison TEN is relaxed and casual, yet alert. He has himself and his skills in hand; he takes things in his stride; he works with executive speed and likes the challenge of mental arithmetic. He often shows a genuine capacity to budget his Time and his energy. His general behavior, his demeanors, his orientation to the household are more modulated.

This greater self-possession shows itself in many ways. Having consolidated certain visual, manual and laryngeal skills, he can attend to a visual task, and at the same time maintain conversation. NINE may have to stop at such a task, in order to talk. For similar reasons TEN is more capable of little courteous amenities which have a motor basis. Since his whole organization is less channelized his attitudes are more flexible, and he is more responsive to slight cues.

This relative fluidity has important cultural implications. It makes the 10-year-old peculiarly receptive to social information, to broadening ideas and to prejudices, good and bad. It is relatively easy to appeal to his reason. He is ready to participate in elementary discussions of social problems,—racial minorities, crime, the relationships of management and labor, the black market etc. Parents often fail to sense the social intelligence of the 10-year-old child. Sometimes they treat him as though he were only eight years old; or they maintain a certain intellectual aloofness which prevents them from organizing his thinking. Yet this is a golden period for planting liberalizing ideas.

Perceptive teachers are aware of the great power which they can wield through suggestion and through the social science studies of the fifth grade, studies which touch the fundamentals of the Four Freedoms and the conditions of human welfare. Social workers also are aware of the critical importance of this age period in the lives of neglected children. The channelized characteristics of the 9-year-old, and the fluidity of the 10-year-old readily lead to bullying and delinquent forms of behavior in an adverse environment. A gang simply organizes these traits for better or for worse.

It is said that the 10-year-old sometimes esteems his gang or his club more than his family. This may be partly true; but on the whole, he has a fairly critical sense of justice. He is cognizant of partialities, and frequently surprises you with the judiciousness of his observations. He sizes up his parents and compares them freely with the parents of his playmates. Many of his comparative judgments are secret; others are expressed. Ask him to describe his teacher and you will get a candid portrait: Miss A. "She's reasonable; she yells a lot, too, but she's really very nice!"—Miss B. "She doesn't like some kids. One kid she doesn't like at all!"—Miss C. "She's pretty big and she has sort of yellow-blondish hair. She never stands up straight. She walks like this." The 10-year-old is evidently aware of individuality in others as well as in himself.

Individual differences, apparent at nine years, become still more manifest at ten. The 10-year-old gives a fair indication of the man (or woman) he is to be. Talents now declare themselves, particularly in the realm of the creative arts. Giftedness in personal-social behavior also reveals itself, if we take pains to read the subtler emotional patterns of the child. He may show fineness of character, graces of deportment, executive ability, perceptiveness of interpersonal relationships, and a wide range of personality traits which have great prognostic import as to his potential vocation and career. In the management of interpersonal relationships he may already show a kind of skill and a sense of justice which signify capacity for leadership. All special skills should be recognized, not for purposes of pre-vocational training but for reasons of psychological hygiene.

A democratic culture will naturally place a premium on all kinds of skill. The schools continue to bestow excessive emphasis on academic skills. The non-verbal child with mechanical skills, however, should have ample opportunity to exercise them and to give them socialized expression. The exercise of skills with social approval serves a valuable double purpose. It serves to strengthen that self-respect and self-confidence which is so important in meeting the perturbing demands of adolescence. Simultaneously, society thereby protects itself against the delinquencies of adolescence. Cultural planning for the teen ages should begin at ten.

The 10-year-old will respond to such planning. As already noted, he takes kindly to liberalizing ideas of social justice and social welfare. Although critical, both of self and of others, the 10-year-old is capable of loyalties and of hero worship, and he himself can inspire it in schoolmates. He can be readily inspired to group loyalties in his club organizations. He likes the sense of solidarity which comes from keeping a group secret, as a member of a group.

Girls and boys alike have a certain fondness for secrets. It seems that in some esoteric way a shared secret intensifies both the private sense of self and the identification with another self. So in radio, movies, comic strips and pictorials, we find that the 10-year-olds like mysteries, conspiracy, practical magic and hero worship. Comics still hold sway with some children, but are losing it with others.

Romance and love in the cinema are spurned, at least by the boys

There is not much companionship between the sexes. They keep apart by intermittent feuds and separatist truces, but they also enjoy group games of one sex against the other and the formal situation of dancing school. Boys express their camaraderie with other boys in wrestling, shoving and punching each other. Girls as pals walk with arms about each other. There is much gossiping in and out of school, among school-mates, with writing and exchange of more or less complimentary notes. Girls are prone to write notes to other girls. True to the secretive-in-group tendency characteristic of the age, the notes are often phrased in cryptic terms understood only by those "in the know." Most of this surreptitious activity is superficial, innocent and spasmodic. It does not result in permanent resentments and enmities. It seems to serve a psychological necessity, if not a constructive function.

When two or three girls foregather with their assorted paper dolls, they dramatize many life situations, in whispered secrets or in outspoken dialogue. By using the dolls as concrete symbols, or by staging plays, they explore the whole family structure, including engagements, brides, weddings and the rearing of children.

Girls are more aware of interpersonal relationships than boys are. They are more aware of their own persons, their clothes, and appearance. They may spend prolonged periods preening a coiffure. At the same time, they are more discerning of their individual relationships with others. If a younger child giggles at the movies, her companionship is spurned. More than boys, girls are interested in family life and they are most perceptive of differences in family living. A less favored child may inspire sympathy and a desire to help.

By such precursor signs girls, and to lesser degree, boys of ten give evidence of approaching adolescence. Too little is known about the concrete steps whereby these children will reach ultimate maturity. Ten years and more of adolescence lie ahead.

The mechanisms of development during those years will not change. The increments will come slowly and often painfully. Endocrine changes will bring about new physical and mental manifestations. But the patterning of behavior will remain a gradual process of architec-tured growth.

Just as the equilibrium of age five gave way to the impulsiveness of five-and-a-half and the creative thrusts of six, and as these in their turn gave way to the subjectiveness of seven, the expansiveness of eight, the self-motivation of nine and the re-orientation of ten, so the eleventh and twelfth years will lawfully manifest themselves in distinctive shapes of behavior. And likewise, each year of the teens and the early twenties will bring forth its characteristic behavior shapes. The psychology of adolescence remains yet to be written, because the morphology of the growing behavior patterns has not been studied in concrete detail.

The culture cannot do justice to the psychological needs of the adolescent without a more realistic knowledge of development as a morphogenetic process, that is a process which produces lawful shapes and configurations of all behavior,—motor, adaptive and personal-social. General dynamics cannot explain the progressively changing structure of the adolescent mind.

The changes are in essence comparable to those which we have described for infancy and childhood. The foundation and most of the framework of the human action-system are laid down in the first decade. The consolidations of those first ten years will not be sloughed off. They will remain an integral part of the action-system of the matur-ing youth. The teens do not transform the child, but they continue him. Herein lies the preventive and the hygienic significance of infancy, the pre-school years, and the years from five to ten.

PART THREE

There was a child went forth every day,
And the first object he look'd upon, that object he became,
And that object became part of him for the day or a certain part of the day,
Or for many years or stretching cycles of years.

The early lilacs became part of this child,
And grass and white and red morning-glories, and white and red clover, and the
*   song of the phoebe-bird,*
And the Third-month lambs and the sow's pink-faint litter, and the mare's foal
*   and the cow's calf,*
And the noisy brood of the barnyard or by the mire of the pond side,
And the fish suspending themselves so curiously below there, and the beautiful
*   curious liquid,*
And the water-plants with their graceful flat heads, all became part of him. . . .

His own parents, he that had father'd him and she that had conceiv'd him in her
*   womb, and birth'd him,*
They gave this child more of themselves than that,
They gave him afterward every day, they became part of him.

The mother at home quietly placing the dishes on the supper-table,
The mother with mild words, clean her cap and gown, a wholesome odor falling
*   off her person and clothes as she walks by,*
The father, strong, self-sufficient, manly, mean, anger'd, unjust,
The blow, the quick loud word, the tight bargain, the crafty lure,
The family usages, the language, the company, the furniture, the yearning and
*   swelling heart, ...*

The strata of color'd clouds, the long bar of maroon-tint away solitary by itself,
*   the spread of purity it lies motionless in,*
The horizon's edge, the flying sea-crow, the fragrance of salt marsh and shore mud,
These became part of that child who went forth every day, and who now goes, and
*   will always go forth every day.*
                                                    —WALT WHITMAN

PART THREE

ORIENTATION

THE Behavior Profiles, assembled in PART Two furnish cross-sectional views of the ascending stages of maturity from five to ten years. PART THREE assembles the Growth Gradients, which are implicit in these stages. But the life career of the child does not begin at the age of five years, and to get a clear view of the trends of growth, the gradients must begin with infancy. The following ten chapters therefore group the growth gradients from birth to ten years in ten major fields of behavior. Special attention is, of course, given to the period from five to ten, but the earlier period is treated in sufficient detail to show the developmental continuities.*

For convenience, each gradient consists of a series of levels arranged by weeks, months or years. This does *not* mean that the itemized gradient levels should be regarded as statistical age norms.

The parent who reads a gradient should never say my child *ought* to be at this particular level of the gradient because he is old enough. The child may well be younger or older than the chronological age assigned by the gradient. It is more important to find the gradient-level which approximately describes the stage of maturity which he has actually attained. The gradients are intended to show the overall

* Further details on the period from birth to five may be secured from the following volumes: Gesell & Ilg: *Infant and Child in the Culture of Today* (Harper); Gesell et al: *The First Five Years of Life* (Harper).

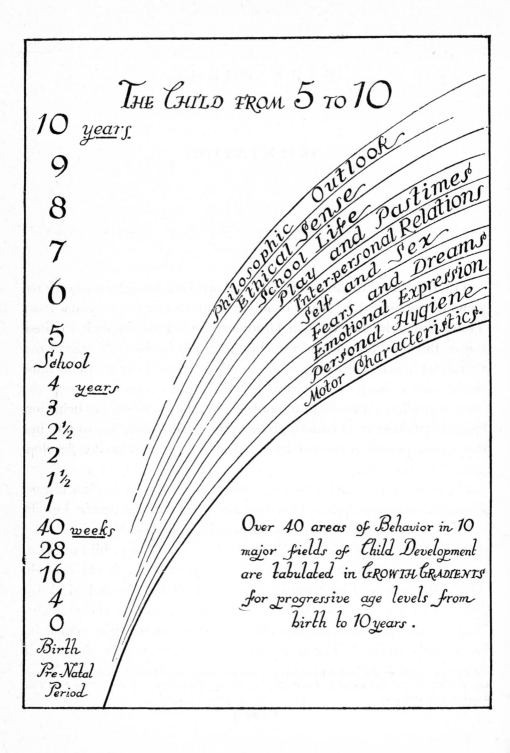

The Child from 5 to 10

Over 40 areas of Behavior in 10 major fields of Child Development are tabulated in Growth Gradients for progressive age levels from birth to 10 years.

developmental *sequences* of behavior rather than rigid standards of expectancy. Individual differences are too great to permit rigid standards rigidly applied. Generous allowances should be made for age variations.

Nevertheless, the gradient-levels are *location points* which help to give us bearings. They indicate, suggestively, the kinds of behavior which precede; and still better they indicate the kinds of behavior which are likely to follow in due course. This orientation, this *forward* look, provides perspective and usually affords cause for optimism. The gradients are not designed to *rate* the child; they are designed as tools to aid interpretation. They are rough charts to sail by.

Each of the chapters of PART THREE is followed by a group of gradients in tabular form for ready consultation. The introductory discussion interprets the general significance of these gradients in terms of child development and of child guidance. No attempt is made to consider specifically each separate item of a gradient. Many of the items have already had concrete mention in other connections. The emphasis is on growth trends over a long reach of time. We are concerned with the developmental philosophy of the behavior under discussion,—the nature of the behavior from the standpoint of maturity, the import of the behavior from the standpoint of the culture. In last analysis the culture consists of home, school and community. So we naturally have had teachers as well as parents in mind in writing these interpretations. We make repeated references to the individual differences among children (and adults) to protect the gradients from arbitrary application.

11
MOTOR CHARACTERISTICS

Most of the readers of this book, to say nothing of the authors, are especially interested in problems of child personality. But one cannot make a frontal attack upon the psychology of personality; because personality is really the sum and resultant of all possible forms of behavior. So one must approach the subject from several angles, which are represented by the titles of the ten chapters in PART THREE. Naturally we begin with the child's motor characteristics, because the very core of his physical and practical self is muscular.

All told he has over 600 distinguishable muscles. Most of them are firmly attached in symmetrical pairs to the skeleton with its elaborate apparatus of joints and levers. Anyone who has tussled with a lively pre-school child knows the versatility of that apparatus. The complexity of the muscular system is beyond imagination, because a child has some 40,000,000 muscle fibers, each of which, in turn, is made up of an immense number of microscopic fibrils, and they in their turn are linked up with nerve fibrils which receive impulses via a veritable jungle of nerve cells in the brain and spinal cord. Because of the myriad of nerve connections the muscular system is really a neuro-muscular system.

Considering its vast complexity, is it strange that it takes literally a score of years to organize this system? Most of the organization takes place in the first ten years of life, and proceeds with an orderly sequence suggested by the gradients of growth. The process of organization really begins before birth, when the deep spinal muscles of the trunk come into action. These muscles are very ancient in the evolutionary history of the race. They antedate even the muscles which move the fore limb and the hind limb. In general, the development of the massive fundamental muscles is basic to that of the finer accessory muscles, such as those which wag the tongue and fingers, purse the lips and move the eyeballs.

But Nature cannot wait until the birth of the child to lay down the primary networks for the coordination of the neuro-muscular system. Accordingly, as we have already seen, even the unborn baby is capable of making movements and of striking attitudes. Some of the movements involve the gross muscles, many involve the fine. The total amount of activity which takes place during the fetal period is considerable; and if we had the requisite information we should find that this activity is already predictive of certain motor characteristics which the child will display in later life.

Soon after the baby is born he assumes active postures which involve eyes, head, arms, legs and trunk. His eyes, which moved intermittently under closed lids while he was still in utero, now assume a fixed posture as he stares at some object. He holds the posture by means of his twelve oculo-motor muscles. These are so tiny that they could go into a thimble, but they are in many ways the most important muscles in his entire body. They have extremely extensive connections with millions of nerve cells (neurons) in the brain. Through these cells the eyes are brought under voluntary control, and they are also brought into association with countless muscle fibers in other muscles.

The eyes acquire their own skills; they also acquire directional skills which are built into the skills of other muscle groups. Having "learned" to hold a posture, the eyes learn to move right and left, up and down, and oblique-wise; they learn to converge, to follow a moving object and to rove in exploratory inspection. In a few years they make hop-skip excursions across the printed page of a book which the reader holds in his tight hands.

This remarkable feat which needs the coordination of eye-head-hands-and-body postures had its humble developmental beginnings in the tonic-neck-reflex of early infancy. The t-n-r (for short) is both a static and dynamic posture. In its most typical form the baby lies supine, head turned to the right, right arm extended, left arm flexed. In general outline this activity bears resemblance to the stances assumed in fencing, boxing, creeping, walking, throwing, golfing and violin playing! In all these motor skills the action-system must strike asymmetric as well as symmetric attitudes in order to maintain poise and to make progressive movements.

At first the infant gazes rather vaguely in the direction of the extended arm; but in two or three months his eyes "pick up" his moving fist, and he begins to look regardfully at his hands—an event which marks an epoch in his mental growth. Later he looks at an object held in his hand; he seizes an object on sight and inspects it. All of this preparatory to the supreme achievement of holding a book simultaneously with eyes and hands,—and perhaps even lifting the head a moment to smile at the teacher. But if the teacher is wise she will not expect the latter amenity too early.

The complexities of postural control are well borne out in the development of throwing,—a motor skill which was of life and death importance to primitive ancestors, and which figures prominently in the play activities of child and adult. Well defined casting begins at about 15 months when the baby is perfecting his capacity to let-go-of-a-hold. Safely seated in his high chair he takes great delight in casting one object after another overboard. His oculo-motor muscles are alert enough to follow through as the objects fall,—a very important visual skill, basic to the eye movements of reading.

At 18 months he can cast while standing; but his throw is a crude forward thrust, and he toddles both before and after the throw. He is nearly four years old before he acquires a definite standing stance for delivery. His leg work, however, is still immature. He tends to use his right foot as fulcrum, and to twist and lean awkwardly with his trunk. At five years he advances with the left foot, shifts weight to the left foot on delivery, releasing the ball when the arm is in full extension. As in so many other behaviors, the 5-year-old prefigures the adult. He shows many of the elements of mature throwing. Boys throw much farther and more accurately than girls, and are obviously more masculine in their style of delivery. Here is a constitutional sex difference in behavior which can scarcely be ascribed to cultural factors. The sex difference becomes evident well before the age of four.

Primitive man not only hurled missiles; he also struck blows with a cudgel. After toss-ball comes bat and ball. Batting requires a higher order of coordination on the part of the eyes, hands, fingers, body posture and feet. Nimble shift of stance, instantaneous perception, accurate timing and flash flood release of energy are demanded. The 6-year-old makes swat-like strokes at the ball from a rather stiff stance; the 10-year-old makes a creditable swing with promising foot work. Batting form during the years from five to ten improves perceptibly, not merely because practice makes perfect, but because the total neuro-muscular system of the child undergoes progressive growth changes. Similar changes affect numerous motor aspects of his school work.

Crayon and pencil require more delicate handling than bat and ball.

The manipulation of graphic tools is highly dependent upon motor maturity. Details will be given in the chapter on School Life (Chapter 18), in connection with the growth gradient for writing. Here again the general form of the motor activity varies with age and with inborn ability, rather than with exercise per se. This accounts for the fact that children at one stage will prefer bold and free flowing strokes with crude crayon; and at another stage, they will enjoy circumscribed finer strokes with pencil. Speed and accuracy also show a tendency to vary with the current maturity of the neuro-muscular system. The 7-year-old doodles, the 8-year-old likes to be timed for speed of performance, the 9-year-old tends to write at top speed without special regard for neatness. Such variations are entirely normal; and if we understood them better, we should not place as much stress on straight line progress in the acquisition of motor skills.

Inasmuch as maturity is such a fundamental factor in determining the motor traits of growing children, we should expect distinguishable differences in the general motor deportment of the various grades of an elementary schoolroom. To be sure, much depends upon the freedom of movement allowed to the pupils. If they are restricted to fixed positions at fixed desks, we should have to observe the tensional outlets of the children,—the ways in which they wiggle, squirm, tap, grimace, etc. Such tensional behavior affords good clues to the motor maturity of a child. But if the atmosphere and the equipment of the room allow a normal degree of freedom, we get a truer picture of the motor characteristics of the children.

In the *kindergarten*, the typical 5-year-old may move from one locus of interest to another, making a transitional contact with the teacher. But when he gets to an area of choice, he stays there for a prolonged period, working smoothly. He is moderately aware of the whole room in his play, relates readily to his teacher, is not disturbed by a visitor.

The motor demeanors of the *first grade* are significantly different. The set-up and the atmosphere of the room are more fluid. Materials are less in evidence. The typical 6-year-old frequently moves from one locus to another. Indeed he seems always to be in motion. Even when he settles down he keeps on settling, continually shifting his posture and sketchily manipulating the material with which he is engaged. He does not build a tower or wind thread on a bobbin as smoothly as he did a year ago. He seems to be over aware of the contexts of his task, and too ready to move to the next task.

There is less scatteration in the *second grade*. SEVEN settles down for longer periods, narrows down to the task in hand, and shows persistence even in the finer use of pencil and scissors. When restless he may push his desk, but he can remain on location better than more mercurial SIX. He is interested to finish his task; if he moves about it is more typically for a round trip to his teacher.

EIGHT is still more sedentary. There is less moving about in a *third grade* room. Performance is more even, group cohesion more evident. The room looks neater, and if it gets out of order from group activity it is quickly put back in shape by group action. The individual children are more poised and self-dependent. There is less opening and closing of desks and fewer round trips for teacher contact; and more communication by an eager raising of the hand in a modified and agitated t-n-r attitude.

The *fourth* and *fifth grades* are more business-like. The pupils remain seated for a much longer period; but for some developmental reason or other, postural proprieties have slumped. A typical 9-year-old raises his hand at the end of a flail-like arm which is so flaccid that it is often supported by the free hand! Perhaps, for temporary developmental reasons, his energies are draining from the proximal spine to the distal precinct of the fingers; for he has a new interest in speedy but skillful performances which require fine coordination. At any rate, if an immature 9-year-old should be in the group, he might give symptoms of his immaturity in his motor demeanors and motor deportment.

The motor characteristics of a child are worthy of observation because they are indicators both of individuality and of maturity status.

By the age of nine a child acts like himself. He reveals his psycho-motor makeup in the way he comes into the schoolroom, and in the gestures which he makes under tension or excitement. Nutritional and environmental factors should always be weighed; but we may also look for the core of individuality which expresses itself in postural and physiognomic demeanors.

Sheldon, however, holds that "postural preferences are unquestion-ably innate." He speaks in terms of three temperament types which are associated with three body types as follows: (1) *viscerotonic*: round, soft body, short neck, small hands and feet; (2) *somatotonic*: square, firm body with rugged muscles; (3) *cerebrotonic*: spindly body, delicate in construction. The extreme viscerotonic has a good digestive tract. He is good natured, relaxed, sociable, communicative. The pronounced somatotonic is active, energetic, assertive, noisy and aggressive. The fragile cerebrotonic is restrained, inhibited, tense; he may prefer soli-tude to noise and company. ". . . . . . and," continues Sheldon, "it is probably as natural and desirable for a cerebrotonic to sit round shouldered on the middle of his back as for a somatotonic to sit square shouldered on the end of his back." Mary Lyon, founder of Holyoke, was a dynamic individual. With characteristic zeal she used to exhort the girls in her Female Seminary with the injunction: "Sit with energy!"

This suggestion is not meant to be taken too literally; but it is a healthy reminder that deep seated constitutional differences are at the basis of the demeanors, the manners and the conduct of children. These differences are infinitely more complex than a threefold classification of types can identify; but the mere acknowledgment of the differences is bound to temper our attitudes toward children. We shall try to understand their postural behavior instead of pressing it into a stereotype.

Posture remains a key concept for the adequate interpretation of child development. But the concept must be enlarged to include the fine muscles as well as the gross,—the tiny muscles of the eyes, the slender fascicles of the fingers, as well as the massive muscles of the trunk. Motor health depends upon a harmonization of the heavy fundamental and of the delicate accessory muscles. To establish that harmony Nature accents now one or the other group, now the flexors, now the extensors; now symmetry, now asymmetry; now the *go* muscles and now the *stop* muscles. School and home may consider the meaning and the trend of these accents. The varying accents come to the surface in all sorts of activity: tossing the ball, batting the ball, moulding clay, painting, scrawling, printing, writing, reading. Even manners and morals have a motor basis. We may well look for a motor ingredient in all the gradients of growth.

GROWTH GRADIENTS

§ 1. BODILY ACTIVITY

4 WEEKS—T-n-r (asymmetric posture) predominates.
   Momentarily lifts head in prone position.

16 WEEKS—Assumes a symmetrical posture.
   Sits propped for short period.

20 WEEKS—Holds head erect and steady in sitting position.
   Extends arms in prone.

24 WEEKS—Rolls to prone from supine.

28 WEEKS—Bounces actively in supported sitting.

32 WEEKS—Pivots in prone position.

36 WEEKS—Sits alone, leans forward and re-erects self.

40 WEEKS—Pulls self to feet at side rail of crib.
   Creeps.

48 WEEKS—Pivots in sitting. Cruises at crib rail.

52 WEEKS—Walks with one hand held.

56 WEEKS—Stands momentarily alone.

15 MONTHS—Walks a few steps and falls by collapse.
   Creeps up steps.

18 MONTHS—Walks; seldom falls. Runs stiffly.
   Walks into rather than kicks a ball.
   Likes to move large toys by pulling, pushing, carrying.
   Explores rooms and closets in the house.
   Seats self by backing into a small chair.

2 YEARS—Runs without falling, and squats in play.
   Rhythmical responses as bending knees in bouncing, swaying, swinging arms,
      nodding head, and tapping feet.

2½ YEARS—Walks on tip toe; jumps on two feet.
   Runs ahead or lags when walking on street.
   Pushes toy with good steering.
   Runs, gallops and swings to music.
   Can carry breakable object.

3 YEARS—Walks erect and is sure and nimble on his feet.
   Walks rather than runs. Can stand on one foot momentarily.
   Throws a ball without losing his balance.
   Gallops, jumps, walks and runs to music.

3½ YEARS—Increased tension and may fall or stumble.

4 YEARS—Very active, covering more ground. Races up and down stairs. Dashes on
      tricycle.
   Enjoys activities requiring balance. Can carry cup of liquid without spilling.
   Prefers large blocks and makes more complicated structures.
   Throws a ball overhand.
   In rhythms interprets and demonstrates own response.

5 YEARS—There is greater ease and control of general bodily activity, and economy of
      movement.
   Posture is predominantly symmetrical and closely knit. May walk with feet pronate.
   Control over large muscles is still more advanced than control over small ones.
   Plays in one location for longer periods, but changes posture from standing, sitting,
      squatting.
   Likes to climb fences and go from one thing to another. Jumps from table height.
   Likes to activate a story. Runs, climbs onto and under chairs and tables.
   Throws, including mud and snow and is beginning to use hands more than arms
      in catching a small ball but frequently fails to catch.
   Alternates feet descending stairs and skips alternately.
   Attempts to roller skate, jump rope, and to walk on stilts.
   Likes to march to music.

5½ YEARS—There is demand to discard tricycle for bicycle, and many enjoy a few experiences on a bicycle.

6 YEARS—Very active; in almost constant motion.

Activity is sometimes clumsy as he overdoes and falls in a tumble.

Body is in active balance as he swings, plays active games with singing or skips to music.

He is often found wrestling, tumbling, crawling on all fours and pawing at another child, and playing tag.

Large blocks and furniture are pushed and pulled around as he makes houses, climbs on and in them.

Balls are bounced and tossed and sometimes successfully caught.

He tries skates, running broad jump, and stunts on bars.

Some boys spend much time digging.

7 YEARS—Shows more caution in many gross motor activities.

Activity is variable and he is sometimes very active and at other times inactive.

He repeats performances persistently. Has "runs" on certain activities such as roller skating, jump rope, "catch" with a soft ball, or hop scotch.

There is a great desire for a bicycle, which he can ride for some distance although he is only ready to handle it within limits.

Beginning to be interested in learning to bat and to pitch.

Boys especially like to run and shoot paper airplanes through the air.

Likes to gallop and to do a simple running step to music.

Many have a desire for dancing lessons.

8 YEARS—Bodily movement is more rhythmical and graceful.

Now aware of posture in himself and others. Likes to play follow the leader.

Learning to play soccer and baseball with a soft ball and enjoys the shifts of activity within the game.

Girls are learning to run into the moving rope and can run out when beginning to fail but cannot vary step while jumping.

Stance and movement are free while painting.

Very dramatic in activities with characteristic and descriptive gestures.

Many enjoy folk dances but do not like rhythms unless of a spontaneous dramatic nature.

9 YEARS—Works and plays hard. Apt to do one thing until exhausted, such as riding bicycle, running, hiking, sliding or playing ball.

Better control of own speed but shows some timidity of speed of an automobile, of sliding and of fast snow when skiing.

Interest in own strength and in lifting things.

Frequently assumes awkward postures.

Boys like to wrestle and may be interested in boxing lessons.

Great interest in team games and in learning to perform skillfully.

§2. EYES AND HANDS

4 WEEKS—Stares vacantly at surroundings. Seeks light of window or a bright moving object. Regards an object brought into his line of vision.

8 WEEKS—Follows a moving person and a nearby object with some head rotation past midline.

12 WEEKS—Regards face-hand in t-n-r position.
Holds an object in hand with brief regard.
Fixates prolongedly on electric light or on a person.

16 WEEKS—Rotates head and inspects surroundings.
Activates arms as regards an object and looks from own hand to object.
Fleetingly perceives an 8 mm. pellet on table.

20 WEEKS—Corrals objects on table and grasps one on contact.
Definitely fixates pellet.
In supine, visually pursues a lost toy.

24 WEEKS—Approaches and grasps a toy and can resecure a toy dropped within reach.

28 WEEKS—Strongly manipulative; banging, shaking and transferring toys. With toy in hand, visually perceives moving free hand.
Extends arms, regards and attempts to secure objects just beyond reach.
Perceptive of new surroundings. Occupied with watching surroundings while in carriage.

32 WEEKS—Holds one object, regards and grasps another.
Bites, chews and regards toys.
Closes eyes on approach of an object to face.

36 WEEKS—Brings one toy against another.
Feeds himself a cracker.

40 WEEKS—Picks up or pokes at tiny bits with newly acquired index-thumb prehension.
Has a crude release.
In carriage, plays with toys as well as watches surroundings.

44 WEEKS—Explores parts of a toy. Probes holes and grooves.
Brings an object into container without release.

48 WEEKS—Takes toys from table to chair and reaches toys to side rail of crib.
Plays serially with several toys. Easy release.

52 WEEKS—Puts toy in and out of container.
In carriage, inspects automobiles, pedestrians and dogs.

15 MONTHS—Casts toys in play.

> Releases one cube over another, and dangles a toy by a string.
> Attempts to imitate a scribble by rubbing or banging crayon on paper.
> Enjoys looking out of window at moving trees and automobiles.
> Pats or manipulates a picture book.

18 MONTHS—Attention is brief, but within its span he encompasses adult performances and imitates them.

> Builds a tower of three or four blocks.
> Turns several pages of a book and looks at pictures, naming or pointing to one.
> Looks out of window at people, airplane, or moon.

2 YEARS—Regards and reaches almost simultaneously.

> Fits toys together.
> Rotates forearm and turns door knob.
> Enjoys watching a moving object. Locates picture in picture book.
> Makes tiny marks with crayon on paper.
> Builds blocks vertically or horizontally in simple line, or tower with a variety of blocks.

2½ YEARS—Over-grasps and over-releases.

> Experiments with vertical and horizontal lines, dots and circular movement in painting.
> Finger painting, clay and water hold special interest.
> Makes simple block structures.
> Enjoys watching trains at a distance. Can identify landmarks on a familiar route.

3 YEARS—Can copy a circle.

> May "read" from pictures in a book.
> Can put on shoes, and unbutton some buttons.
> Strokes are varied and rhythmical in painting.
> Manipulates clay and makes flat "cakes" and balls; rolls narrow strips.
> There is order and balance in block building.
> Enjoys watching men at work or steam shovel or cement mixer in operation.

3½ YEARS—May show mild tremor in fine motor coordination.

> May use non-dominant hand, or shift handedness.
> Some identify *D* for daddy, *M* for mommy, *J* for Johnnie (own name) and *S* for Susan (sister).

4 YEARS—Draws objects with few details. Can copy a square.

> In painting, works with precision for some time, but shifts ideas. Makes crude designs and letters.
> Enjoys having name printed on his drawings and begins to copy. May sense number of letters in name and may print first two letters, making marks for remainder. Identifies several letters.

Uses scissors and attempts to cut on a straight line.

Builds extensive complicated structure with blocks, combining many shapes in symmetrical form.

Laces shoes and buttons front buttons.

Fingers piano with both hands.

5 YEARS—Coordination has reached a new maturity. He approaches an object directly, prehends it precisely and releases it with dispatch.

Builds with blocks usually on the floor and builds graduated towers or low rambling structures with roads and small enclosures.

Manipulates sand, making roads and houses. Molds objects with clay.

If cannot do puzzle with precision and dispatch, he will ask for help or abandon it.

Likes to color within lines, to cut and paste simple things but is not adept.

Makes an outline drawing, usually one on a page, and recognizes that it is "funny." Likes to copy simple forms.

Paints at an easel or on the floor with large brushes and large sheets of paper. May enjoy making letters in this manner.

Can "sew" wool through a card by turning it over.

Can manipulate those buttons on clothes which he can see, and can lace his shoes.

Places fingers on piano keys and may experiment with chords.

5½ YEARS—Awkward in many manipulations.

Boys especially are interested in tools, in tinker toys and in watching an electric or wind-up train.

Girls like to dress and undress dolls.

Many show an interest in learning to print own first name and in underlining capitals and words in a familiar book.

6 YEARS—In many of his performances he makes a good start, but needs some assistance and direction to complete.

He is now more deliberate and sometimes clumsy.

Handles and attempts to utilize tools and material.

Cuts and pastes paper making books, boxes; and likes to use tape to fix things.

Hammers vigorously but often holds the hammer near the head. Can join boards and make simple structures.

Is beginning to use pencil crayons as well as wax crayons for coloring and drawing.

Can print capital letters which he commonly reverses. Likes to write on the blackboard as well as to use crayons and pencils.

Attempts to sew using a large needle and makes large stitches.

7 YEARS—Manipulation of tools is somewhat more tense, but there is more persistence.

Pencils are tightly gripped and often held close to the point. Pressure is variable but is apt to be heavy.

Child can now print several sentences with letters getting smaller toward the end of a line. There are individual differences in size of printing: some print very small and others continue to make large letters.

Boys are especially interested in carpentry, and many can now saw a straight line.

Girls prefer to color and to cut out paper dolls.

Several show marked interest in the piano. Usually both hands are used with unequal pressure.

8 YEARS—Increase in speed and smoothness of eye-hand performance, and an easy release.

Holds pencil, brush and tools slightly less tensely.

Enjoys having a performance timed but does not compete with time.

Likely to be a gap between what he wants to do with his hands and what he can do.

Writes or prints all letters and numbers accurately, maintaining fairly uniform alignment, slant and spacing. Likes to do neatly but sometimes is in too much of a hurry.

Beginning to get perspective in drawing. Draws action figures in good proportion.

Girls can now hem a straight edge in sewing.

9 YEARS—Individual variation in skills.

Can hold and swing a hammer well. Saws easily and accurately and uses knee to hold board. Makes finished products.

Garden tools are used and handled appropriately.

Builds complex structures with erector set.

Handwriting is now a tool.

Beginning to sketch in drawing. Drawings are often detailed. Especially likes to draw still life, maps and designs.

Girls can cut out and sew a simple garment and can knit.

Can dress rapidly. Some interest in combing own hair.

Interest in watching games played by others.

12

PERSONAL HYGIENE

EATING

By the time a child reaches the age of five years, one might well suppose that "he should know how to eat!" In a happy-go-lucky household perhaps he does know. But in another household with exacting standards, he falls at least short of expectations! Even when permitted to eat with the family (a mark of promotion), he dawdles, he talks too much, and he may even ask to be fed. He wiggles in his chair, and his napkin must be tucked in at the neck to stay anywhere at all! Well, perhaps he will improve in another year.

But at the age of six he stuffs his mouth; he spills, he masticates grossly, grabs for his food, knocks things over, teeters back in his chair,

Besides he is reputed to talk altogether too much, and to kick the table legs. Well, well, perhaps he will improve in another year.

At seven he may talk less at meals; but his mouth is still likely to be full to capacity when he does talk. He may bolt his food,—and also the table; but he is "quieting down." His napkin is variably below his chin, on the floor, or it lies neglected beside his plate.

At eight and nine he is not impeccable, but the napkin gradient registers an advance. The napkin has moved from its earlier position at the chin to the lap or the vicinity of the lap. The 8-year-old anchors his napkin by sitting on a corner of it.

And so each year brings its achievements and its new promise. Meanwhile year in, year out, parents punctuate the meals with admonitions, reminders, frownings and disciplinary dismissals from the table. An incredible amount of emotional tension disturbs the equanimity of mealtimes of many American homes. All because of an exaggerated emphasis on table manners for their own sake.

In most instances the child is not truly ill-mannered. He is inept, immature. The demands of decorum made upon him are often out of all proportion to his skill. It takes not only motor skill but a certain degree of maturity to coordinate smoothly and with precision the following components of faultless table manners: (a) poised sedentary posture (b) immobilization of napkin (c) cutting, spearing and loading with one or two feeding utensils (d) graceful transit of the load to the mouth (e) timing of the next load (f) agreeable conversation (g) simultaneous timing of conversation in relation to mastication and to the conversation of others (h) swallowing (i) social deference to elders (j) inhibition of kicking table legs (and nearby sibling!) (k) satiety (l) conventional request to be excused.

It is safe to say that the eating behavior of children would tend to improve and not deteriorate if less strenuous stress were placed upon the formal aspect of manners. A friendly atmosphere at mealtimes is of importance, because enjoyment (rather than strict discipline) is still the best aid to appetite.

From a developmental standpoint graceful table manners constitute a minor problem. They depend primarily upon the maturity of the child's motor skills and his tensional controls. Under ordinary conditions the "manners" improve with age (rather than with scoldings). Even at the age of eight, the child eats tolerably well in public; and by ten he usually eats acceptably both at home and abroad. Viewed in this developmental perspective, the sternness and exasperation of the supervising adults seem wasteful and misplaced. (The family life does not need to be ruined after all.) The chief guidance rule is preventive. Make gradual rather than excessive demands; avoid complexities; make concessions; simplify the mealtime situations; rely on favorable atmosphere and attitudes. When parents themselves have highly emotional attitudes with respect to good manners, the problem has shifted from child to adult.

Many feeding problems vanish as soon as parents reduce their own determinations, and place more faith in the lawful fluctuations and the favorable trends of development. The *level of appetite* for example fluctuates from year to year but shows a tendency toward overall improvement. It may be low at 18 months and at four years but there is usually a steady rise from five years on. By nine years nearly all children have a vigorous and generous appetite. Nor is it wise to expect uniform levels of appetite throughout the day. Breakfast is often "the poorest" meal, even though one might wish to insist that it be otherwise. At many ages there is marked variability from meal to meal. But, again, such variability tends to decrease with increasing age.

Closely related is the question of *speed in eating*, which in turn is "manners," because parents become impatient with dawdling and equally impatient with bolting. There are marked individual differences, based on constitutions and on maturity. Speed however, tends to pick up with appetite, and accordingly varies with age. The 5-year-old may eat very slowly. The 8-year-old likes to eat with dispatch and directness, and without deferment of dessert. One must not expect an orderly and uniform progression in eating behavior between the ages of five and ten. Many of the complications of infant feeding have been transcended, but the organism is still in a state of formative variability. There is a constantly changing ratio between appetite, motor skill, social amenity, and tensional control. This results in unavoidable fluctuations in the general pattern of eating behavior. FIVE reflects the logic of these fluctuations; we should be more tolerant and optimistic with respect to table manners.

A closing word about *preferences and refusals*. They cause no end of worry and vexation. The cultural elevation of spinach, aided and abetted by Pop-Eye, betrays a tendency toward induced feeding, which is not warranted by the science of nutrition. Carefully controlled studies (notably those of Dr. Clara Davis) have demonstrated that a healthy child will voluntarily and unaided select an adequate diet. Under favor-able conditions he is likely to select an optimal diet.

This fact should give pause to strenuous efforts to overcome honest aversions to certain kinds of food. To be sure, we cannot always deter-mine whether the refusal is whimsical or due to imitation, custom or to some other environmental factor. But if it is based on bio-chemical incompatibility it should be respected. The phenomenon of allergy has shown that some supposedly wholesome foods are positively harmful to the organism. Even here, developmental factors modify the symp-toms. The allergic reaction tends to diminish with age; the organism builds up its immunity and the child tolerates the hitherto inimical substance. Sometimes a parent and child may have very similar allergic symptoms, suggesting the hereditary transmission of bio-chemical consti-tution.

Preferences and refusals become less marked and less frequent after the age of eight years. In the preceding years there are significant fluctuations. A food preferred at one age is often discarded at a subse-quent age. There are temporary periods of strong passions for certain foods. The 5-year-old may manifest a strong dislike for stringy and lumpy foods. This may coincide with a special susceptibility to throat difficulties at this time. The 6-year-old tends to emotional reactions in relation to the taste of food. He makes rather fine taste discriminations, and he behaves somewhat ritualistically in regard to them. The 8-year-old likewise has emotional reactions to the smell of food. Such reactions, however puzzling and unwarranted they may seem, suggest the presence of physiological factors.

From this brief survey it is clear that eating, in our modern culture is a curious mixture of simple, complex, primitive and cultivated patterns of behavior. The whole child eats. Psychic and somatic factors are intimately blended. And it is difficult to separate environmental from intrinsic origins. Consider the authenticated story of the 2-year-old infant, who survived many weeks at sea in a life boat which escaped a torpedoing. After long experience, he cried for sharks to make their appearance, and he cried when he did not receive his anticipated ration of hard tack!

Differences in cultural experience and differences in race and individual constitution are reflected in the patterns of eating behavior. Sheldon writes almost a paean describing the alimentation of the viscerotonic, who attends and exercises to eat. (While the cerebrotonic eats and exercises to attend; and the somatotonic eats and attends to exercise!) The viscerotonic has a love of food and a warm appreciation of the process of eating for its own sake, which is not to be confused with mere voracity of appetite. "Digestion is excellent and is a primary pleasure."

But all children are not viscerotonics, so we may end on a broader note, based on the famous self-selection study already cited: "The joys of eating bulk large beyond our adult power to remember; they are our best ally in getting children to eat heartily, and it would seem that some latitude should be allowed in the matter of the conventions of eating in the interest of that enjoyment which is after all the best sauce for appetite."

SLEEP

The appended gradients give ample indication that sleep is not a simple function. It is a growing function which undergoes many changes from year to year. Sleep is not simply a clever trick, which can be learned with practice. It is a complex behavior trait, which was built up through long ages of racial evolution. Every child must rebuild his sleep structures as he matures The culture helps him as best it can.

The term "sleep structure" is not altogether figurative. To begin with, sleep depends upon certain structural arrangements in the central nervous system. Sleep is not merely a cessation of activity, a turning off of a switch. It is a positive method of inhibitory control, which must be adaptively related to other concurrent functions of the organism, especially those of nutrition, of movement and of mentation (mental activity). And the structure of the sleep mechanisms inevitably changes as all these related functions change. Sleep is not an isolated function which grows by itself.

The newborn baby is sometimes characterized as being an expert sleeper. In a restricted sense this is true. He surely shows marked ability to stay asleep; but should he be considered less competent because as he grows older he becomes more wakeful? Sleep is an intricate behavior complex, which comprises four distinguishable phases: (a) going to sleep (b) staying asleep (c) waking (d) staying awake.

All skills are relative. The newborn infant is most skillful in phase *b*. He shows a simple kind of ability in phase *a*, but often falls asleep in the very midst of nursing, after an intermittent onset. He is likely to cry as he wakens and may continue crying until the next feeding. He has not made a clearcut differentiation between feeding and sleeping.

By the age of 16 weeks the pattern of his sleeping behavior undergoes remarkable changes. He displays increased competence in all four phases of the sleep cycle. He is likely to finish his meal before he sleeps (phase *a*); he stays asleep for a long but not overlong stretch (phase *b*). He may awake without crying from hunger; and he stays awake talking to himself and playing with his hands until the next feeding. He has two or three naps during the day, and a corresponding number of periods of awakeness. This remarkable gain in phases *c* and *d* is based upon structural changes in his nervous system. The brain cells in his "waking center" have reached a new stage of maturity. Consequently he can be more easily awakened; and he also wakes himself up more often and more easily. He is really a much more highly talented sleeper than he was as a newborn.

If sleep were an independent faculty this would be the end of our story. But as the child's action-system changes his sleep problems change. Awakeness becomes more and more demanding, and it is more difficult to operate those brain cell controls which govern release into sleep. Nature's problem and the culture's problem is to keep phases a and b in equilibrium with phases c and d. Now one, now another phase is apparently over accentuated. For example, at 15 and at 21 months the child often wakes up spontaneously during the night, and in an apparently capricious manner remains awake for an hour or two.

During the second and third years release into sleep proves to be a complex process, because it entails a voluntary inhibition of the wakeful cerebral cortex. Going to sleep from choice is a release act comparable to prehensory release. The child first learns to seize an object and then he learns to let it go. At the age of two-and-a-half years he is in a peculiarly unsettled developmental stage. He not only shows difficulty in going into sleep, but he may have difficulty in getting out of sleep! He temporarily loses some of his knack in waking up.

This brief analysis is made to suggest that we need to make a similar analysis when confronted with the sleeping problems between the years from five to ten. It is the whole child who sleeps; but it does not follow that his entire organism slumbers homogeneously with simultaneous equality of depth. He stirs, he dreams, he smiles, laughs, frowns, grimaces, talks in his sleep. He is rarely completely quiescent. Fears disturb his sleep, taking the form of nightmares and night terrors. Whether pleasant and wishful dreams should be considered guardians of sleep must be left in doubt. It is true that at about the age of eight or nine a child may protest on being awakened in the midst of an enjoyable dream; but whether he wishes to go back to sleep to finish the dream or his sleep is not altogether clear.

Many of the management problems of the middle years (from 5 to

10) have to do with bedtime preliminaries. Here, as elsewhere, there are great individual differences, but also there are developmental trends in the demands made by the child upon the parent. The demands are variable from age to age; but they are definite and they usually denote a real need at the time. The nature of the need is not always apparent. One child makes a quick jump into bed so that the man under the bed won't get him. Another child shakes his head to shake out the bad thoughts before going to sleep!

The fall of night, the impending separation from the parent and the prospect of the blackout of sleep itself all combine to soften the texture of daytime morale, and open the way to apprehensions, imaginings and clinging behavior. The 5½-year-old likes to be read to or talked to prior to going to sleep. He seeks reassurance. He even finds comfort in the companionship of a toy animal as bedfellow.

Such props and preliminaries do not necessarily become habitual because with the expansion of personality the pre-sleep demands take on a more constructive character. The bedtime hour may transform into a kind of social hour during which the household is, however, in danger of over stimulating the child. But it may also become a more quiet witching hour, when the rapport between parent and child is sensitized by a heightened feeling of interdependency. The competitive strivings of the day abate. The child becomes more receptive, and emotionally more aware. It is a favorable time for confidences and for organizing mental processes by questions, answers, discussions and hints. Routine prayers have a function; but the more mundane inter-communication also serves a spiritual purpose.

No set rule can be offered. All depends on good timing, which means finding the psychological moment, which in turn depends on recognizing a developmental stage.

Although the 7-year-old may show a certain fondness for his bed, he is quite likely, in another year, to exhibit increased ingenuity and energy in an effort to stave off bedtime. Often this is legitimate because the quantitative need for sleep is decreasing. Given some leeway the

8-year-old helps to settle this problem satisfactorily. He tends to adjust if granted the privilege of some pleasant self-regulated pre-bed occupation. This is a fair tribute to his self-dependence.

But as his self-dependence grows, his self-assertiveness may increase. Unless carefully managed this may precipitate a sharp resistance to going to bed at the expected time. The problems of sleep and personality again reveal their close union. The rebellion is not so much against sleep as against the domination of a parent-imposed task. If the parent meets the challenge wisely he will widen the area of his strategy.

And this principle holds for the management of sleep throughout the whole period of childhood. Sleep difficulties cannot be handled by direct assault. The whole child sleeps,—and wakes. Sleep is a complex of four phases: release into sleep—staying asleep—waking—staying awake! It took ages of evolution to produce these phases. The child needs a befitting allotment of time to organize these phases into his own developing personality.

ELIMINATION

A physiologist would include under the heading of elimination the excretory functions of perspiration, respiration, micturition and evacuation. These functions are seemingly so automatic that one might wonder whether they need to be included in a volume on child behavior. The first two mentioned do indeed take care of themselves to a marked degree; although they always retain a significant relationship with the psychological states of the individual.

The functions of bladder and bowel, however, are not allowed to take care of themselves. They are so heavily complicated by superimposed cultural controls that they undergo a tortuous course of organization and of reorganization throughout the periods of infancy and childhood. The controls are not fully established even during the first five years of life.

These excretory functions are governed by a combination of voluntary and involuntary mechanisms. When bladder and bowel are empty or partially filled, the urethral and anal sphincters (ring-like muscles) are kept in tonic contraction by the sympathetic nervous system. This mechanism takes care of itself; it is involuntary. When the contents of bowel and bladder reach a certain level (which varies greatly with conditions and individuals), the sphincters relax; the smooth muscles of the containing walls contract; the contents are expelled. Here again the basic mechanism is involuntary. It is essentially the only mechanism which operates in the early months of infancy.

As the child grows older, a higher mechanism is gradually superimposed upon the lower. Increasingly complex connections are made with nerve fibers which go to and from the brain. Voluntary control becomes possible only as these nerve connections take shape. Sphincter control, as we sometimes call it, therefore depends not upon "will power" but upon nerve cell structures which have to grow. All toilet training must defer to the maturity of the child's central nervous system.

This principle holds even during the middle years. The lapses which come at the age of six, for example, are readily explained in terms of current developmental changes which affect the entire organism and therefore involve the sphincters.

Parents do not have to be neurologists in order to appreciate the difficulties which confront the child in the acquisition of sphincter control; but a brief tabulation of the progressive steps toward mature control will throw light on problems of guidance and prevention:

a) In the newborn infant the excretory acts are numerous and apparently irregular.

b) They decrease in number and tend to occur during periods when the child is awake.

c) Being awake he attends to the accompanying internal sensations.

d) He associates the act with a particular place and with customary events in his daily routines.

e) He "learns" to delay, as inhibitory neural mechanisms mature. He delays by inhibiting the otherwise spontaneous relaxation of the sphincters.

f) Lengthens the period of his delay.

g) Learns to terminate the inhibition at will. This is true voluntary release; but the occasions when he can exert that will are few and limited in scope.

h) Uses gestures, vocal signs, general names, and later distinguishing names for the products of bladder and bowel, *after* excretion.

i) Uses such words *during* excretion.

j) Uses the words *prior to* excretion, "tells," at first not soon enough; but eventually he tells in good time.

k) Dry all night.

l) Wakes by himself and asks to be taken to the toilet.

m) Develops a curiosity about the excretory functions of others. He takes a special interest in strange bathrooms. He experiences a sense of privacy and of modesty.

n) Lengthens the span of retention and facilitates voluntary release.

o) Foresees urgencies long in advance and plans accordingly.

p) Adjusts and controls despite changes of scene and the hurly burly of school life.

q) "Accidents" decline almost to the vanishing point.

It requires nearly all of the letters of the alphabet to list the progressive stages of organization in bladder and bowel control for the first ten years of life. Even so, our listing greatly oversimplifies the underlying developmental processes. Progress does not proceed in a straight and steady line. There are many fluctuations and apparent lapses, due chiefly to the ever changing accents and patterns of growth. Sphincter control does not develop independently, but must always be incorporated into the total action-system. For example, the infant often "forgets" his toilet training when he learns to walk. The drive to walk is so strong that it temporarily interferes with apparently established skills. The excretory act must be re-adapted to postural and other changes.

Moreover, reciprocal interweaving of opposite skills (e.g. inhibition versus release) is going on all the time. At times inhibition takes the upper hand: the child withholds valiantly for a long period but is unable to release at will. Later the release mechanism dominates: inhibition is overpowered and release becomes expulsive. These are normal growth fluctuations. They are not due to perversities. They are expressions of physiological awkwardness.

Similar awkwardnesses beset the child even after he is old enough to go to school. In spite of a sharp strengthening of cultural inhibitions the organism seems to lose some of its previous inhibitory capacity. Accidents of bowel as well as bladder increase during the sixth year. They are comparable physiologically to the accidents already mentioned, which occur in the infant with the emergence of the powerful walking drive. Once more, at the age of six, the organism is undergoing profound transformation. Sphincter controls are affected.

Needless to add, individual differences in this field of personal-social behavior should be recognized both at home and at school. The tonus of the sphincters is highly susceptible to reflex stimulations. Psychic activity tends to increase their tone; but in temperamentally susceptible individuals the bowel and bladder organ systems react as tensional outlets. We must, therefore, think in terms of physiological status and maturity, as well as in terms of cultural propriety.

Parents are unduly mortified by lapses in children of school age. The lapses are most likely to occur following an afternoon session at school. It is not so much the child as the adult who fails to foresee these mid-afternoon urgencies. Similar urgencies and instabilities re-appear among 8-year-olds. Many teachers aggravate these difficulties by unnecessarily rigid restrictions. The toilet arrangements, mores and practices which prevail in many elementary schools need liberalizing revision.

BATH AND DRESSING

Birds and four-footed animals frequently exhibit forms of behavior which are ascribed to instincts of cleanliness and adornment. The human species may be credited with comparable instinctive tendencies;

but under the conditions of modern culture these tendencies in the young do not always come to spontaneous and clear cut expression! Sometimes the infant displays a positive aversion to clothes; and although he may enjoy the aquatic aspects of bathing he may soon resist the sanitary. At any rate the tugging, the pulling, the dawdling, the bribing, the exhorting and the scolding which, at varying ages are occasioned by the demands of bath and dressing, are sufficiently impressive to warrant a brief examination of underlying causes.

The causes are primarily developmental, and they are exacerbated whenever parents and caretakers become too exacting. The child's failure to meet expectations must always be considered in relation to his sense of time and timing, and the maturity of his attention patterns. The ultimate goal is self-dependence, but it must be reached by gradual stages.

For a baby the bath has many facets of interest,—social, dermal, athletic and playful. He delights in the water play and in gross motor activity. At the age of one he plays exploitively with washcloth, soap and floating toys. Needless to say he has no appreciation of the more practical purposes of the bath. At 18 months he may show resistance to the bath for brief periods, because of the strength of new gross motor drives. At two years he takes a positive interest in helping to wash himself; he especially likes to wash his hands at a bowl,—but not from motives of cleanliness. At two-and-a-half years he is likely to be in a ritualistic phase of development. He does not entertain an image of the objective of the bath. He imposes more or less elaborate and irrelevant rituals upon the whole situation. If his caretaker thinks solely of the relevant objectives and not of the ritualisms, child troubles ensue. By three the rituals abate. By four and five the bath is an easy routine; and often so pleasant that it is difficult to terminate. By eight years some children can take over completely.

The 5-year-old washes his hands before meals, if reminded. Reminders are necessary for the next two or three years. The 8-year-old, however, prefers a very mild reminder in the form of a faint and tactful hint. Cleanliness is not yet next to godliness; but it is approaching the zone of personal sensitiveness.

Children between the ages of five to nine still need some assistance in the niceties of cleanliness, neatness and manicuring. There are individual differences in the degree of docility shown. Some children react with extreme resistance to help about the ears, and even to combing and brushing of hair. In some instances this extraordinary resistance is based, not on personality negativism, but on a temporary hyperesthesia, which probably has a developmental basis, and is exacerbated in certain individuals.

The development of self-dependence in dressing is roughly parallel to that of self-dependence in cleanliness. It depends first of all on motor abilities, and secondly, on consciousness of social approval. Interest in adornment and display serve to motivate the child at certain ages, even though earlier he may have shown a predilection for no clothes at all. Individual and sex differences become apparent in the pre-school period, and pronounced during the elementary school period. Adolescence brings a host of elaborating manifestations.

The 5-year-old usually can dress himself almost completely; but he is somewhat careless or indifferent about attire. His mother daily selects the clothes to be worn and lays them out in advance. The 6- and 7-year-olds need similar assistance. The 6-year-old, characteristically enough, presents special problems, due to the transitional phases of his current development. He is more clothes conscious than at five, but he does not readily accept the help he needs. By nature he dawdles. He is very easily distracted from the task of dressing. He needs management (and forbearance) more than direct pressure. Time brings changes. SEVEN likewise dawdles; but is more likely to end with an effective spurt. EIGHT is more efficient in dressing,—even though boys may affect disdain of neat and tidy clothes once they have them on. From eight to ten there is a marked increase of responsibility in selection of clothes, disposal of soiled clothes and adaptation of garments to weather and occasion.

Although culture plays a powerful role in the shaping of customs and costumes, the spontaneous child is likely to disclose certain trends of natural man. Even in the removal of clothes we glimpse, at least darkly, a developmental gradient! FIVE-AND-ONE-HALF casts his garments all over the room. SIX drops them on the spot or flings them aside. SEVEN drops them more decorously. EIGHT puts them on a chair (where they may accumulate from day to day in some households. NINE may even hang them up neatly.

And for the record it should be added that the boy who *never* would comb his hair is reputed to give it altogether too much attention, now that he is in his teens.

SOMATIC CONDITIONS

Under this heading we shall sketchily consider some of the somatic, that is, bodily conditions, which are intimately related to the development of the child's behavior characteristics. The subject is much too vast and complicated for summary treatment. We simply wish to suggest, somewhat concretely, how the maturity of the child reacts upon his physical and mental well being.

From an anatomical and physiological standpoint the child's organism consists of a collection of organ systems—skeletal, muscular, gastro-intestinal, urogenital, pulmonary, circulatory, etc. The various organs are, of course, closely interrelated; indeed they are knit into a single living unit through the nervous system and the humoral system,—that is, by the blood and body fluids. When all these organ systems function in ideal harmony, the child is ideally healthy. When the harmony is disturbed by disease, injury or excessive strain the child reacts with illness, with somatic "complaints," with tensional symptoms of varying severity. Sometimes the symptoms are signals of danger; very often they are methods by which Nature attempts to compensate or to restore an optimal working balance. Sometimes also the symptoms are passing, normal indicators of growth changes. These latter symptoms are very interesting. We wish that we knew more about them.

It is certain that the child's body chemistry undergoes alterations with age. This is demonstrated by shifting allergies, by fluctuating appetites and food preferences, by changing susceptibilities and immunities to disease. There are certain diseases seen in infancy and childhood which are seldom or never seen after adolescence. The severity of a given disease also varies with age. Contagious diseases are, in general, more dangerous before rather than after five years of age. This is partly due to differences in the "immunologic maturity" of the tissues. Fatigue, psychologic stress and shock, malnutrition and other factors may precipitate illness, but the primary susceptibilities of the organism are determined by bio-chemical defenses, which are closely correlated with age and constitutional type.

With modern medical techniques the incidence of infectious diseases is reduced by protective inoculations. Nevertheless, conservative opinion holds "that hereditary factors, influenced by the age of the host, may be of importance in determining whether an individual is capable of forming antibodies when stimulated by infectious agents." The marked individual and age differences in allergy reactions lend support to this point of view. Some writers use the term "serological maturation" in much the same way that we speak of behavior maturation.

Although the organism may be described as an interdependent collection of organ-systems, this does not mean that the several systems mature at a uniform rate. On the contrary each system has a more or less unique and independent curve of growth. Now one system or function is in the ascendancy, and now another. It is these very deviations from lockstep which produce both commonly observed, and also commonly unrecognized irregularities of child development.

Four-year-old children often prove to be peculiarly susceptible to colds. A child may have one cold after another throughout the winter. At five he may show excellent health, escaping, perhaps, with one cold. In the period approximately from five-and-a-half to six-and-a-half years there is marked increase of susceptibility to infectious diseases, and the child is sicker with illness when it strikes. The mucous membranes of throat, bronchi and ears appear to be peculiarly vulnerable at this age.

This is not surprising, because much other evidence corroborates that the 6-year-old is in an active stage of developmental transition. At seven and eight years illnesses are fewer. The total death rate is lower in the age period from five to ten years than in the years under five, and it is lowest of all in the half decade from ten through fifteen years.

The statistics for injuries and fatalities from *accidents* also show significant age trends. These trends again are based on maturity factors. Parents and educators should realize that the incidence of accidents is determined by three sets of interacting factors: 1. the child's physique 2. his behavior traits 3. exposure to risk. Even the preferred site of injury may be affected by the child's body build and motor characteristics (factors 1 and 2). For example, the 2-year-old still leans forward when he runs. Should he fall he is likely to bruise his forehead. As he grows older his running stance becomes more erect; at two-and-a-half years he is more likely to hit his nose; at three or four years his teeth; at four-and-a-half years his collar bone. A 6-year-old may break his fall with his arm (and his arm with his fall); the 8-year-old is more likely to jeopardize his legs.

A recent government report of the Children's Bureau has shown that accidents represent the leading cause of death among school children, and therefore constitute a public health problem of the first rank. The second leading cause of death (pneumonia and influenza) for children from five up to ten years of age shows a rate of 10.2 (boys) and 9.0 (girls), as compared with accident rates of 39.3 (boys) and 20.0 (girls). This sex difference is even more marked for the two principal accidents, namely, motor-vehicle fatalities and drowning. Boys are more daring and reckless. Girls are more cautious, and age for age, are physically and psychologically more mature. Girls, accordingly, incur fewer risks, with one outstanding exception: the rate of fatalities for accidental burns is more than twice that of boys for the five to ten years age group.

These trends must not be taken too literally because many accidents unfortunately contain unpredictable elements of physical place and circumstance. The most predictable areas lie in the field of behavior. Among pre-school children the amount of exposure to risk (factor 3) is largely determined by their immature behavior traits and lack of parental foresight. It is not surprising that fatalities and injuries from burns, scalding, poisons, knives etc. are excessive for the household age from infancy to five years. Automobile, bicycle and street accidents, on the other hand, play a leading role in the period from five to ten years. Six and Eight are notoriously "careless" ages, not because the children are willfully heedless, but because they lack the capacity to take adaptive heed. In fact a 6-year-old may take very conscious heed before he runs across the street to meet his mother who is waiting for him. He may close his eyes, clench his fists and dash; but he may fail to make adequate allowance for an oncoming car. Perhaps the parent did not make adequate allowance for the limitations of the child's psychology. Here are two sets of behavior factors which can be recognized and brought under preventive control. A similar control should be extended to the 8-year-old. He is in an expansive hurry-up, dash-away age. He does not look far enough ahead. Frequently he is given altogether too much freedom in the use of his bicycle. He needs more delimitations and supervision to reduce exposure to risk.

This entails planning and management. Parents and teachers are inclined to place too much reliance on admonition and explanation. Children need help in acquiring attitudes of caution; but mere words, even emphatic words, do not suffice. Sometimes the repetitive, worrisome, scolding insistence on caution is only a form of relief for the mother, expressing her subchronic state of anxiety. Often there is excessive appeal to fear. Caution has elements of fortitude as well as fear. If the child is unduly afraid he cannot be duly cautious, that is, duly prudent and wary. The parent-child relation should not be fearsome in either direction; there should be mutual confidence, so that children will freely and promptly report home even apparently minor accidents or injuries regardless of the "guilty" circumstances under which they may have occurred.

The organism of the child rarely remains for a prolonged period in smooth equilibrium. Even in the absence of accidents and frank disease the child is subject to tensions which express themselves outwardly in different forms of *tensional activity*. These tensional manifestations are varied in kind and degree. Some are transient and benign; they may even be part of the mechanisms of adjustment. They take on an abnormal character when they become stereotyped and over compulsive. It is difficult in many instances to determine the origin and basis of any given tensional activity. There are enormous individual differences based on temperamental characteristics, as already suggested by the so-called qualities of viscerotonia, somatotonia and cerebrotonia. Well organized children who show a favorable balance of these qualities show the least pronounced tensional symptoms. Conversely, poorly organized children show marked, frequent and even multiple symptoms. On the other hand an over rigid and generally tense child may enjoy very few specific tensional outlets. He may show a more general collapse under stress. All of which suggests that such outlets may serve a function in normal as well as abnormal behavior.

The classic tensional activity of the pre-school period is thumb-sucking. In so far as it is definitely related to the functions of eating and sleep, it may be attributed to somatic conditions. But this easy generalization does not do justice to the changes and elaborations which occur in connection with teething, excitement, ennui, fatigue, variations of appetite, association with rituals and accessory objects and with other modes of tensional release. We have shown that this behavior, in ordinary instances, follows a developmental sequence toward resolution. This lawful sequence has an encouraging import, although it does not preclude that other forms of tensional behavior will not assume a similar role in the school years.

Temper tantrums which might also be listed among pre-school tensional outlets show a comparable developmental course. They vary in nature and severity with age and temperamental type. They are extremely prevalent up to the age of two-and-a-half years. Their later manifestations may be considered in the following chapter, which deals with the expressional aspects of emotional behavior, including crying, anger and aggression.

Rocking, head banging, head rolling, various forms of rhythmic and pre-masturbatory movements, stuttering, finger nail biting and psychic tics like repetitive eye blinking may occur before the age of five, with resolution during the middle years after five.

Tensional behavior is at a relatively low ebb at five years, and is ordinarily limited in scope; but it shows a marked increase in the period from five-and-a-half to seven years. School entrance is frequently accompanied by temporary speech tensions, nail biting, an exacerbation of thumb-sucking, hand to mouth gestures, chewing of pencil, chewing of hair, tongue protrusion, pulling of mouth corner, pursing of both lips and biting the lower one! This cataloguing of the various patterns exaggerates the gravity of the reactions, and yet conveys a healthy reminder of the tensions under which the school-beginner is laboring. Many of these tensions escape by the mouth outlet in the form of clicking, blowing through the lips, heavy breathing, gasping with excitement, and throat clearing and insufflations. But the tensions also involve the eyes which dart with horizontal thrusts, and the legs which shift and jiggle, the knees which knock, and the feet which tap restlessly. For no apparent reason a child may make somewhat peculiar throat noises and may even repeat them so often as to suggest a convulsive tic. But usually such a "nervous habit" proves to be a temporary manifestation, on a par with his general restlessness and the clumsiness which, so it is said, causes him to trip over a piece of string.

The tensional behavior of the 7-year-old is less pronounced throughout. If thumb-sucking, nail biting or stuttering persist from earlier years, he now makes a voluntary effort to bring them under control. The outlet activities of hand to mouth are less emphatic, but lip pursing, whistling and throat noises may become very persistent. Fingers and hands are perhaps more restlessly active than feet. Some SEVENS show a marked sensitivity and tensional overflow into the hand. They may not like to be touched, but they themselves like to touch objects in an exploratory manner. A characteristic tensional expression of the 7-year-old at school is a mildly pensive sigh, head resting in hand, elbow propped on desk, eyes averted obliquely.

The 8-year-old, true to his expansive, highly-geared nature, displays a larger variety of tensional outlets. Many earlier patterns reappear, but with a fluidity of shift which makes them less noticeable. His tensional behavior is more diffuse, and much of it is channelized in chatter, gestures and mimetic expressions. There is grimacing, scowling, raising of eyebrows, humming and smacking of lips. The eyes not only dart, but also roll. No somatic member seems to be free from tensions. He plays with a gadget, he jiggles his legs, he shoves his body; he may feel an urgency to urinate when confronted with an unpleasant task. It is as though every one of his organ systems were permeable to the inner tensions which ordinarily are a relatively normal feature of his behavior day. The diffuseness and diversity of his reactions are in character with his somatic make-up, his physiologic maturity.

At nine and ten there is a quieting down of tensional manifestations. They are less diffuse and ubiquitous; they are more closely associated with specific situations, and they tend to reflect the idiosyncracies of the individual. Several reactions are rather characteristic of this age period: pianoing of the fingers, fiddling at a button, blowing of lips and cheeks, picking at fingernails and cuticles, tiny gestures of plucking at eyelid, and a sweeping gesture of clapping the hand on the head in pseudo-dismay. Equally characteristic are the emotional refinements of worry and anxiety; for the fields of tensional behavior and of expressional behavior inevitably overlap. The 9- or 10-year-old can grimace with mock deprecation of his failures; he can smile and laugh at situations and at himself.

Thereby he registers his increased maturity. This type of smiling and laughing is an excellent form of somatic tensional outlet! It denotes a more cultivated mind; it is also reminder that some of the cruder physiological tensions of earlier ages, if not excessive, have a certain sanction in the economy of child development.

GROWTH GRADIENTS

§1. EATING

1 YEAR*—*Appetite* Usually good for all meals though may be less for breakfast.
Refusals and Preferences May refuse milk from a bottle, especially if some change as a shift in style of nipple has been made. May also refuse milk from a cup. Preferred bottle is the 6 P.M. bottle. Preferences for certain foods are becoming well defined: certain kinds of cereal, certain vegetables.
Self-Help May finger feed for part of one meal. A few boys refuse any help. Many insist on standing while eating. May need a toy—or preferably two toys—to occupy his hands while he is fed.

18 MONTHS—*Appetite* May be decreasing and is usually less than the robust infant appetite. Appetite for milk from the bottle may be better than for milk from the cup. Noon meal usually the best.
Refusals and Preferences Fluctuating and not clearly defined.
Self-Help Most children enjoy feeding themselves and may do so for all three meals, though mother may need to fill the spoon. Child hands empty dishes to mother as he finishes with them.

2 YEARS—*Appetite* Fair to moderately good. Noon meal usually the best.
Refusals and Preferences At this age many children are "finicky" or "fussy." Child can name foods and can verbally express likes and dislikes. He prefers whole separate foods; does not like puréed foods, or several foods mixed together. Preferences may be related to taste, form, consistency or color. Goes on food jags. May prefer red or yellow foods.
Self-Help Some can feed themselves and will accept no help. May not even want mother nearby as they eat. Others need help. Two extreme groups now discernible: the "messy" and the "spotless" eaters.

2½ YEARS—*Appetite* Often fluctuates between very good and very poor. Usually one good meal, noon or evening. May eat better in-between meals than at meals.
Refusals and Preferences Even more definite than at two. Meat, fruit and butter are usually favored; green vegetables refused. Preferred foods, child will feed himself; other foods, he will eat if fed; some he absolutely refuses. Food jags continue, first one food, then another being favored.
Self-Help May feed self entire meal, or may want to eat part and then call parent for help with the remainder. Marked ritualism: child demands the repetition of foods, of dishes and of arrangement of dishes.

* For further details on all gradients—ages one to four years—see *Infant and Child in The Culture of Today.*

3 YEARS—*Appetite* Fairly good—less variable than formerly. Breakfast and supper may be the best meals. Milk intake increasing.

Refusals and Preferences Less marked than earlier. Meat, fruit, milk, desserts and sweets are favored. Vegetables are now accepted. Child likes foods which require chewing. May ask for special foods he likes as meal is being prepared.

Self-Help Can feed himself and can eat well by himself. May be too demanding, both of food and of attention, if allowed at the family table, or may dawdle.

4 YEARS—*Appetite* Appetite is fair. Child drinks his milk rapidly and well.

Refusals and Preferences Food jags or food strikes indicate marked and definite preferences for certain foods and dislike of others.

Self-Help Child is beginning to help plan his meals. Helps set the table. May dawdle if eats alone though does not need to be fed.

Table Manners May be able to eat several meals a week with family—often breakfast, or Sunday dinner. However, talking usually interferes with eating and child usually has to interrupt his meal to go to the bathroom. Much leaving table.

5 YEARS—*Appetite* Usually good though varies markedly from meal to meal with breakfast often the poorest. Child cleans his plate.

Refusals and Preferences Refusals definite: cooked root vegetables, gravies, casseroles and puddings.

Prefers meat, potatoes, raw vegetables, milk and fruit.

Self-Help Feeds himself slowly but persistently and with a fair amount of ability. May need help toward end of meal or with certain foods. Beginning to use a knife for spreading.

Table Manners May eat most meals with family, but may have supper early in the kitchen. Talking interferes with eating. Napkin tucked in at neck.

6 YEARS—*Appetite* Usually large (child said to be a "wonderful" eater); but may eat more between meals than at meals. Likes a snack before bed. Takes more than he can handle. Wants the biggest piece. Breakfast often continues to be the poorest meal.

Refusals and Preferences Refuses foods by spells; dislikes certain foods because of texture. Likes and is willing to try new foods. Dislikes cooked desserts and cooked vegetables. Prefers meat, potatoes, milk, raw vegetables, peanut butter, ice cream and candy.

Self-Help Many prefer to finger feed, though some will not touch food with their fingers. May prefer a fork to a spoon. May be awkward in spreading.

Table Manners Manners are poor. Child talks too much, spills, stuffs mouth, chews with mouth open. He grabs for food, knocks things over, wriggles in chair, or teeters back in chair. Kicks table legs. Criticizes behavior of siblings and adults. Dawdles. May refuse napkin or bib, or may have it tucked in at neck.

7 YEARS—*Appetite* Moderate. Extremes of poor and excessive appetite in different children.

Refusals and Preferences Beginning to accept disliked foods, though dislikes strongly flavored cooked vegetables or cheeses. Likes milk, meat, ice cream and sandwiches, especially peanut butter.

Self-Help Very little difficulty with implements. Pushes food onto fork or spoon with free fingers.

Table Manners Improving, though may spill, bolt food, stuff mouth, talk with mouth full. May want to bring his last activity to the table with him. Leaves the table with any distraction. At times he may be interested in the table conversation. May quarrel or fool with siblings. Sometimes prefers to eat by himself so he can continue listening to radio or reading. Prefers napkin beside the plate and uses when needed.

8 YEARS—*Appetite* Excellent. Poor eaters for the first time have a good appetite. Increase in intake as well as increase in weight. Some may need to have intake restricted.

Refusals and Preferences Fewer refusals. Preferences about as at seven years. Will attack new foods. Judges food by the odor. Expresses "love" for certain foods.

Self-Help Less frequently needs to use fingers. Beginning to cut meat with a knife, but is not skillful. Can "fix" own baked potato.

Table Manners Variable. Definite contrast between poor table manners at home and good table manners abroad. At home he bolts his food, spills food, pushes it around on his plate, takes large mouthfuls and talks with his mouth full. Plays with silver. Aware of good table manners but unable to put them into practice. Wants to have his turn to talk and tends to interrupt adult conversation. May anchor napkin by sitting on it.

9 YEARS—*Appetite* Under better control. Now eats approximately an adult meal and even poorer eaters settle into more balanced intake according to their needs.

Refusals and Preferences Frankly refuses certain foods. May refuse a food cooked in a different way from what he is used to. Usually prefers and looks forward to a sweet dessert.

Self-Help Good control of implements. Tends to saw meat with a knife and cut too large pieces, therefore may need help.

Table Manners Generally improved but may still be better away from home than at home. May become too absorbed in listening or in talking.

§2. SLEEPING

1 YEAR—*Nap* Usually one a day, from 11 or 11:30 to 12:30 or 2:00.

Night Baby falls asleep between 6 and 8 P.M. Sleeps well through the night, till 6 to 8 A.M. Then cries or vocalizes for mother. After toileting may remain happily in bed for another hour before breakfast.

18 MONTHS—*Nap* Follows the noon meal. Child may take toys to bed with him, but usually goes right to sleep. Nap lasts 1½ to 2 hours, child waking happy and wanting to get right up.

Night Bedtime comes between 6 and 8 P.M. Child may play with teddy bear or other toy briefly before dropping off to sleep. Frequent night waking, especially after an exciting day. Child is easily quieted. Wakes in morning between 6 and 8 A.M., lies quietly till he feels that it is time to get up, then calls parent.

2 YEARS—*Nap* In afternoon. Child may sleep for two or three hours. Some may not sleep for periods of several weeks, or for several days a week, but at these times will usually play in their room for an hour or so. A long nap tends to displace night sleep.

Night Does not fall asleep till late, often 8 or 9 P.M. Many bedtime demands. May want to take several toys and books to bed with him, and may call parent back several times to ask for toileting or for a drink. May cling to mother at bedtime. Difficult for him to get to sleep. Long play period may precede sleep. May wake several times during the night and demand toileting. Usually wakes at the slightest sound.

Wakes between 6:30 and 7:30 A.M.; plays happily alone. If he calls, is easily satisfied till breakfast time with being changed and given a cracker and a few toys.

2½ YEARS—*Nap* Child willing to go to bed for nap but may not stay in bed long. After a short play period may be ready for sleep, especially if some novelty, as a blanket-bed on the floor is introduced. Once asleep may sleep too long and may need to be awakened lest nap interfere with night sleep. Slow to wake up, feels miserable and often cries.

Night Bedtime should not be delayed past 8 P.M., although hour of going to sleep may vary from 6 to 10 P.M. depending some on length of nap. Bedtime is complicated by elaborate rituals. Some call mother back after she has left. Child sings and talks to himself before falling asleep. Takes toys to bed. Considerable night waking with crying or demand for toilet or drink.

Most sleep the clock around and may not awaken till 8:30 or 9 A.M. If awake earlier, may play till time to get up.

3 YEARS—*Nap* The beginning of "play naps," though some may actually sleep for one or two hours.

Night Fewer bedtime rituals than at two-and-a-half. Doll or teddy to bed. Much waking during the night. Child may lie and talk to himself; may get into mother's bed; may wander about the house.

Morning waking, between 6 and 7 A.M. Child may be whining and fretful. He may call to be picked up.

4 YEARS—*Nap* Usually enjoys a "play nap" alone in his room, with books or toys, from 1 to 3 P.M.

Night May go to bed willingly at 7 P.M.; enjoys hearing a bedtime story. May then enjoy half an hour alone in bed with books or crayoning. Takes dolls or teddy to bed.

Wakens in night only for toileting; usually needs only a little help from adult.

Morning waking between 7 and 7:30 A.M. Gets up and plays in own room till time to go to parents' room.

5 YEARS—*Nap* Many nap once or twice a week for an hour or more. A few, especially boys, may nap several days a week.

Bedtime Variable from 7 to 8 P.M. dependent on nap and activity of the day. Now may go to bed without pre-sleep activity though some "read" or crayon for a while. Less taking of toys to bed.

Night Some sleep through but many waken for toileting usually after midnight and may have difficulty returning to sleep. May have frightening dreams and wake screaming.

Morning Most waken at 7-8 A.M. and can busy themselves with play materials until time to get up.

6 YEARS—*Nap* A few have half hour nap on occasion at five-and-a-half years. At six years an hour's "play nap" may be desirable.

Bedtime At five-and-a-half rarely resists bedtime hour which is usually between 7 and 8 P.M. May prefer supper in bed followed by play. May want mother to talk or read to him.

Return to taking toy to bed. May enjoy prayers.

At six years most usual bedtime is at 7, though some wait till 7:30 or 8:00. Enjoys some activity with adult. May tell day's experiences.

Night More can sleep through night. Child disturbed by bad dreams and gets into mother's bed, or mother goes to him. Several still waken for toileting and usually manage by themselves.

Morning At five-and-a-half, two extreme groups: one wakens very early (5-6 A.M.), the other has to be awakened (8 A.M.). By 6 years, usual time is 7 to 7:30 A.M. Gets right up and can then dress self if clothes are laid out, but apt to dawdle.

7 YEARS—*Bedtime* From 7-8 P.M. Gets ready for bed by himself with little adult help. May like to be read to. Two extreme groups: one group falls asleep rapidly; the other sings, listens to noises in house or sees shadow objects in room prior to sleep. A few take toys to bed.

Night Usually sleeps soundly with less waking with nightmares or for toileting.

Morning Wakens by himself at 7 A.M. as a rule, but may sleep later on Sunday mornings. Some like to waken early on occasion to read or do some special thing. Needs some reminding to get dressed.

8 YEARS—*Bedtime* Later, usually 8-8:30, occasionally 9 P.M. Getting to bed now more difficult. Wants to put off, stay up later, read one more chapter, etc. Can get ready unaided but needs motivation. Mother tucks him in. May need quieting down time of reading or music before ready to fall asleep.

Night Usually undisturbed.

Morning Awakens 7-7:30 A.M. and dresses self.

9 YEARS—*Bedtime* Knows bed hour which is usually 8 P.M. or later; but may need to be reminded. Gets ready by himself. Reads or listens to radio until 9 P.M. May continue this too long and need reminding. A few need to be asleep by 7:30 P.M.
Night Usually quiet, though some waken screaming from nightmares.

§3. ELIMINATION

4 WEEKS—*Bowel* Earlier, bowel movements were numerous, occurring somewhat sporadically.
Now more closely associated with act of waking. Occur in daytime, three to four a day.
Bladder Infant may cry during sleep on occurrence of micturition. There may be a glimmer of wakefulness.

8 WEEKS—*Bowel* Two movements a day, at waking or in close association with a feeding.

16 WEEKS—*Bowel* Delay between feeding and evacuation. This may allow temporary "success" if mother places child on a receptacle at this time.
Bladder Number of daily micturitions has decreased and volume of any one has increased.

28 WEEKS—*Bowel* Temporary irregularity. No longer closely associated with waking or eating. One may occur early in morning in play period; another in afternoon.
Bladder Soaking wet diapers. Intervals of dryness from one to two hours in length.

40 WEEKS—*Bowel* May respond to training for a period of several weeks; may grunt and look at mother's face during the act.
Bladder May be dry for a whole hour after a nap or after a carriage ride. Mother may have temporary "success" placing child on pot.

1 YEAR—*Bowel* Postural developments introduce complications. Functions best standing or lying down. "Successes" less frequent; resistance again appears; relation of looking at mother disappears.
Bladder Dryness after nap. Intolerance of wetness at certain times of day.

15 MONTHS—*Bowel* Resistances and irregularities lessen. But infant may show sphincter contraction when on toilet, releasing only after diaper is put on.
Bladder Postural difficulties (insistence on standing) have lessened. Likes to sit on toilet, and responds at optimal times. At other times may resist. Retention span has lengthened to two or three hours. Placement on toilet may stimulate child to withhold urine. May release urine as soon as removed from toilet. May be exaggerated release. Points with pride to puddles; may pat puddles.

18 MONTHS—*Bowel* Contraction may be very strong; release explosive. Articulate children may say "Toidy," increasing voluntary control. Such children may have few accidents from this time on.

Bladder Can respond with nod of head or "No" if asked if he wants toilet. May even ask, saying "uh," etc. May feel shame at puddles and may report accidents by pulling at pants.

21 MONTHS—*Bowel* May have temporary diarrhea.

Bladder Child reports accidents by pointing at puddles. Tells after wetting and sometimes before. Pleased with successes. But number of urinations increases and lapses may multiply.

2 YEARS—*Bowel* Trainable. Parent may remove child's pants and leave him to his own devices near the toilet facilities. Some children do best if divested of all clothes.

Bladder Better control. No resistance to routines. Tells in advance. May go into bathroom and pull own pants down. May express verbal pride in achievement: "Good boy." May call puddle, "Bad boy."

2½ YEARS—*Bowel* Extremes and exaggeration. May skip a day between movements.

Bladder Retention span lengthening. May be as much as five hours. Child can stop and then resume in the act of micturition. May have difficulty initiating release.

3 YEARS—*Bowel* Tendency to withhold and postpone. Daily movement may occur in afternoon. Child asks for and accepts help.

Bladder Well routinized. Accepts assistance if needed. Few accidents. May be dry all night; may wake by himself and ask to be taken to toilet.

4 YEARS—*Bowel* This function has become a private affair. But there is curiosity about the functioning of others.

Bladder Still routinized but may insist on taking over routine himself. Curiosity about strange bathrooms.

5 YEARS—*Bowel* One movement a day, usually after a meal, most commonly after lunch but may be after supper. When irregular, may show increased constipation. Many still need help with wiping.

Bladder Takes fair responsibility but may need reminding during day. Few daytime and only occasional nighttime accidents. Less reporting to mother. A few girls have reddened genitals. Many waken for night toileting and report to parent.

6 YEARS—*Bowel* Time of occurrence variable. Many have one movement a day usually after lunch though may be earlier. Some now have in early morning or at night. Some may be unable to complete at one time. Functioning may be rapid. Occasional accidents. Uses words suggestive of function such as "stinker," etc.

Bladder Mostly takes responsibility though may have to dash.

Accidents are rare and if occur child is disturbed by them.

May need reminder before going out to play.

Some giggling at sound of urine stream and may mention this function in a humorous or angry attack.

Some require night toileting, but these can attend to themselves.

7 YEARS—*Bowel* One regular movement a day, consistent with own individual timing, usually after lunch or after dinner. A very few have a movement at school; many wait until they reach home in afternoon.

Bladder Definite increase in span. Accidents rare. May forget to go to bathroom at times such as before school in morning but accepts suggestion. Only a few now need to get up at night and these can care for themselves.

8 YEARS—*Bowel* Two groups: one functions after breakfast, the other after supper.

May now be able to function at school if necessary. On occasion may have a rapid release.

Bladder Manages by himself with occasional reminder before he goes out or on a trip. May have to urinate before or during an unpleasant task.

9 YEARS—Both functions are well under child's own control. One or two movements a day—usually after breakfast or late in day. Rarely needs to be reminded to go to the bathroom.

§4. BATH AND DRESSING

1 YEAR—*Bath* Any time of day; often late afternoon.

No longer interested in water play or gross motor activity. Now plays with washcloth, soap, water toys.

Dressing Interest in taking off hat, shoes, pants.

Cooperates in dressing: puts arm into armhole or extends leg for pants.

18 MONTHS—*Bath* After supper. May be brief periods of resistance to bath.

Dressing Removes mittens, hat, socks; unzips zipper.

Cooperates in dressing: puts on shoes.

2 YEARS—*Bath* Likes to help wash himself. May prefer washcloth to water toys. Likes especially to wash and dry hands.

Dressing Removes shoes, stockings, pants. Likes to undress.

Can put on some clothes though may put both legs in one pant leg and may get hat on backward.

Cooperates in dressing.

2½ YEARS—*Bath* Evening bath. Child enjoys it. Wants to "take over" even though not very capable.

Interest in fixtures and rituals built up around faucet, plug, etc.

Slides back and forth in tub. Less interest in mere washing.

Dressing Better at undressing than at dressing: can take off all clothes.

Can put on socks and perhaps shirt, pants, and coat though not always accurately. Allows mother to lay clothes out, correctly oriented.

May be completely independent or may demand total help. May run away as he is being dressed.

3 YEARS—*Bath* Fewer bath rituals. Child insists on washing self, at least in part. Does not like to get out of the tub.

Dressing Undresses himself rapidly and well.

Can put on pants, socks, shoes, sweater, dress. Can unbutton front and side buttons. Cannot tell front from back or lace shoes, though might try.

4 YEARS—*Bath* Now an easy routine. Child can wash though mother needs to supervise lest he get marooned on one part of body. Can dry self in part.

Dressing Dresses and undresses with little assistance, especially if clothes are laid out.

Can distinguish front from back, lace shoes; may button front buttons.

5 YEARS—*Bath* Can with encouragement and reminder wash face and hands before meals.

Cannot bathe self, though tries to participate. Likes to wash parts of body—hands and knees.

Can scrub fingernails with a brush but cannot cut or file them.

Dressing and Care of Clothes Dresses self completely, lacing shoes, buttoning front buttons. Cannot button back buttons or tie shoe laces.

Motivation may be lacking. "He can but he doesn't." Mother responsible for selecting clothes, laying them out, picking them up after they have been removed.

Careless about clothes.

6 YEARS—*Bath* A few can bathe themselves if mother gets tub ready. Many need to be bathed entirely. Some wash own arms and legs.

Many do not like bath—or other routines.

Dawdling in bath. May refuse to leave till all water has gone down drain.

Most wash faces and hands before meals, if reminded.

Dressing and Care of Clothes Can dress self except for tying shoe laces and buttoning very difficult buttons. If they do tie shoe laces, tie them too loosely.

May need some help and is unwilling to accept this help. Mother needs to be nearby to give some assistance.

Dawdling.

Boys brush hair; girls need to have hair combed.

Careless about clothes even though may be clothes conscious.

Drop clothes off as they remove them, or fling them about.

Not responsible for keeping clothes clean and tidy, except for a few girls.

Mother needs to select clothes, and may need to lay them out.

Accessories are frequently lost.

7 YEARS—*Bath* Washes face and hands before meals *if* he hears mother's reminder, though he may protest.

Some bathe without help and with only a little supervision. Others still need considerable direct help or may prefer to be bathed.

Dawdle in tub.

Girls still like to be clean and neat; some boys prefer not to be.

[267]

Dressing and Care of Clothes Many can dress without any help if clothes are selected for them. Others dawdle, lack interest, and need help. May dawdle till he gets ready to dress, then actually dresses quickly.

Variable in appearance. Some girls like to look neat; children often neater than at eight; some boys like to look sloppy.

Still careless about clothes: drop them as they remove them; do not report tears. A few put away clothes after removing them; hang up pajamas.

Can tie shoe laces but does not like to bother.

Slow and distractible about dressing. May suddenly speed up and finish.

8 YEARS—*Bath* Washes face and hands less thoroughly than when younger, because in a hurry. Does not yet wash spontaneously. Needs to be reminded but insists on mother wording reminder in a certain way, just a hint.

Can keep fingernails clean and may be able to cut nails on one hand.

More than half now bathe themselves. May even draw own tub. Others need help. Dawdle in tub, playing with soapsuds, sliding back and forth in tub. May be slow to get to bath but likes it once in tub. Likes warmer water and feeling of water on skin.

Dressing and Care of Clothes Can dress without assistance. Can choose what dress or suit to wear and may be able to select out-of-door clothing suitable to the weather.

Girls with braids still have hair combed.

Some children (mostly girls) can take good care of clothes, hanging them up, or piling on a chair on removal. Some take full responsibility: select clothes, hang them up, put dirty garments in hamper, report on tears or missing buttons.

Many are completely careless. Clothes may be dirty and torn, and not tucked in.

May hang up clothes at night, but not hang up outdoor clothes in daytime.

No longer allows mother to lay out clothes, and may insist on selecting wearing apparel himself.

Can and do keep shoe laces tied without reminder.

9 YEARS—*Bathing* Is not resistant to a bath. Bathes two or three times a week.

Is fairly independent but likes to have an adult around. He still needs reminding to brush teeth well and wash hands thoroughly.

Dressing and Care of Clothes Does complete job of dressing.

Boys and girls are interested in doing their own hair, but the majority do not do it completely until ten years of age, and then only if it is uncomplicated.

Is careless with clothes, and apt to throw them around. Not concerned about how clean they are. Fairly good at reporting tears and holes.

§5. HEALTH AND SOMATIC COMPLAINTS

18 MONTHS—Convulsions may accompany illnesses, especially those with high temperatures.

21 MONTHS—Elimination difficulties; frequency of both functions; diarrhea common.

2½ YEARS—Elimination difficulties. Long retention span; constipation more common in girls.

Frequent colds with ear complications, especially in slow speech children.

Wants to be carried and treated like a baby (33 months).

3 YEARS—Expresses fatigue by saying, "I'm tired."

4 YEARS—May have one cold right after another, all winter.

Stomach ache in social situations.

Needs to urinate in difficult situations or at mealtimes.

May have "accidents" in emotional situations.

Knocks out front teeth if falls.

Breaks collar bone if falls (4½ years).

5 YEARS—Good, or even excellent health is characteristic.

Many have only one or two colds all winter.

Some increase in whooping cough, measles, chicken pox.

Occasional stomach aches or vomiting in relation to disliked foods, or just prior to elimination.

Constipation—girls.

5½ YEARS—Complains that his feet "hurt" him.

Some have frequent colds.

Headaches or earaches beginning.

Stomach aches with some nausea and vomiting in connection with school.

Somatic symptoms may appear after a week or two of school.

Whooping cough, measles, chicken pox the most common communicable diseases.

Hyper-sensitivity of face, head, neck region to washing, hair combing, etc.

Child may endure large pains yet fuss about a splinter or nose drops.

6 YEARS—More susceptible to diseases and sicker with illness than earlier.

Frequent sore throats, colds, with complications (lung and ears); increase in allergies.

Chicken pox, measles, whooping cough. Diphtheria and scarlet fever; German measles and mumps.

Stomach aches and vomiting in connection with going to school.

Toilet "accidents" with over-excitement.

Breaks arm if falls.

Hyper-sensitivity of face, neck region if washed or touched. (Some become hysterical with laughter if tickled.)

Increased redness of genitals—girls.

7 YEARS—Fewer illnesses than at six, but colds of longer duration.

German measles and mumps frequent. Chicken pox and measles may occur.

Complaint of headache with fatigue or excitement; complaints of muscular pain.

Minor accidents to eyes, but fewer gross accidents; eye rubbing.
Extreme fatigue.

t YEARS—Improving health. Fewer illnesses and of shorter duration. Less absence from school because of illness.

Increase in allergies and otitis media.

Headaches, stomach aches and need to urinate in connection with disagreeable tasks.

Accidents frequent; from falls, drowning, and in relation to automobiles and bicycles.

Breaks leg if falls.

9 YEARS—Improving health and few illnesses, but marked individual differences.

Some have a prolonged illness or show marked fatigue.

Very few general somatic complaints, but innumerable minute ones related to the task at hand (eyes hurt when tested; hands hurt when gripping); often say "It makes me feel dizzy."

§6. TENSIONAL OUTLETS

1 YEAR—Thumb-sucking strong, with or without accessory object. In daytime, just before sleep, and during the night.

Transient and somewhat accidental stool smearing.

Pre-sleep rocking in crib, bed shaking, head banging or head rolling.

Handling genitals and possibly some masturbation, usually very slight.

Crying.*

18 MONTHS—Thumb-sucking reaches a peak. May go on for several hours a day as well as just before sleep, or even all night.

Occasional episodes of stool smearing.

Rocking, bed shaking, head banging or head rolling may occur.

Furniture moving. Takes objects out of bureau drawers. Grabs at objects.

Sit-down temper tantrums.

Tears books or wall paper.

21 MONTHS—Tears bed apart.

Removes clothes and runs around unclothed.

2 YEARS—Thumb-sucking less during the day. Has a positive association with hunger, frustration, fatigue, excitement.

May be some stool smearing.

Rocking, bed shaking, bouncing, head banging, or head rolling. Many pre-sleep demands.

Fewer tensional outlets at this age.

Left alone in a room, removes everything from drawers and cupboards.

* For crying gradient see Expressional Behavior.

2½ YEARS—Thumb-sucking less during day. May be associated with an accessory object. At night strongly associated with accessory object.

Rocking, head banging, in some. Some masturbation.

Stuttering may come in with high language children.

Tears wall paper.

Completely disrupts playroom, both large and small objects.

Sudden aggressive attacks—may "sock" a stranger.

Temper tantrums.

3 YEARS—Thumb-sucking, associated with accessory object, at night or occasionally in daytime. Can tolerate having thumb removed from mouth during sleep.

Fewer tensional outlets.

May wander around house during the night.

3½ YEARS—Thumb-sucking at night with accessory object. Can suck in daytime without object.

Considerable stuttering.

Nose picking, fingernail biting.

4 YEARS—Thumb-sucking only as he goes to sleep.

Out of bounds behavior:

Motor—runs away, kicks, spits, bites fingernails, picks nose, grimaces.

Verbal—calls names, boasts and brags, silly use of language.

Nightmares and fears.

Needs to urinate in moments of emotional excitement.

Pain in stomach and may vomit at times of stress.

5 YEARS—*Home* Not much tensional overflow. Often not more than one type in any one child.

No total facial grimace; more broken up into segments.

Hand to face: nose picking, nail biting.

Thumb-sucking, before sleep or with fatigue, often without accessory object.

Eye blinking, head shaking, throat clearing at meals.

Sniffing and twitching nose.

School or Examination Little tensional overflow: hand goes briefly to various parts of face and body.

Grasps thighs or scratches arm or leg. Pulls at clothes.

General restlessness, lifts buttocks from chair.

Nasal discharge; needs to blow nose.

5½ YEARS—*Home* Number and severity increasing. One child may show several types of overflow.

Hand to mouth, nose picking, nail biting increasing.

Some throat clearing, sometimes tic-like.

Mouthing of tongue and lips, tongue projection.

Less pre-sleep thumb-sucking.

School entrance may cause increase in stuttering, nail biting, and thumb-sucking.
School or Examination Many hand to face gestures, especially hand to mouth.
Some tongue protrusion, pulling mouth at corners, mouth pursing, biting lower lip.
Chews, bites or taps pencil. Chews hair.

6 YEARS—*Home* Numerous and quite constant. (Increase begins at 5½.)
> Total body wriggling with thrusting of legs and kicking at table legs and piano, swinging arms and striking out or pushing.
> Clumsiness, "falls over a piece of string," also falling off chairs.
> Facial grimacing, throaty noises, gasping, sighing and tongue mouthing.
> Hands in almost constant activity, especially about the face: chewing fingers, ties, hair, pencils; picking nose; biting fingernails.
> Also an occasional outburst of screaming and temper tantrums.
> May be an increase in stuttering.
> *School or Examination* Overflow in mouth region: tongue extension and mouthing, clicking, blowing through lips, biting lips. Throat clearing and throaty noises.
> Biting, chewing or tapping pencil.
> Gasps with excitement.
> Hand to mouth lessening.
> Shifts legs: jiggling, knocking knees together, tapping feet.
> Throwing and kicking.
> Eyes shift horizontally.

7 YEARS—*Home* Very few tensional outlets reported. Old ones dropping out.
> With fatigue or absorption may still suck thumb, pick nose, bite nails or stutter, but are attempting to control.
> Touch and manipulate objects: rubbing, tapping, jabbing, raking.
> A few show tensional chorea-like movements.
> Eye rubbing, scowling, some blinking.
> Make throaty noises such as grunting, whistling.
> Gross bodily outlet: hangs from doorway, tilts chair back, athletic stunts.
> *School or Examination* Less hand to mouth, though some fingering of teeth.
> Less tongue protrusion, but mouth movements, lip pursing, whistling.
> Hands finger pencil, roll it over mouth, rub or tap it on table, and usually drop it. Hands rub over desk. Touching anything seen.
> May rest head on hand, elbow propped on desk, or put head down on arm.
> Throaty noises, grunting, whistling.
> Jiggling of legs but less kicking, though may kick people.
> Oblique or horizontal eye thrusts.

8 YEARS—*Home* Very diffuse. Any of the earlier patterns may appear: blinking, nail biting, eye rubbing, but all less persistent.
> A few persistent thumb-suckers still suck during reading or listening or during illness or fatigue.

Crying with fatigue.

Making faces when given unwelcomed command.

Stomach ache and headache. Need to urinate before unpleasant task.

School or Examination   All five to seven year patterns of overflow are seen, and many in one child during some one situation.

Now more expression through verbalization and gesture.

Grimacing, scowling, raising eyebrows, eye rolling, humming, smacking lips.

Leg jiggling prominent, though may be controlled by pressing feet against furniture or crossing knees.

Fiddling with gadgets. Shoving.

9 YEARS—*Home*   Marked individual differences. Some boys "let off steam" by wrestling around. Girls may wander around house, restless and moody. Fiddle around, can't sit still.

Some growl, mutter, sulk, find fault, stamp feet, or may actually destroy things.

Specific personal habits fewer,—cry, pick at self, suck tongue, pick at hangnails.

School or Examination   Pianoing of fingers; fine distal activity.

Draws in breath, blows lips and cheeks; or hums, sings, whistles, whispers.

External rotation of leg and crossing ankle to knee; jiggles and swings legs.

Grimaces with failure; smiles and laughs at material and at self.

Large gesture of clapping hand on head; or tiny gesture of plucking at eyelid.

13

EMOTIONAL EXPRESSION

A CHILD cannot tell us exactly how he feels, even after he has learned to talk. For that matter, the adult has difficulty in describing his own emotions. Emotions are elusive. They are not entities which can be neatly classified and labelled. The dictionary does not have labels enough to do justice to their infinite variety.

Nevertheless, the emotional life of the child is not altogether hidden from view. It comes to expression in numerous tokens of visible behavior. If we read these outward signs aright we gain a glimpse of his inward states of feeling. In this sense his expressional behavior is a form of communication. It constitutes a kind of radar screen which reflects his inner electronic storms and tensions!

If the outward activity consists of a blinking of the eyes, chewing of the lips, or jiggling of the feet, we may think of it as a kind of tensional outlet,—an overflow escape. In the previous chapter we have shown how these simple forms of tensional behavior reflect the "somatic conditions" of the organism. One cannot draw a sharp line between tensional behavior and emotional expression. So-called emotion arises from a complex state of tensions: a) The organism (i.e. the child) assumes an attitude of expectancy or a readiness to act; b) the expected does not happen immediately; the intended action is delayed; c) this suspense combined with readiness produces a peculiar state of tension which is felt as an emotion; d) the tension, whether pleasurable or painful, expresses itself in characteristic ways,—tears, frowns, fists, screams, smiles, shouts, blushes, gasps, etc., etc. The expressional reaction is so closely identified with the felt emotion that the famous psychologist James ingeniously suggested that we do not cry because we are sorry, but that we are sorry because we cry. A recent writer (Nina Bull), however, suggests the thesis that the sorry feeling comes *with* the readiness to cry and not because of the actual crying. This might explain why a "good" cry does indeed relieve the tensions of the sorriness.

Emotion is not an entity; it is a process. From the standpoint of child guidance we must consider the total sequence of the process. The premonitory and preliminary phases of the emotional sequence are often more significant than the end products. They are more subtle and pliable, making preventive measures possible. On the other hand we may also be thankful, within limits, that the child declares himself, now and then, with an outburst of emotional expression, which after all constitutes his most basic language. As he grows older his expressional behavior becomes more refined; he uses words as well as gestures, not only for communication, but also as controls, symbols and embodiments of his emotional life. And thus his "emotions" grow. They take on pattern and texture, through dynamic relationships with his ideas and intellectual orientations. Emotions are not independent forces which in some mysterious way take possession of the child. They are structured modes of reaction which, like his perceptions, yield to the organizing influences of experience and education. They have had an awesome evolution in the history of the race. They have a biographic development in the history of the individual.

The subjoined growth gradients of affective attitudes, crying, anger and aggression will strongly suggest their ancient racial background. But we should point out that our discussion of the child's "emotions" is not confined to the present chapter. Emotional processes pervade all his life, private and social, genial and elevating, as well as violent and disturbing. For full perspective we must consider in later chapters the emotional formations which pertain to fears and dreams, to the child's play life, to his interpersonal relationships at home and school, his ethical and philosophic reactions to good and evil, and to the true and beautiful. But inasmuch as emotions are not self-subsisting entities, we shall focus our attention throughout on the processes and the patterns of development.*

CRYING

Life begins with a cry. During the first fortnight which he spends in a hospital nursery, the new-born baby cries on the average about two hours of each day. This is his most eloquent expressional behavior. We know that he does not cry without reason. He cries from hunger, pain, discomfort,—and also from denials which are not too well understood. If we arrange his day so that he spends more time with his mother and less time in the congregate nursery, his crying decreases in amount and insistence. Such a rooming-in-arrangement (as described in the *Infant and Child* volume), shortens the interval between distress and attention;

---

* The concept of growth is the indispensable key to the comprehension of the emotional characteristics of the child. We are indebted to Charles Darwin for important observations which he made on his several children. The tenderness and sympathetic insight which he displayed as a parent are well known. "My first child," he writes, "was born December 27, 1839, and I at once commenced to make notes on the first dawn of the various experiences which he exhibited, for I felt convinced, even at this early period, that the most complex and fine shades of expression must all have had a gradual and natural origin." Darwin studied these shades for thirty-three years and then published his classic volume, "The Expression of the Emotions in Man and Animals." Indeed, his patient investigations of emotional expression were marshalled to show that man is derived from lower animal forms.

and if the baby is reared on an individualized self-demand schedule throughout the first year his various cries become more meaningful to his mother. He does not need to assert himself too violently and too frequently. He is permitted to "oversleep"; his hunger cries are promptly answered. Thereby he is granted so many experiences of satisfied expectation that he acquires a sense of security, a simple kind of faith in the universe. This sense of security is comparable to a felt "emotion," even though it is not as dramatic as a fit of rage.

Crying tends to arouse so much emotion in the adult that it is easily misconstrued. In earlier centuries it was regarded as one of the major signs of the imperfection, "the pettishness" of childhood. It figured in the discussions of infant damnation. St. Augustine believed in "hereditary guilt," but held that the crying of a baby is *not* sinful. Susannah Wesley took matters into her own efficient hands. She relates of her numerous offspring, "When turned a year old (and some before) they were taught to fear the rod and to cry softly. . . . and that most odious noise of the crying of children was rarely heard in the house. . . ."

But this was over two hundred years ago. A more rationalistic view is slowly gaining ground; because the liberating concept of organic evolution has made us conscious not of hereditary guilt, but of the biologic basis of the frailties of the child's nature. In the light of that liberating knowledge it is almost incredible that so many children should still be severely punished *because they cry*! Yes, children are punished *because* they cry!

Crying is expressional behavior. It is a symptom, not a vice, and it can be understood only if interpreted in terms of its developmental determinations. Individual differences of temperament, fatigue and physiologic irritability will naturally influence the incidence of crying episodes; but maturity factors are primary. In the first few months the infant cries on slight provocation; a mere startle may evoke a screaming cry. The infant may wake with a hunger cry; in time he also cries or fusses before he goes to sleep, as though he were actively perfecting his growing ability to stay awake. At about the age of 16 weeks there is a quieting down; there are fewer crying episodes and they are shorter. Why? Because the infant is now in a state of relative equilibrium, as shown by many other aspects of his behavior. He is under less stress and tension. With new growth increments his equilibrium again becomes less stable. Such developmental fluctuations occur throughout the first ten years of life, with an overall trend toward diminution of frank crying as a mode of emotional expression. The 9-year-old usually does not cry unless he is extremely tired, or severely hurt, physically or mentally.

The characteristics of the act of crying and of the associated behavior also undergo some developmental changes. At first the cry is tearless and the vocal component of call is prominent. Later come tears, sobs, lump in the throat, and a large variety of body attitudes and motor activities. The physiologic reactions are similar to those which accompany the rejection of food. The mechanism of weeping deeply involves the digestive apparatus, whether it registers pain, displeasure, sorrow, helplessness, resignation or self-abasement. In the crying act the child tends to use the motor and verbal equipment available to him at his stage of maturity. A very premature infant may exhibit all the facial contortions of weeping which culminate, however, in a perfectly soundless cry or a faint bleat. The lusty neonate cries with a scream and thrashing of legs and arms. The 8-month-old infant may shift precariously from crying to laughter. Ten months later he uses his gross postural muscles tantrum-wise to supplement his cry. The 3-year-old is more equable. The 4-year-old cries rather freely, and supplements with whining verbalization. The many pattern changes which take place in the pre-school years suggest that the child rarely deserves the epithet "cry baby"!

The 5-year-old already has himself much better in hand. His cries are typically sun showers. His moods are fleeting. He can consciously hold back tears. At six years we witness again the phenomenon of paradoxical regression. The child "reverts" to tearful tantrums and outright bursts of loud crying; not because he is sinking to a lower level, but because, paradoxically, he is in transit toward a higher. This is no time to shame him for being a cry-baby. (Crying itself is not the vice, but an outward sign.) And, of course, he should not be punished *because* he cries.

At seven years he is usually able to pull himself together; but he is in a sensitive phase which results in overtones and moods of sadness, and sometime in broken-hearted sobs. There can be no doubt that he has problems of emotional organization, for he is variably sweet and good, or cross and tearful. He even declares, "I feel like crying," an infallible sign of increasing control. The 8-year-old further extends the control by dramatizing his emotions, and curbing his tears after they well up. By ten years the child, though not a stoic, is still nearer to an adult level of self-control.

Throughout the period of infancy and early childhood the causes of crying are diverse. Sometimes they seem very trivial and apparently superficial because the infant readily changes from crying to laughter. But this should rather remind us of the underlying immaturity of the child's nervous system.

A wise quatrain from Samuel Johnson calls for citation here:

> If the man who turnips cries
> Cry not when his father dies,
> 'Tis a proof that he had rather
> Have a turnip than his father.

ASSERTION AND ANGER

Self-preservation is the first law of life. The second law is self-expansion. When an infant declares himself on one or both counts with a vigorous burst of crying, we are likely to say, "The Baby is showing his temper." Some babies, of course, show a larger amount of this so-called temper than do others; but no normal child is altogether devoid of it. Temperaments and tempers differ. Ages likewise differ. As a child grows older, he displays his temper in new modes of expressional behavior, by violent and then less violent bodily attitudes, by facial contortions, by gestures, words and muted words! With maturity he advances from one order of self-assertion to another. If at a later school age he persists unduly in using the expressional channels of the nursery, his behavior is properly regarded as infantile. Whatever his mode of expression he behaves as he does, not because he has a "temper," but because he has organized his personal-social reactions in a given manner.

In the aftermath of the most tragic of all wars the subject of Anger and Aggression takes on a solemn importance,—even in relation to child development. In the early patterns of naive rage and pugnacity we see not only retrospectively the vestiges of the combativeness of pre-human progenitors; we see also the foretokens of organized human warfare. If we ever hope to control the primary origins of systematic war, we must comprehend the mechanisms of anger and aggression in infancy and childhood.

We cannot, of course, annihilate these mechanisms by any known device of appeasement or exorcism. We can, however, forestall the worst consequences by adequate measures of developmental guidance. Even without adequate guidance there is a natural tendency toward refinement in expressional manifestations and provocative causes during the pre-school years. The infant in a fit of rage thrashes arms and legs and arches his back; at 15 months he pulls himself forcibly free from a thwarting adult; at 18 months he cries, stamps, casts himself on the floor. In a tantrum of the first magnitude he hits, kicks and struggles furiously. Fortunately even such hopeless behavior is not beyond the reach of psycho-technology! The 18-month recalcitrant is responsive to gross motor humor: his struggle dissolves if you pick him up as a bag of rags with a light-hearted, executive maneuver. He cannot be controlled by hypnotism or solemn injunctions. The whole episode might have been avoided in the first place by utilizing methods of gradual transition,—for his rebellion was against a too sudden change. That was the critical maturity factor in his management.

At 21 months the anger pattern is already somewhat different. He is disappointed by an unwitting omission in his accustomed bedtime routine; he reacts by freezing into resistance or by "howling." The reason is so obscure that the parents are sorely perplexed. But from the child's standpoint there *is* a reason: You don't brush your teeth unless you are in your pajamas.

At two-and-a-half years he may resent interference with his activity or with his possessions. His tantrum reactions are more aggressive, especially when precipitated by his mother. He may be destructive with objects and surroundings, not excluding wall and wall-paper. In disputes over toys he may attack other children with rather indiscriminate hitting, biting, kicking. (We are describing his conduct, without condoning it. Our readers will grant that such things can happen, and they will agree with the gentle Darwin when he says: "Everyone who has had much to do with young children must have seen how naturally they take to biting, when in a passion. It seems as instinctive in them as in young crocodiles who snap their little jaws as soon as they emerge from the egg.")

Inasmuch as we are compelled to report yet other manifestations of anger and aggression we should, in further parentheses, assure the reader that these drastic forms of emotional expression are amply offset by more estimable forms of behavior detailed in later chapters. But at the moment, we must proceed realistically with manifestations of defiance and aggression.

The age of three, being a period of relative equilibrium, shows a temporary decline in physical aggressiveness. Interference with plans and belongings still arouses anger; but by and large the 3-year-old displays much more self-control than he did several months earlier. He also uses language to a greater degree to solve his personal emotional problems. At five years and at seven, eight and nine there is a similar constructive or substitute use of language with a diminution of frank physical aggressiveness. The stimuli which arouse the child's anger are becoming more social in context and vary with the development of his personality.

The relationships between language and aggressiveness are rather complex. Words should not be taken at their face value when first used by children. The 3½-year-old, flourishing his new found verbal sword, says "I'll cut you in pieces." To be sure, he may be angry at the moment; but that he is truly sadistic may be honestly doubted. In his recent past he may have dismembered a ginger bread man, but his verbal threat is probably not as gory as it sounds. Indeed, there is a strange, shallow matter-of-factness about young children which often causes them to use words glibly at the very time when they least appreciate the social import of the words. For example, a child may talk blithely about his mother's death, until he begins to comprehend. Then he denies that his mother will die, or he worries in silence. Children's silences are often more eloquent than their words.

At five-and-a-half and at six years, aggressiveness takes both physical and verbal forms: "You're a dope;" "I'll shoot you;" "Get out of there!;" "I wish you were dead,"—illustrate the winged missiles which are directed toward friend and foe. Some of these missiles may even be hurled at grandmother. Even so, the roof of a peaceful household should not fall. Now, if ever, one should calmly consider the true and, in essence, temporary psychology of the crisis.

Temporary in the sense that the 7-year-old already shows less crude and less frequent aggressive behavior. He has, or should have, very few tantrums, and he offers less resistance to his mother's commands. He is not equally pacific with his siblings; and on occasion he may even throw a stone, which is indeed an ancient behavior that probably antedates the stone age. But the 7-year-old is more in character when he mutters an aspersion and withdraws from the scene of irritation. Withdrawal is, to be sure, the opposite of aggression; it partakes less of courage and more of fear; but it has a useful function in the economy of development, to say nothing of the perfection of morals.

The typical 8-year-old is inquisitive rather than boldly aggressive. He illustrates the second, rather more than the first law of life. He accomplishes his self-expansion by fluid, multiple contacts with his social environment. He invades his environment, not to dominate, but to gain new experiences, new insights. There is a quality of aggression in his argumentativeness, his alibis, and his occasional epithets and disagreeable remarks. But when he is eagerly and loudly confabulating with his confreres he does not wish to quiet down on command. There is little animus in his heated discussion. He is really rising above brute levels. He and the 9- and the 10-year-olds at their best, give encouraging evidence of human capacities which make for peace and mutual understanding, instead of war and bloodshed.

By the same token we must look to the period from five to ten years for the developmental beginnings of juvenile delinquency and adult crime. Now that aggressive war has become a crime the psychology of childhood anger takes on impressive import. All long range policies, cultural and educational, directed toward the prevention of war must deal fundamentally with the emotional life of children before they reach the stage of adolescence, which brings forth new forces for good and evil.

THE STRUCTURALIZATION OF EMOTION

Emotions are not self-subsistent entities which in some mysterious manner suffuse or attach to patterned states of consciousness. They are themselves patterned; they are structures which grow in the same manner in which percepts, concepts, motor skills or any other configured behavior takes shape. An *emotional attitude* is simply a more or less habitual tendency to react and feel in a particular manner in a given situation. When the attitude is excessively emotional or unreasonable we call it a *prejudice*. When the attitude tends to occur time and time again in much the same way under varying circumstances we call it a *stereotype*. Racial antagonism readily becomes a prejudice or even a stereotype. *Racism* is a systematized, dogmatic attitude,—"the dogma that one ethnic group is condemned by nature to congenital inferiority and another group is destined to congenital superiority."

These simple definitions suggest the far flung extent of the problem of so-called "emotional education." We are dealing with structured modes of behavior which have their developmental basis in the instinctive constitution of the child; and which are only secondarily transformed or redirected by the sanctions and tabus of culture. For this reason we greatly need more knowledge of the innate determinants, racial and constitutional, of all emotional or affective traits,—particularly the traits of sociability, affection, pride, jealousy, sympathy, curiosity, competitiveness and creativeness, anger, fear and humor, which have such an important influence on the health or well-being of society.

Emotions are structured responses to concrete situations. Emotional patterns of behavior are displayed in the social settings of home, school and community. A discussion of emotions in the abstract would serve no useful purpose in the present volume. We shall therefore portray the emotional life of the growing child in terms of his specific reactions to other children, to his parents, to teacher, to school groups,—to the conjoined world of things and persons.

Anger and fear, however, are so basic that they call for special consideration. Crying and laughter likewise. We cannot close the present chapter without a brief reference to the saving sense of humor which is not only an affective response in its own right, but which plays an important role in the hygiene of the emotions,—the emotions of parent as well as of child.

In smiling, laughter and humor we are dealing with fundamental elements in the pleasurable aspects of emotional life. If crying had evolutionary roots in the rejection of food, primitive laughter was associated with the enjoyment and digestion of the feast. The well-fed infant tends to smile from sheer satisfaction; he smiles socially on the sight of caretaker at the age of 8 weeks; at 12 weeks he chuckles; at 16 weeks he definitely laughs aloud, and throughout infancy he participates in various grades of nursery humor from rollicking rough house to many kinds of peek-a-boo and mock-scare games, addressed to his eyes, ears, skin or his total physical (and mental) self. But, be it noted that both the child and his opposite must be in a playful attitude, or the nursery game comes to grief and tears, rather than to fun and laughter. Laughter, humor, relaxation reflexes and tensional behavior are all closely allied.

Children would not indulge in so much spontaneous and (apparently to us) meaningless laughter if it did not have a wholesome effect upon their behavior and mental growth. Some of this laughter might be set down as private or physiological; but it tends to spread and to increase in social situations. Even at the age of one year the child likes to repeat performances laughed at by his elders. At two years he can initiate humor and "carry on" with his playmates. At three years an abundance of laughter accompanies his play. At two-and-a-half all is not well with the world and he does not laugh quite so freely. He is caught in the rigidities of ritualism, perseveration and negativism. One might wish he were not so humorless. If the responsible adult meets this behavior with an equivalent insistent rigidity matters go from bad to worse.

Here is the ideal time to utilize the biological function of humor; namely, to dissolve tension and to increase the pliancy of the mind and to keep it from overstretching. Here humor becomes a technique in child management,—a technique which either prevents or atomizes an impasse.

The child cannot as yet summon therapeutic humor out of his own resources; but the parent can supply the lack in critical situations. Since humor is based on innate factors (instinctive and physiologic), individuals will show enormous differences in responsiveness; but this still leaves ample scope for teachers and parents. Within limits the humor sense can be educated, because with age it becomes increasingly identified with language and thought.

The early plays of Shakespeare were full of low comedy, buffoonery, mistaken identity, broad punning and rustic horseplay. Later plays show a ripening and the jester becomes an exalted humorist. A similar trend toward maturity is reflected in the humor of childhood. The 3-year-old is already refining the gross motor humor of the 2-year-old. His humor is becoming more verbalized. He enjoys the verbal play of tossing a word (like "golly") back and forth with someone who will play with him. At five years he enjoys slapstick humor, more or less verbalized, which he himself initiates. SIX is not notably a humor age, for reasons already indicated. SEVEN somewhat ineptly perpetrates hackneyed jokes. He seems to sense the social aspect of humor and will deliberately do something ludicrous in order to get a laugh; but he is still somewhat bound by his subjectivity. He will make a better show and use of humor in another year.

The typical EIGHT has a high humor sense. He loves humor stories and relishes the way Brother Fox fools a victim. By the same token he rather likes to catch a teacher in a mistake. But the emotional fabric of the self is complicated. Particularly at home where he has a status and prestige to protect, he still dislikes humorous references to himself.

At nine and ten the humor sense, if it matures, becomes more robust. The child is not only able to perpetrate a more or less practical joke, but he can take one on himself. He may even be able to laugh off teasing,—which is an excellent achievement. Some philosophers have located the origins of humor and laughter in the domain of derision, superiority and degradation!

If then, the sense of humor is subject to the laws of growth, it will in some measure yield to training. Education in humor must come through suggestion, atmosphere and experience. At home the child has innumerable social experiences which call for impromptu humorous handling. An institutionally reared child misses out sadly because he does not have the unscheduled experiences which normal family life yields.

At school nearly everything depends upon the teacher, because humor is not an official subject of the curriculum. A vital teacher naturally and also deliberately establishes an atmosphere of cheerful give and take. In such an atmosphere humor comes somewhat by contagion. Many unpredictable social situations arise which can be exploited to release humor. There is hardly an art which does not have a place for the expression of humor in the schoolroom: drawing, music, sculpture, dancing, dramatics, broadcasting and television, but above all literature.

By literature we do not, of course, mean the *Funnies*. The so-called Comics deal rather in anger, fear and adventure as their stock in trade. They tend, if anything, to give their readers an undue, untrammelled sense of power. Whatever their merits they usually do not introduce the child to that fine territory where humor verges on philosophy.

English literature and also foreign literatures contain materials for this enriching type of humor. But much remains to be done to create new humor materials based on the developmental characteristics of the child, and his developmental needs, both moral and philosophic. The techniques of humor applied by himself and others are needed to safeguard sanity. This has always been a function of laughter and of humor.

GROWTH GRADIENTS

§1. AFFECTIVE ATTITUDES

4 WEEKS—Baby appears stable and relatively well coordinated.

8 WEEKS—Much crying and apparent emotional disequilibrium.

16 WEEKS—Vocalizes happily.
  Smiles at sight of a face.
  Seems to enjoy people, but self-contained.

20 WEEKS—Much disequilibrium and crying.

28 WEEKS—Self-contained; plays contentedly alone.
  Affectionate, smiling response for people.

32 WEEKS—Easily becomes over-excited.
  Close interplay between crying and laughter.
  Fears strangers.

40 WEEKS—Smiles when watching or participating in nursery tricks.
  Girls show first signs of coyness by putting head to one side as they smile.
  Shy with strangers. Most smiling and *affectionate* with family group.

44 WEEKS—More fearful, less smiling, more crying.

52 WEEKS—The heyday of smiling and social give and take: "Where's the baby?" and other social games.

Indiscriminate *affection* and social smiling response.
Repeats performance laughed at.

15 MONTHS—Demanding, assertive, independent. Not in good emotional equilibrium.
Discriminates against almost everyone; does not get on well with people.

18 MONTHS—Very mobile, with sketchy, short-lived attention span; impulsive.
Constantly moving, "into everything," busy, self-contained, independent.
Helpful in small ways.
Becoming more *affectionate* with mother. May hug doll or teddy.
May respond to gross *humor* approaches from adult: hiding, peek-a-boo, being lifted bag-of-rags fashion.

21 MONTHS—Definitely lacks equipoise. Less independent.
New awareness of persons and fear of strangers.
Sense of possessiveness about own things and knows about possessions of others.
Conscious of adult approval and disapproval.
More responsive to mother, yet more demanding. Quiets with *affection*.

2 YEARS—Better emotional as well as postural equilibrium. More sedate than formerly.
Shy.
Non-cooperative in play; but helpful with adult.
Real show of *affection* toward mother, especially strong at bedtime. This may spread to other adults. Even his voice has affective tones. May take affectionate care of toys.
Possessive of his own things but *not jealous* of others.
Proud of new clothes, as shoes, etc.
Humor largely gross motor, as peek-a-boo and chasing; but may be initiated by children themselves and may be carried on by them without adult support.

2½ YEARS—Disequilibrium. Extremes of aggression and withdrawal.
Child is domineering, imperious, bold. Is also rigid and ritualistic.
Is selfish, possessive and demanding.
Affection is expressed in rigid form as a kissing ritual.
May express *jealousy* of younger siblings.
Is *proud* of own abilities to do things.
Can be handled by *humor*. "No, no, no" may be answered effectively with "Yes, yes, yes."
Verbally asserts domination over members of his family.

3 YEARS—Good equilibrium. Happy and contented, enjoys self quietly.
Emotional as well as physical self-control.
Friendly, helpful, conforming, wishes to please. *Mildly* affectionate.
May be *jealous* of younger siblings.
Proud of own increasing abilities.
Enjoys friendly *humor*. Much laughter accompanies play.

Early gross motor humor giving way to verbal. Enjoys humorous word play. Likes riddles, and guessing. Humorous wrong guess by adult causes much amusement.

3½ YEARS—New unsettledness. Voice quavers, he stutters, speaks in high-pitched voice. Fears and fearful dreams increase.

Leads an elaborate imaginary life with much emotion involved.

Very *affectionate* toward and possessive of parent. Says "I love."

Humor is involved in imaginary play.

Tries to control emotion of others, "Don't talk," "Don't laugh."

May withdraw from adult or may demand, "Hold my hand."

4 YEARS—Out of bounds. Quarrelsome, Argumentative.

May be selfish, rough, impatient with younger siblings.

Expresses *affection* at bedtime: goodnight kiss and strong hug.

May be *jealous* of mother and father together.

Proud of own products and creations.

Silly boisterous *humor*. Wild laughter accompanies play.

Enjoys silly rhyming, "mitsy, witsy, bitsy" and play on words.

Likes to call silly names; exaggerations amuse him. Silly showing-off.

Out of bounds verbalization: Tattles a great deal, exaggerates, boasts, tells tall tales, calls names, threatens, is profane, or mildly obscene.

5 YEARS—Serious, businesslike, realistic, literal. Well equilibrated, poised, but may be resistant.

Dependent on adult (proximity of adult) company and support. Cooperative.

Likes and invites supervision.

Friendly, sympathetic, *affectionate*, helpful.

Strong feeling for family. Likes to be with family. May be very proud of mother.

Proud of his own appearance, nice clothes, etc.

General curiosity and eagerness for information.

Enjoys slapstick *humor*, which he initiates.

Mother reports that he "loves" to be read to.

Likes to talk and will talk to anyone. Some talk "constantly."

Excited in anticipation of future. Knows own mind and sticks to it.

Calling names: "skunk," "rat," "I'll kill you."

6 YEARS—Highly emotional. Marked disequilibrium between child and others.

Expansive and undifferentiated. Good or bad; sweet or horrid; adoring or cruel.

He knows "everything"; boasts, brags.

Likes praise and approval; resents correction and is easily hurt by a cross word.

Loves or hates mother.

Rapidly explosive with crying, strikes out physically or verbally, or has temper tantrums.

Quarrelsome, argumentative, explosive, rebellious, rude, "fresh," stubborn, brash.

Noisy, boisterous and easily excitable.

Silly, giggling, grimacing, showing off.

Resents direction, but is also over-conforming.

Domineers, blames and criticises others, alibis.

Glowers and glows; has fire or a twinkle in his eye.

At times angelic, generous, companionable.

Jealous of possessions of other children.

May not be too responsive to *humor* at this age.

Uses language aggressively: calls names, threatens, contradicts, argues, uses mild profanity.

7 YEARS—A "feeling" age. Gets on better with others, though disequilibrium within own feelings.

Serious, absorbed, thoughtful, inhibited, empathic.

Sets too high goal for self.

Self-protection by withdrawal from situation. "Deaf" ear.

Anger directed toward self. Throws or breaks something if he cannot perform.

Often moody, sulky and unhappy.

Sensitive to praise and blame. Cannot take compliments, but can be reassured.

May not be able to accept *affection*, though he gives it.

Anxious to please and considerate of others.

Jealous of privileges or abilities of siblings.

Little sense of *humor* and cannot be handled with *humor*.

Worries about place in family or school group.

Uses language complainingly: nobody likes him, people are mean and unfair, he has nothing to play with. If angry may retreat into silence instead of, as earlier, into angry verbalization. May be given to "screeching." Complains of headache.

8 YEARS—Tendency to disequilibrium between self and others.

Attacks life with some courage, also feels he is being attacked.

Thinks he knows "everything" but beginning to recognize that others may know more.

Impatient especially with self. "Snippy," careless.

Dramatizes anything. Tall tales are dramatic but usually with a grain of truth.

Demanding of mother; fresh and rude, or strongly *affectionate*.

Some *jealousy* of mother and father being together.

Critical of others and also of self. Selfish and demands much attention. Bossy or helpful. Quarrelsome.

Bursts into tears; has laughing jags.

Often gay and cheerful.

Very curious about personal activities of others: phone calls, conversations.

Feelings of guilt.

High *humor* sense. Enjoys humor in stories, especially when one person is fooled by another, making someone uncomfortable.

Likes to catch teacher in a mistake. At home dislikes humorous references or jokes about himself.

Out of bounds verbally: talks a great deal, exaggerates, boasts. Raises voice when angry or tired.

9 YEARS—Becoming more independent. Better equilibrium.

Quick extreme emotional shifts, short lived.

Impressionable, reasonable, explosive, empathic.

More responsible, independent, cooperative, dependable.

Evaluates own performance, may be disgusted or apprehensive about own actions. May be ashamed of past behavior.

Wants things to be proper. Disgusted with others who deviate even slightly from his standards.

Gets mad at parents, but is also *proud* of them, brags about them, *affectionate* toward them.

Enjoys competition.

Protective and loyal to friend or to younger sibling.

Responds well to compliment.

Has passions for certain activities. Often overdoes to point of fatigue.

Many complain a good deal: headaches, eyes hurt, hand hurts, etc., while doing a task, but continue to do required task.

Enjoys *humor*—if he thinks something is funny, repeats it over and over. Likes surprises in a story. Beginning to accept jokes about self.

Uses language to express subtle and refined emotions: disgust, self-criticism, pity, envy.

§2. CRYING AND RELATED BEHAVIORS

1-4 WEEKS—The hunger cry almost universal.

4 WEEKS—May fuss half an hour a day. May cry one or two hours a day.

4-12 WEEKS—Differential crying for different causes. Crying before sleep as well as hunger cry.

8-16 WEEKS—Much crying and fussing, but less than formerly. Perhaps one hour a day. May cry at almost any provocation.

16 WEEKS—Brief period of equilibrium. Less crying and for shorter periods.

20 WEEKS—Stage of disequilibrium. Any stimulus—the mere appearance or disappearance of an object—may evoke crying. Transitions difficult.

28 WEEKS—Less crying. May cry if left supine, if he prefers sitting.

32 WEEKS—Instability of emotional make-up suggested by close interplay of crying and laughter.

40-52 WEEKS—Less crying. Cries more with specific irritations or frustrations. May cry for attention.

15 MONTHS—May fuss or vocalize when disturbed, instead of crying.

18 MONTHS—Tantrums, with violent crying, if things go wrong.

21 MONTHS—Crying very violent—"bawling." "Frozen" into inactivity by inability to verbalize.

2 YEARS—Child is sensitive, dependent, tearful.

2½ YEARS—Crying from temper. Stormy. May awake crying after nap. Whining.

3 YEARS—Less crying and less show of temper.

4 YEARS—Much crying. Also may whine if his wants are not met or if he has nothing interesting to play with.

5 YEARS—Less crying, though may cry if angry, tired, cannot have own way. Crying now of shorter duration and can sometimes be controlled, tears held back.
Little moodiness. "Gets right over" crying.
Some whining, though less than at four years.

5½ YEARS—Abrupt onset of temper tantrums, with loud angry crying.
Much crying at routines. Also excitement and fatigue bring on crying.
Some moodiness, whining, expression of resentment.

6 YEARS—Tears and tantrums. Tantrums involve loud crying. Adult can often get child to laugh when he is crying.
Child is called a "cry-baby"; he cries at "any little thing."
Some whining and fussing, but more outright crying.
Brave about real injuries to themselves but cry at small hurts.

7 YEARS—Less crying. Becomes moody, sulky, "in the dumps."
If cries, sobs broken-heartedly, but can control crying and can pull himself together.
Sensitive about crying and ashamed to be seen crying.
May merely say, "I feel like crying."
Moods very variable: sweet and good, then cross and tearful.
May cry if spanked or spoken to sharply; or if he is unhappy or cannot make up his mind. Less because of routine requirements or small disturbances.

8 YEARS—Less crying, but sensitive, feelings hurt, and tears well up.
Feelings easily hurt by careless remarks or by criticism.
Less temper and less moodiness. But may say, "I'm not in the mood to do so and so."
Dramatization of own emotions.

9 YEARS—Cries only when emotions are over-taxed. May then cry if angry, over-tired, feelings hurt, or if wrongly accused.
Complaints of: "That's no fair."

§3. ASSERTION AND ANGER

1-12 MONTHS—Loud angry crying; thrashing of arms and legs.

15 MONTHS—Casts objects.
Demands to do things himself, in his own way.
Pulls free from adult grasp.
Anger chiefly aroused by interference with his physical activity.

18 MONTHS—Tantrums: cries, casts self on floor, hits, kicks, struggles. Caused chiefly by resistant objects, (may kick the objects); also caused by imposed transitions.
Inadvertently destructive of objects.
Rough with children or animals: stamps or steps on them; pokes, pulls, pushes them. Does not clearly distinguish animate from inanimate.

21 MONTHS—Pulls hair, knocks children over head, hugs too tightly, "bear hugs."
Real approach to other children.
Intense crying. Cries because he can't verbalize his wishes, which are often for repetition of certain things (bib, spoon).
May stand rigid and frozen.

2 YEARS—Not characteristically aggressive.
May hit, pat, poke or bite other children.
Engages in tugs of war over materials.
"Messes up" the house but does not necessarily destroy things.

2½ YEARS—Tantrums: extremely aggressive whole-body response. Caused chiefly by mother.
Attacks other children aggressively with intent to hurt: bites, hits, kicks, especially in disputes over toys.
Very destructive with objects, especially with plaster and wall-paper.
"Grabs" objects from others. May without warning walk up to and hit a stranger.
Anger chiefly aroused by interference with his physical activity or with his possessions.

3 YEARS—Increased self-control and less aggression.
Increased use of language may take place of physical aggressiveness.
Anger now aroused less by interference with physical activity and more by interference with plans and possessions.

3½ YEARS—Verbal threats, such as "I'll cut you in pieces."

4 YEARS—Physically aggressive: bites, hits, kicks, throws.
Verbally aggressive: calls names, brags, boasts.
Rough and careless with toys.
May aggressively exclude others from group.

[293]

5 YEARS—Not characteristically aggressive.
> May stamp feet, slam door. An occasional tantrum.
> Verbal aggressiveness: "I'll kill you."

5½ YEARS—Transition from calmness of five to aggressiveness of six years.
> Calls names: "Stinker," "You're a dope."
> Verbal threats: "I'll hit you," "I'll shoot you."
> Resists directions: "I won't," "Get out of here."
> Temper tantrums. Slams doors. Strikes parents or other children.
> Destructive in play.

6 YEARS—Extremely aggressive, both physically and verbally.
> Tantrums: throws self to floor, hits, kicks. If sent to room, may not stay there unless door is locked. Then may destroy furniture.
> Says, himself, that he is "mad."
> Calls names.
> Verbal threats: "I'll kill you."
> Contradicts, argues, resists: "No, I won't"; "Try and make me."
> Hits and kicks,—adults or playmates.
> May exhibit considerable cruelty toward animals, insects, children.
> Destructive with objects.

7 YEARS—Less aggressive behavior. Few tantrums and less resistance to mother's commands.
> May be considerable fighting with siblings.
> May threaten to "beat somebody up."
> May kick or throw stones.
> Verbal objection: "That isn't fair," "It's a gyp."
> If angry may leave the room, or the playground.

8 YEARS—Contacts environment curiously rather than aggressively.
> Responds to attack and criticism with hurt feelings rather than with aggression.
> Aggression seldom physical, chiefly verbal. Argues, alibis, calls names or makes disagreeable remarks.

9 YEARS—Fighting and "beating somebody up" common (with boys) but may be in the nature of play.
> Aggression chiefly verbal. Objects to what people say and do. Criticizes.
> Verbally expresses indifference to adult commands or adult standards.

14

FEARS AND DREAMS

EMOTIONS are so ubiquitous and at the same time so fluid and elusive that it is difficult even to enumerate them. The dictionary is full of hundreds of adjectives and nouns which designate various emotional states; and there are countless emotional states in children and adults, for which there are no words in the dictionary. No wonder that psychologists cannot agree on a satisfactory classification of the emotions. But all listings give a leading position to fear.

One convenient classification recognizes six primary emotions: fear, disgust, wonder, anger, subjection, elation and tenderness. The child manifests these emotions in various patterns of behavior: he seeks, he avoids; he desires, he rejects; he is inquisitive, aggressive, joyous, affectionate, fearsome.

The baby is born with a capacity to startle, to feel pain, to feel pleasure. This threefold capacity lies at the basis of emotion; because in all emotion there is an element of shock or excitement issuing in feelings of the agreeable or disagreeable. The startle pattern is very fundamental, very primitive. It is exhibited by adults as well as children (to say nothing of the lower animals). Eyes blink, head bends sharply, mouth opens, abdomen contracts, elbows, fingers and knees flex into a startled attitude. The organism thus assumes a preparatory postural set, and if in a moment it also feels distress or anticipates pain or danger, we call the reaction fear. At the same time the heart may begin to pound, blood pressure rises; the spleen releases red corpuscles, the liver releases glycogen into the blood stream. Many other physiological changes take place. The reaction may be mild and temporary; it may be violent and prolonged. It may result in cries of terror, in efforts of flight and escape; or it may assume a more chronic and refined form of timidity, anxiety and worry. Fear is protean. In yet other developments it contributes to the exalted sentiments of awe and reverence; and to the homespun virtues of caution and vigilance.

From the standpoint of child guidance, fear should not be too much feared. Fear is normal. Fearing is natural. Often it has a wholesome influence on the life of the growing child. Fear, like fire, is useful in the right place at the right time; harmful if misplaced and out of control.

The early fears of childhood change with age. These changes depend on the maturity of the child. Some of the fears seem entirely reasonable, and others which seem irrational may have a deep developmental justification. Possibly we should look for a rationale even in inexplicable night terrors and nightmares. Significantly enough they too diminish with increasing age.

The organism reacts with fear (or with fancies) whenever it senses insecurity or the threat of insecurity. A baby hears a *door slam*; he startles, cries. Likewise, if he sees an abrupt movement or feels a sudden loss of support he cries. At 16 weeks he may cry time and time again, whenever he hears the *kitchen clock* strike. At 24 weeks he listens un-afraid to the self-same clock; but he cries at the sight of an *approaching stranger*. At 32 weeks he is afraid of his own mother when she dons a *new hat*. Similar changes in the content of fears take place throughout the whole span of childhood. The child sheds old fears because experi-ence teaches him true meanings. The child acquires new fears because he detects novelty and portent, which formerly he was too immature to apprehend. The new perceptiveness actually denotes a growth ad-vance. Significantly the word *apprehension* means grasping with the intellect as well as distrusting with dread!

Our gradient of fears therefore shows a progressive trend toward increasing sophistication. An infant fears sinister sounds,—his father's deep voice, the roar of the vacuum cleaner. As a pre-school child he may fear the wrinkled visage of a withered old woman, or a Hallow-e'en mask. Later he is awed or even terrified by the ominous roll of thunder or the vague obscurity of attics and cellars. Still later he fears the burglar or spy who hides there; or who comes over the air in a too thrilling radio program. By the age of ten he can laugh retrospectively at these "childish" fears which he has outgrown. But his mental structure has probably been enriched and strengthened by some of these very fears. As he matures he does not banish fear altogether; he refines and organizes its patterns.

A further glance at our gradient reveals developmental fluctuations in types and degrees of fear susceptibility. During periods of relative equilibrium fears are not as prominent as at the ages when the organism is actively crossing frontiers into strange new territories. Susceptibility also changes in type: there is a trend of emphasis from *auditory* (2–2½ years) to *spatial*, to *visual* (3 years), to *auditory* (4–5½), to *personal* (7 years).

Even within any one type of fear, significant developmental changes take place. For example, consider fears of sounds. At first the child fears especially loud or sudden sounds or those outside his natural range (1–6 months); then sounds of mechanical gadgets (18 months); sounds of trains, trucks, flushing of toilet, barking dogs (2–2½ years); fire engines (4 years); rain and thunder (5 years); doorbell, telephone, static, ugly voices, bird and insect noises (5½–6 years). A similarly elaborating development, based on the child's increasing perceptiveness, is apparent in his visual fears and fears about his mother.

All these trends are, of course, highly subject to individual differences in temperament, and environmental conditions and experiential association. Fears are notable for their individuality. (We know of a 3-year-old who had a highly organized fear of rubber boots; and another older child who was obsessed by the fear that our government could not pay its national debt!) When fears reach an overpowering intensity, or when they take the form of protracted anxiety, special aggravating factors must be looked for.

The basic variations in ordinary fears, however, are attributable to maturity factors. Growth processes determine in a broad way what and when a child will fear. They determine also the what and the when of his reveries, his imaginary companions, his day dreams, his night dreams, his nightmares. There are profound parallelisms and interactions between these various modes of behavior in normal child development. All afford a sidelight on the formation of personality.

For example, at about the age of two years the child begins to play Imaginatively with objects. Month by month his dramatic phantasy elaborates, because his nervous system is a growing structure: a) he animates a material object, b) he plays the role of a baby, c) he plays with an imaginary object, d) he plays with an imaginary animal (30–42 months), e) he impersonates an animal, f) he has an imaginary human companion, g) he personalizes an object (36–48 months), h) he impersonates another person, i) he has an alter-ego type of imaginary companion (5–10 years).

The daydreams of the child reflect a similar sequence. And so do his fears and night dreams, which show a trend from wild animals, to domestic animals, to separation from mother, to bogey man, to witches and ghosts, to burglars, and finally to personal and to private worries.

Vast areas of the child's dream world are never reported; but when he is old enough to report reliably, we find that while the content of his dreams is influer ed by his personal experiences, the general format of the dreams has a deeper determination. In the deepmost sequences we dimly see the impress of millions of years of racial evolution when the elemental fears of man took shape, in his struggle with nature, with beasts, and with his own kind. The last world war has added an awesome page to this ancient unrecorded history of human fears.

Far from being banished with civilization, fear remains an important factor in child behavior. It figures prominently in the dreams of infants and children. Fear dreams greatly outnumber anger dreams. Indeed we have found few purely aggressive dreams in the five to ten year age group. A typical dream is a fear dream in which the child is chased. He flees, he runs, he pedals his bicycle, he flies toward safety. Or he is paralyzed to the spot. But he does not fight to conquer. If his dream is blissful, it is not because he victoriously destroys or annihilates. It is rather because he enjoys a full release from the clutch of fear and revels in the free use of his dreamed activity. Many of his dreams are pleasant not because they fulfill a wish but because they activate an unimpeded power. Such dreams we would not rudely interrupt.

All of which suggests that in fears and dreams we are dealing with a natural function, which in moderation is harmless if not actually useful. Perhaps the dreams themselves may prove to be a natural device for organizing and resolving fears. Even the milder forms of nightmare may serve as a tensional outlet and facilitate a fuller development of ultimate inhibitory control. Conceivably a nightmare takes the place of more serious and more chronic somatic complaints. Or is a nightmare an acute, dramatic somatic complaint?

A night terror is a more extreme sleep experience than a nightmare. The child sits up in bed; or jumps out and clutches at the furniture or at a person. His face is terror stricken. He stares with wide open eyes but without recognizing his caretakers or surroundings. He cries; he hallucinates; he perspires. The episode may last for fifteen minutes. It terminates sharply. He returns to bed without memory or recall of the event. Peaceful sleep ensues immediately.

An ordinary nightmare is much less dramatic. The episode lasts only a minute or two. It is preceded by brief crying or moaning and body stirring. The child wakes up without perspiration; he recognizes his surroundings and is fully oriented to them. But there is often a long period of waking and a verbalized going over of the frightening dream before the child goes back to sleep. Peaceful sleep is delayed.

All these symptoms, whether of nightmare or night terror, indicate that we are dealing with a phenomenon more fundamental than either fear or dreams, namely, *sleep*. Contrary to popular belief, sleep is an extremely complex function, because it is inextricably bound up with the complicated mechanism of *waking*. Sleep is a component of an organic cycle which consists of four interacting phases: *a*) *going to sleep, b*) *staying asleep, c*) *waking, d*) *staying awake, a*) going to sleep *b*) staying asleep . . . etc. Now as shown in chapter 12 all these phases depend upon a coordinating neural mechanism which undergoes progressive organization throughout infancy and childhood. The child from five to ten is still "learning" to sleep. If he has recurrent nightmares, phase *b* (*staying asleep*) and phase *a* (*going back to sleep*) are out of normal adjustment. If he is subject to recurrent night terrors phase *b* (*staying asleep*) and phase *c* (*waking*) are faulty. He wakes with spastic, almost convulsive intensity and yet in such a narrow zone of his total personality that we may truly say "he doesn't know how to wake up." Fortunately he is likely to do so in time, with further developments of his complex nervous system.

Ordinary night dreams are milder, more comprehensive and better modulated despite their grotesqueness and despite the fact that the super-lord cortex is sleeping on the job. We incline to the belief that the cortex is not entirely asleep, and that its lackadaisical participation is constructive and puts method in the apparent madness of the dream. This participation is at once a physiological and a developmental device. We need not worry too much about either the luxurious or the dreadful dreams of normal children.

But what about the daytime fears, when the cortex is wide awake? Here, the cortex of the adult must supply controls which the immature cortex of the fearing child lacks. Many childhood fears seem inconsequential and amusingly absurd. They should, however, always be taken seriously by the adult. They should never be laughed out of court. Nor should the child be shamed for cowardice. Valiant fathers, in particular, are likely to get too tough with their fledglings in the supposed interest of the nation's morale. "What, is this boy afraid of the water? Even with water wings? I'll toss him in and he will swim!"

We may well wonder whether the child's fear of water should not be respected. It is an ancient fear in the history of the race. The child may tremble at its impersonal vagueness, darkness and the vast expanse which spreads before him. At any rate, before the age of seven under certain conditions of temperament and experience, it may take a year or two before a young child overcomes his terrified screaming and his timorousness at the water's edge. The fear seems entirely irrational (to us). But we might well hesitate to cast it out altogether even if we could; because there should always remain a residue of controlled fear in the form of self-protective caution. We would not set up a completely fearless child as a paragon. Water is a danger as well as a delight.

The same philosophy applies to all forms of safety education. The everyday dangers of the home (falling, burning, scalding, injury from sharp and pointed objects, etc.) cannot be controlled by mere admonition. They call for concrete training and insight. The dangers of street and traffic likewise call for calm training in the art as well as attitude of caution. Caution also has a place in moral education. Children should

[301]

not be kept too innocent of evils which, after all, are comparable to physical dangers.

The preventive hygiene of fear, therefore, is many sided. A happy and secure home life is the best general safeguard against unreasonable fears. A sense of humor combined with sympathetic common sense helps to forestall the misgivings which lie at the root of exaggerated fears. Fatigue, also, may undermine fortitude. A warm bath and a glass of milk may help to banish an unaccountable fear.

Do not unnecessarily expose the child to manufactured fears. Keep him from movies, radio, comics and televisions which are absurdly terrifying. Good stories, however, provide fear experiences which enlarge the child's imagination. Literature, like life, introduces him to pain and evil and helps him in the task of surmounting both.

A final word about the dynamics of fear and the resolution of fear. To understand fear we must also understand anger. The preceding chapter dealt with aggression and anger reactions. Anger is in some respects the counterpart of fear. In fear the organism avoids; in anger it attacks a danger. The dilemma is fight or flight. Life calls for a working balance between these opposed tendencies. When they are not well coordinated the result is indecision, confusion or a conflict emotion like jealousy. Jealousy seems to be a subtle mixture of anger and fear.

Of the two opposing impulses fear is by far the more complex and the more fertile in its end results for human behavior. It is more subjective, more flexible and tentative, and therefore more consequential in the organization of personality. Certainly it needs more insight and subtle management on the part of parents and educators. The regulation of anger is by comparison simpler in scope. Anger leads to drastic, definitive responses,—some of them destructive and irreparable. Fear leads to withdrawal, and to avoidance responses, but withdrawal does not preclude a return to the scene of danger and a final resolution in terms of conquered and compensated fear.

What is the dynamics of fear in such instances of resolution? Let us assume that an angry dog barks at a timid child as though to devour him. The child is so afraid of the sound and the sight that he runs away. Even on a better day he runs away at the mere sight and sound of a dog. During this period of withdrawal an injudicious parent forces the child to touch and pet a harmless dog. The withdrawal is thereby intensified. Left to himself and aided by more subtle reassurances, the once affrighted child begins to feel impelled by curiosity and tenderness. Inner forces reverse: he approaches the dog almost compulsively. Now he is actually drawn toward the dog. The intensity of this reversed behavior probably varies with the intensity of the original withdrawal behavior. If the latter was pronounced, the child may overdo his reconciliation. The child whose withdrawal was exacerbated by ill-timed interference is most likely to react with marked and prolonged compulsion. Whether the fear be normal or abnormal, its dynamic course tends to follow the same sequence: "shock"→withdrawal→compulsive return→and then, finally, resolution.

GROWTH GRADIENTS

§1. FEARS

1-12 MONTHS—Loud or unexpected noise: squeaky toys, clock, father's deep voice, any sound outside the usual range.
  Strange objects, situations or persons.
  Familiar person who is in any way changed,—i.e. wearing a hat.
  Falling objects, dangers of falling, sudden movement.
  Threats of bodily harm or pain.

15 MONTHS—Seeing mother depart.

18 MONTHS—Sound of mechanical gadgets as electric sweeper.
  Seeing mother depart.

2 YEARS—Many fears. Chiefly auditory as: trains and trucks, thunder, flushing of toilet.
  Visual fears: dark colors, large objects, large buildings, trains, hats, the dark.
  Spatial: toy moved from usual place, crib moved, moving to new house, fear of going down the drain.
  Personal: mother's departure and especially separation from her at bedtime.
  Rain and wind.
  Animals, especially animal noises.

2½ YEARS—Many fears. Especially spatial: fear of movement, or of having objects moved from usual place, as a toy or piece of furniture.

Any different orientation: someone entering house in an unusual or unaccustomed way; taking a different route in a car.

Large objects, as trucks, approaching.

Many auditory fears as at two years.

3 YEARS—Visual fears predominate: people of a different color, old wrinkled people, the grotesque, masks, bogey men.

The dark.

Animals.

Specific individuals described to the child as harmful, i.e. policemen.

Mother or father going out at night.

4 YEARS—Auditory fears: especially of fire engines.

People of a different color, old people, bogey men.

The dark.

Animals.

Mother leaving, especially going out at night.

Uses word "afraid" or "scared" and then is afraid.

Enjoys being mildly frightened by the adult in play.

5 YEARS—Not a fearful age.

Less fear of animals, bad people, bogey men.

Concrete down to earth fears: bodily harm, falling, dogs.

The dark.

Sounds: thunder, rain, siren, especially at night.

That mother will not return home, or be at home when he gets there.

5½ YEARS—Very fearful. Especially auditory fears: doorbell, telephone, static, ugly voice tones, flushing of toilet, insect and bird noises.

Spatial: fear of being lost, fear of the woods.

The dark.

Fear of sleeping alone in a room or of being only one on a floor of the house.

Domestic animals.

Deprivation of mother: that she will not be at home when he gets home.

6 YEARS—Marked increase in fears, especially auditory and spatial. May stem from one experience.

Fear of supernatural: ghosts and witches.

Large wild animals and large dogs.

Woods and tiny insects.

Elements: thunder, rain, wind, fire, especially sound of elements. May cover ears or comfort another.

Sound of sirens, static, telephone, flushing of toilet.

Fears that mother may die, or that something will happen to her.

Fear of man under bed, or hiding in woods (especially girls).

Injury to self: splinters, little cuts, blood, administration of nose drops.

Afraid of being late to school.

7 YEARS—Deeper, worrisome fears.

Many visual and spatial fears: shadows, ghosts and creatures in attic or cellar, heights.

War, spies, burglars, people hiding in closet or under bed.

Beginning to resolve fears by getting someone to precede him into feared place, or by using flash light.

Worries about not being liked by parents, teacher, playmates.

Fear of new situations: Starting second grade, new school work.

Worries about being late for school, or of not finishing school work.

Fears now stimulated by reading, radio and cinema.

8 YEARS—Fewer fears; less worrying.

May still have fear of fighting, of failure, of not being liked.

Less fear of elements and fewer visual and auditory fears.

Now shy of dark, but likes to be out at night with parents.

Girls may fear strange men.

Enjoy frightening others with "boo!" or by telling frightening tales.

Compulsively repeat fear situations to resolve them.

May worry in the midst of an experience: that he won't catch train, that he will be punished etc.

9 YEARS—Few fears, very variable from child to child.

Worry mostly about school failure. Some about trouble at home. Worry that they cannot meet demands of a competitive situation, about report cards. Upset by own mistakes.

Enjoy frightening each other: spying, hiding.

Spontaneously report that they were "frightened to death" of something. Seem to enjoy this and feel proud of it. Also say, "I don't frighten very easy."

§2. DREAMS

1 YEAR—Wake in night, cry, apparently in response to sound, usually a loud sound. There may be early sleep disquietudes.

2 YEARS—Wake up with the slightest sound. They may be dreaming.

3 YEARS—Children begin to report occasional dreams.

Dreams may wake the child.

Dream of parents, daily play.

3½ YEARS—Some wakefulness and crying caused by dreaming.

Only occasional reporting.

[305]

4 YEARS—Less wakefulness caused by dreams; more reporting, probably fairly reliable.
Reports of dreams may be confused with fanciful tales.
Dream of parents, playmates, play.

4½ YEARS—Considerable dreaming and can report dreams.
Dream of animals, especially of wolves.

5 YEARS—Nightmares which awaken and frighten child. Child often cannot tell dream.
Has difficulty going back to sleep.
Animals, especially wolves and bears chase the child.
Strange or bad people—may be of odd color or appearance.
Activity in regard to elements: fire, water.
Child may still confuse dreams and his own waking imagination.
A few dream of ordinary daily events.

5½ YEARS—Dream of things in their beds. Waken and go to mother's bed. Can usually
tell dream. Less disturbed than earlier.
Wild animals (wolves, bears, foxes, snakes) chase or bite the child.
Domestic animals, especially dogs, hurt him or his dog.
Some pleasant dreams of everyday events.
Talking in sleep: "Mommy" or say names of siblings.

6 YEARS—Dreams are funny or ghostly; nice or bad; few nightmares.
Fewer animal dreams. Foxes, bears, lions or snakes chase, bite etc.
Domestic animals often in "nice" dreams.
Fire, thunder and lightning, and war.
Dream of ghosts, skeletons, angels.
Girls especially, of bad men trying to get into room.
Mother getting killed or injured, or that she has abandoned him.
Pleasant dreams of everyday people, sibs and playmates; may laugh and talk.
Can usually go to mother's bed if disturbed, and also usually able to tell what
dream was about.

7 YEARS—Less dreaming; fewer unpleasant dreams; may be last nightmare age.
Some still dream of animals; of being chased or threatened and cannot move or
speak.
Dreams mostly about himself. He is the central figure.
He flies, swims, dives into ocean, floats through air, walks above ground.
Daily events and often embarrassing situations.
Ghosts and supernatural; burglars and war.
Movies and radio affect dreams.

8 YEARS—Very little dreaming reported.
Varies from child to child. Some like to dream and to tell about dream.
Chiefly pleasant dreams about experiences, possessions, playmates. Some about
personal difficulties or worries.

Some boys have returned to animal dreams or the fantastic.

May have frightening dreams from cinema, radio or reading.

Do not want to be wakened during dream.

9 YEARS—Many have horrid scary dreams of being hurt, shot, or kidnapped. Not only child himself, but his mother or friend may be the victim.

Motion dreams: whirling, swimming, flying.

Daily experiences and personal worries.

Dream of natural events (storms, fire) or of being chased or threatened.

Aware that dream is stimulated by radio or cinema.

Some like to dream, especially in early morning, and may want to go back to sleep to finish a dream. Like to tell dreams.

15

SELF AND SEX

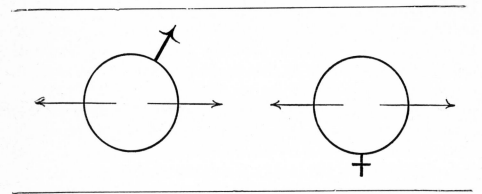

WHEN asked to give the very shortest definition of life, Claude Bernard, a great physiologist, answered "Life is creation." A newborn baby is the consummate product of such creation. And he in turn is endowed with capacities for continuing creation. These capacities are expressed not only in the growth of his physique, but in the simultaneous growth of a psychological self. From the sheer standpoint of creation this psychological self must be regarded as his masterpiece. It will take a lifetime to finish, and in the first ten years he will need a great deal of help, but it will be his own product.

What is the self made of? And how is it made? Basically, of course, it is made of the attributes and potentialities which were inherited from the baby's ancestors. But a baby does not come into his inheritance all at once, not even on his birthday. He comes into it gradually, over a long period of years through the impulses and organizing processes of growth. He has impulses to look, and listen, to touch and to explore the physical world. He has equally irrepressible impulses to explore the world of persons. Paradoxically, the development of his self depends upon the impact of other selves.

At first, he is so closely bound up with the milk that nourishes him, the bassinet that contains him, and with the internal sensations that suffuse him, that his embryonic self is virtually in a state of Nirvana. With the growth of the waking center of his brain (referred to in the earlier section on Sleep) he emerges out of this beatific absorption. He begins to take notice of the hands that minister to him, and a little later he stares intently at his own hands, as though he had made an important discovery. And so he has. Through sight, and active and passive touch, through ceaseless experimental contacts with the external physical world of things, he steadily builds up a fund of experience which becomes the core of his sense of bodily self-identity. It is a long process. We recently saw a bright but totally blind infant who, at the age of one year, was still in a state of confusion with respect to his relationship to his hands and to his feet. The seeing child has many advantages in arriving at a knowledge of his physical self. A looking glass is one advantage. Yet he will chase his own mirror image before he becomes wiser. And even as late as the age of three years, he cannot qualify for a hide-and-seek game, because, ostrich-like, he thinks he can conceal himself by simply covering his eyes with his hands! Picture him as he stands there, to the amusement of an older sib. His naivete in this interpersonal situation reveals the developmental complexity of the psychology of the self and its dependence upon social insight.

The social insight grows and patterns through a countless succession of interactions between the Baby and Some-One-Else. Nursery games illustrate the mechanism, and actually help the Baby to find himself. Peek-a-boo sets up an acute expectancy which is realized. *How-big-is-the-baby?* produces self-approval. *Give-it-to-me!* stimulates response to

some one else. *Rolling-a-ball* to and fro sets up reciprocity. The situations are simple but they reveal universal dynamisms of development
which continue to operate throughout childhood and youth. Sometimes the dynamism accentuates the ego; sometimes it accentuates the
social group or some member of the group. The accents vary with age,
with individual temperament, and with the specific situation. A child
may behave "socialized" in one situation, but reacts infantile in another
because of a specific immaturity. These variations are extremely interesting (rather than irritating) to the perceptive parent.

The 15-month-old infant provides an example. He no longer plays
the "Give-it-to-me" game as of yore. He intensifies his hold on the
object, because he has a new sense of possession, which, by the way, is an
important component of the sense of self. Conversely, he may even
refuse to take a cracker from his mother's hand! He will only accept
it if the cracker is proffered on a plate! Is he individualizing himself
at the moment by accentuating his detachment from her? Many of his
quirks of resistance and his assertive "me do it myself" are symptoms
of reorganizations going on in the territory of his ever changing self.

He also has his moments and spells of accentuated dependence. These
are not necessarily regressions to a lower level of behavior. He has to
strike a balance between two opposite tendencies: attachment to apron
strings and detachment therefrom. It is not surprising that occasionally
he overstresses one of the bipolar trends. Development does not pursue
a straight line course.

The adult offers his hand to a child. Note the fluctuating course
of the resultant behavior patterns between the first and the tenth year.
The 1-year-old accepts the adult hand as an aid to walking. At 18 months
he spurns the hand but accepts a run-about harness. At 21 months he
takes the initiative himself, comes to the adult and takes his hand and
leads him to a point of interest. At two-and-a-half years he refuses or
pulls away; at three years he accepts; at four he won't; at five he will. He
also shakes hands on request. At six he is refractory or unready to
shake hands; at seven he does so responsively, but not with ease. At

nine he shakes hands spontaneously. Not until ten is he certain to extend the right hand! Noting these variations which have their root in the motor as well as the social self of the child, adults need not be unduly sensitive nor insistent at failures to establish manual contact.

Language is a cultural tool which works in a reciprocal way. It helps, by communication to keep the social group together; it helps the individual to define his own status and to do his own thinking. Words are useful labels. They also are indicators to the observant parent. A child who over uses the pronoun *you* may be lagging in the concept *I*. At two-and-a-half years his speech may be imperious because he has difficult self problems to solve.

Many of his thinkings and feelings in regard to himself never come to utterance. He likes his name before he can speak it. He could scarcely realize himself if he didn't have a name. In the beginning was his name. He hears it so often that he finally identifies it with himself. Step by step he interprets other names and makes significant distinctions between pronouns in the first, second and third persons, and in nominative and accusative cases. The progress which he makes from the first to the tenth year might be summed up in a series of propositions which reflect his advancing insight:

1. "*Johnny*"—that's me. 2. I am I. 3. That's my mother. 4. That's my father. 5. He is a man. 6. I am a boy. 7. Susan is a girl. 8. She has a father and mother too. 9. I was a baby. 10. I grew. 11. I came from my mother. 12. I am going to get bigger. 13. I am going to school. 14. I am in the first grade. I have a mother and a teacher. 15. I am in the second grade. I hope my teacher likes me. I hope Freddie is not mad at me. 16. I am eight years old. I want to grow up. 17. I am ten years old. I read the . . . . . . magazine. I want to be an engineer when I'm a man, like my father.

In rough outline these statements show how the self expands, differentiates and incorporates new dimensions into its structure. The first differentiations have to do with the *me* and the *not me*. But very early the child has to reckon also with the distinctions of sex; at the age of two he distinguishes boys from girls by clothes, hats, and style of haircut. Soon he detects more fundamental physical differences. All this helps him to understand what he himself is. His early interests in sex are by no means purely sexual; they are part of a wide ranging curiosity which comprehends his whole environment. He cannot get his bearings unless he makes certain elementary observations and inferences, concerning mommies and daddies, boys and girls, animals and persons, men and women.

Of great psychological significance is his gradual realization that he has an *historical* self as well as a *present* self. *He* was once a *baby*! A little recapture of that babyhood by questioning, or even by dramatic revival helps to impart a new dimension to his enlarging self. At four or six his interest expands into the family tree from which he himself stemmed, and so he inquires about his relationships to parents, grandparents and great-grandparents. A 7-year-old observing his newborn brother taking a first meal at the breast, asked with astonishment, "Did I do that? And Mommy, did you do that too; and you too, Daddy?" He was in the throes of assimilating a tremendous fact. His questions reveal how closely the development of the self is intermeshed with the phenomenon of sex.

This does not mean that the whole, far ramifying structure of the self is built about a single framework of sex. The processes of generation and growth, to be sure, are so all important for the perpetuation of the species that they are strongly entrenched in the organism. But sexual functions do not necessarily play a despotic role in the patterning of child development. Instead the vast array of realities and attitudes which directly or indirectly pertain to sex must be assimilated into a yet more intricate complex, namely, the growing self. The problems of sexual hygiene cannot be rationally approached unless we see the facts of sex in perspective and recognize the subtle gradations by which they are incorporated into the total development of the individual self.

"Are you a little boy or a little girl?" This is a question which

Binet made famous. One addresses it to a child about the age of three years. Usually he (the boy!) responds correctly. But even at this age many children reply by giving their own names. Others respond in terms of an emphatic negative, "Not a girl!" (Does this vehement denial reflect the traditional jest indulged in by relatives who tease small children by attributing the wrong sex to them?) A bright child may counter with a jokingly incorrect response. An older child may indignantly deny the implication of the wording of the question with "No, I am a *big* boy!" Girls are a little more likely to reply "I'm a boy!" Whether this latter is a masculine protest, we do not know! But the variations and tenor of all these responses show how diversely self and sex are interrelated.

Having made a correct intellectual discrimination as to sex, it will still take years for the child to define and establish his proper role as a boy or a girl. Nothing follows automatically. Some writers even hold that it is the culture which impresses this role. Our own studies indicate that there are differences in temperamental predisposition, in psycho-motor demeanor, and in developmental timing which are intrinsic in nature. The differences may not be great, but they can be decisive and they cast doubt on any hypothesis which derives the sex differences in personality solely from environmental or cultural factors.

But the psychological differences between the two sexes are by no means simple. In children as well as in adults they vary enormously in kind and degree. By means of an elaborate masculinity-femininity test consisting of no less than 456 items Terman and Miles investigated the sex temperaments of groups of adolescents and adults, and found many statistically distinctive sex responses. To what extent the manifold differences are due to a cultural bias the statistics do not disclose. The bias itself must have been originally produced by innate differences in the sexes. In any event, the end result is that each sex tends to play the role assigned to it.

The child, however, must actively find and adapt himself to the role, which again is not a simple matter, because each individual of each sex has a distinctive equipment of innumerable qualities of maleness and femaleness. These qualities manifest themselves in behavior tendencies, which to some extent compete with each other, at least in the eyes of the culture. The 2-year-old begins to identify his own sex by making elementary distinctions based on dress, haircut, and possibly voice. A few months later he becomes interested in the differences between boys and girls in their mode of micturition. Still later each sex may imitate the other in an effort to understand this difference, and a great many other differences. Many of these imitations are simple dramatic projections, even when they happen to include the genitalia.

A young child when confronted by two rival alternatives, tends to try out both when he is relatively unfamiliar with the behavior in question. And so during the formative pre-school years, before the so-called sex role is well established, the child shifts rather readily from one sex role to another. Our guidance nursery staff is frequently amused to see how often the domestic corner of the nursery is occupied by the dominant males, age two-and-a-half to three years. This corner is equipped with nothing but dolls, beds, brooms, ironing board and general house-keeping facilities; and it is the boys who are doing the house-keeping, including laundry.

Four- and 5-year-old children often play the role of the opposite sex. Many a 4-year-old boy has asked for a doll for Christmas; and the 5-year-old often wants a doll house. The 4-year-old may know he is not orthodox; so he keeps his doll somewhat out of sight. He may also be conscious of the excessive cultural pressure exerted by the disapproval of his parents. (It is easy to overstress the virtues of masculinity and gallantry at this age.) Girls from five to six years old may want to wear boys' clothes and tuck in their hair. By the age of seven, the shifting in roles becomes less frequent. The assigned sex role is usually established, a little earlier in girls, who at about this time are likely to object to having their hair cut. This too is the time when girls in particular may manifest an intense desire to simply hold a baby, and to have a baby in the family. Which reminds us again that the area of sex-interests is wide and growing. It is not limited to the so called sex act; but relates to the whole complex network of interpersonal relations, and especially those of family life.

The problem of the parents is to help the child, be it boy or girl, to find his or her role in this broader family setting,—a role which is progressing toward marriage. The child needs guidance all along the way. Parents sometimes think they will wait until the child can understand, and then they will tell him the whole story! And that will be that! But it is never so simple and decisive. Something unexpected is likely to occur; and fortunately it often is much less serious than it appears to be at first blush. To be forearmed the parent should know in advance the sort of things which do happen at least to other children. The growth gradients and maturity traits deal with the concrete situations.

Even before the age of four, questions about marriage begin. The 4-year-old may ask questions about how a specific baby arrived into the family. He may not accept too factual information. He may think the baby is really born through the navel. Or he may prefer to think the baby was purchased. At five years his curiosity is less intense than at six years. At six his questions become more specific, and may show some interest in the mechanics of mating in animals. At seven these interests are less openly expressed; but the child reflects and muses on sex relationships as he does about many other aspects of life. If he has heard about "seeds" he thinks about one or two seeds. At eight his interest in the father's function in procreation becomes more realistic. He is more aware of the marital relationships of his mother and father; and perhaps more susceptible to a jealousy reaction. At nine and ten he naturally feels a deepening identification with his family. He displays it, paradoxically, by withdrawal tendencies, and by a heightened sense of shame at any shortcomings on the part of the household. *He is now tragically sensitive to disharmonies and antagonisms between his mother and father.* And this may have a more devastating effect upon the development of his personality than some minor and unintelligent sex episode on his part.

The period from five to ten years is not a dormant or a latent sexual period. It is a period of progressive organization. Unremitting elaborations of the self and sex attitudes are laying the foundation for the more acute developments of puberty. The guidance during this pre-critical period should consist in progressive orientation. Information must be skillfully imparted and also skillfully withheld; because it should be graduated to suit the occasion and the child's maturity. The same story needs to be told and retold in changing versions. Some facts should be given in advance as a buffer against misinformation. The chief goal, however, should be to preserve easy, mutual confidence between mother and child, father and child (sometimes the latter relationship is the more vital). If sex exploration or an adventure in nudity is reported or discovered, the parent should so far as possible rationalize it calmly in her own mind as well as in that of the child. Orientation, rather than mere instruction or discipline is the key to a solution. Often the supreme psychological moment for effective "sex" guidance arises when there is no sex problem at all. The child is taught by suggestion and by indirection. The two extremes to be avoided are over protection through silence and evasion; and over reliance on excessively candid information. The reticences and the securities of wholesome family life are the best long range guarantee of a normal development of self and sex. Reticence as well as information has a role in sex education.

There are enormous individual differences with respect to the strength of sexual characteristics among adults as well as children. Sheldon, for example, states that the viscerotonic temperament is "notably greedy for routine outward affection by members of his family." The attitude of parents will naturally color their outlook on the problems presented by the child. Misdirected emotion can be avoided only if the parent carefully interprets the individuality and developmental background of the child, as each problem arises. Intelligent, outgoing, factual children want and comprehend many facts

[316]

early. Other children are so slow or naive that they must be told a little at a time, with much repetition, and sometimes even a little skillful prodding. Some children again assimilate best by making their own deductions from a realistic knowledge of reproduction in animals. Sometimes the father is a better channel of information than is the mother.

A few children of both sexes seem blind to the implications of sex until a relatively advanced age. Boys are more likely to get sex "information" from non-parental sources. They are more active and persistent in experimental play and exploration. They bring home tales they have heard, new "bad" words they have learned. They ask for specific explanations; and parents can be of service in helping the boy to a suitable vocabulary. Comparing boys and girls as groups, girls tend to show a more precocious interest in sex than boys. Their questions are more comprehensive, and less dependent upon the stimulus of information picked up from other children. The questions seem to come from a more integrated curiosity.

It is evident, then, that the acquisition of a mature sense of self is an extremely intricate process in which the sphere of sex figures importantly, but not omnipotently. The younger the child the less developed the self, even though the vigor of self-assertion may be strong. With increasing age and social experience this self becomes less shallow; it grows in depth; it consolidates the past; it orients to the future. The child's awareness of his self expands with deepening awareness of others. At the age of two he takes an extra spoonful of gruel for Jackie, and another for Jane. Gradually he acquires a sense of hierarchy. He senses his seniority over his baby sister; but, he tends to defer to an older boy. At six years he has been known to say, "I hope they won't ask me to do baby things in school." By the age of ten he is so aware of standards that he is capable of hero worship. He begins to use the word *person* in a new way. The word is coming to represent a new concept, a new relationship to himself and to others. He may even ask, "Am I the type of person who could . . . . . or, who would . . . . . ?" An inarticulate child does not formulate the question; but he virtually asks it in numerous ways as he confronts the situations of his life. His increasing interest in the far-off future indicates that an irrepressible impulse to grow up is part of his irrepressible self.

GROWTH GRADIENTS

§1. SELF

8 WEEKS—Social smile at sight of another person's face.

12 WEEKS—Regards own hand; vocal social response.
Knows mother and recognizes her; enjoys evening play with father.

16 WEEKS—Fingers own fingers; spontaneous social smile.

20 WEEKS—Smiles at mirror image; cries when someone leaves him.

24 WEEKS—Smiles and vocalizes at mirror image; pats mirror and regards hand in contact; discriminates strangers.

28 WEEKS—Grasps feet.
Fingers mirror, regarding imaged fingers.

32 WEEKS—Withdraws from strangers.
In mirror, regards image of parts of body which are not in contact with mirror.

36 WEEKS—Responds to own name.
Regards hand as it moves along surface of mirror.

40 WEEKS—Waves bye-bye and pat-a-cakes.
Regards reflected movement of hand in mirror.

44 WEEKS—Extends object to person without release; again withdraws from strangers.
Placed before mirror, sits back and regards total image.

52 WEEKS—Gives object to another on request.

18 MONTHS—Hugs and shows affection toward doll or teddy bear.

21 MONTHS—Calls all other children "Baby."

2 YEARS—Can call himself by his own name.
Calls all men and women "Daddy" and "Mommy."
Feeds and toilets doll or teddy.
Says "I want" (27 months).

2½ YEARS—Calls self "I" and has an increasing sense of "I" especially in relation to immediate abilities.

Defines his sense of "I" by his imperiousness.

Calls other people "You."

A few, who have a slowly developing awareness of self, **confuse** "I" and "You."

Calls women "Lady" and men "Man," as distinguished from mommy and daddy.

Knows that he is a boy, like father and that he is different from girls and mothers (and vice versa).

Says "I need," and "I don't like."

Domestic play with doll or teddy; or plays with imaginary animal.

Relives babyhood verbally. May want to be a baby. May play role of baby (33 months).

3 YEARS—Sense of "I" becoming stronger.

Combines self with another in use of "We."

Says "I like."

Can tell difference between boys and girls but makes no distinction in his play.

Plays the role of an animal; or may play with an imaginary animal or imaginary human playmate.

Still appears to assume that others see the world as he does.

3½ YEARS—Beginning of temporary attachments to some one playmate, often of opposite sex. Girls more often the initiators of these attachments.

Interest in marriage and marrying. Proposes to parents and others.

Says "I love."

Interchange of parent-child role.

Plays the role of animals or of other people.

Plays with imaginary animal or imaginary human playmate.

4 YEARS—Expanding sense of self indicated by bragging, boasting and out of bounds behavior.

Tendency in play groups for a division along sex lines.

Beginning of strong feeling for and boasting about family and home.

Exhibits some self-criticism.

Begins to realize that other children are separate entities, like him in some ways but different in some ways. That they too have mothers and fathers, and thoughts and feelings of their own.

Is interested in growing older.

5 YEARS—Rather impersonal age. Self and others taken for granted.

Not as interested in own name or in names of others. "I am five" may be more important than "I am Johnnie."

Close and secure relationship with mother (or another adult); even blames mother for what he does. Mother center of the child's universe.

Believes that he and mother are "eternal." Likes to hear of mother's babyhood.

Self-contained, serious about himself, impressed with ability to imitate grownup behavior.

Needs, invites and accepts some supervision. Likes to ask permission and to help.

Likes to have things go smoothly.

Interest in immediate experiences. Realistic. Undertakes only what he can do.

6 YEARS—Child is center of his own universe. Is expansive, undiscriminating.

Interest in own babyhood, stories pertaining to himself, anything pertaining to himself. May act like a baby.

Conceives of himself as always living, past and future.

He knows everything, wants everything, wants to do everything his own way. Possessive of belongings and likes to display them.

His name is important to him. Likes to be called by own name and to write name on all his products.

Relationship with mother most difficult. May behave worst with her. Resists with "No I won't;" acts like a baby, is rude and argumentative. Also fears that she may die, or may not be at home when he returns.

Mother describes him as "changed for the worse."

Does not know when to ask for assistance. May not accept help when he needs it. Is domineering, stubborn, aggressive.

Wants and needs to be first, to be loved best, to be praised, to win.

Does not know what to do but resists direction of others; accepts direction only when it coincides with his idea of what he is doing.

Emotionally excitable, defiant.

Physically and verbally aggressive; belligerent and resistant when attacked.

Interest in good and bad behavior in himself and playmates.

7 YEARS—More aware of and withdrawn into himself. Absorbs impressions from what he sees, hears and does. Seems to be in "another world." May not hear commands.

Self-conscious about own body. Sensitive about exposing body. Does not like to be touched. Modest about toileting.

A definite minor strain: believes that others are mean and unfair.

Ashamed of fears, mistakes, or to be seen crying.

Protects himself by withdrawal. Spends more time alone. May be unwilling to expose knowledge for fear of being laughed at or criticized; or suddenly responds and withdraws. Leaves a scene when things are going badly.

Fear of losing own identity. May dislike new clothes, having hair cut. Begins to suspect that he will one day die. Denies this.

May believe that he is adopted, does not belong to his family.

Loses or hoards products. Forgets to put name on them.

His world is broadening and he is trying to place himself in the social and physical world.

Worries that his mother, teacher or playmates do not like him.

Wants his own place in family group and in school group. Wants his own place at table, in a car; wants his own desk, his own room.

Cautious in approach to anything new.

Less responsive to mother's demands. May say "Why should I?", "I don't feel like it."

Wants responsibility, especially at school, but concerned that he may not do well.

Slight skepticism about religion and Santa Claus.

Senses a goal but has little evaluation of it. Wants to complete a task if he starts it, but does not judge his capacity to do so. Apt to expect too much of himself.

8 YEARS—More outgoing, contacting people and places. Cannot stay out of contact with any part of environment. Seems to be trying his "self" against the environment.

Conscious of himself as a person, and recognizes some of his differences from others and voices them. Talks more freely about himself. Thinks about his "self."

Interested in his own inner anatomy.

Personality more expressive. Facial expressions and gestures are "like him."

Dramatizes. May seem to consider himself the center of the stage.

Belittles himself, expecting praise.

Wants adult to be a part of his world. Makes many demands of mother and wants her to act in certain ways.

Chief interest in relationships with others—children and adults.

Resents being treated as a child. Wants to be like adult. Begins to recognize that adult may know more than he does. Can't wait to grow up.

Can make up mind easily and can respond to reason. May respond with, "Oh all right, if you insist" if instruction is given in a way that suits him.

May have sudden shower of tears at "undeserved" criticism.

Give and take with another person needs to be in balance.

Tries to live up to standards of others. May feel guilty if he thinks he doesn't.

Concerned not only by what others do to him but what they do to others as well.

Expanding information and experience lead to knowledge that standards differ. Increasing identification with social, political groups and exclusion of those who are different.

Increased interest in distant and long-ago people and places.

9 YEARS—A "change for the better" at nine. Many earlier tangles smooth out. Less tension. Life simpler. Child more independent, self-sufficient, dependable, trustworthy. Frequent spurts of better behavior.

More responsible: can have key and let self into house, get a meal, go downtown, make simple purchases, phone if going to be late.

Very busy with own concerns. Doesn't have time for routines or parents' demands. Many are becoming "workers" and may prefer work to play.

Active and interested in many things: school work, succeeding at any task, the future, history, mechanical things, electricity, making things.

Much planning, in great and practical detail: for the immediate future or about going to college and what he will do when he grows up. Making of lists.

"Don't care" attitude, bold front; at other times anxious to please, wants to be liked. Loves to be chosen.

[321]

Increasingly self-conscious: about own activities, own body, own home, parents' and siblings' behavior.

Self-criticism: "I would do that," "Oh that's my poor memory." May be over-ambitious in demands of himself.

May be apprehensive about work and health.

Short-lived but innumerable complaints about many aspects of life.

Wants to succeed. Will work for a reward.

Sensitive and embarrassed by correction.

Some self-projection in beginning of crushes on others, or hero worship for others.

Child now oriented more toward his contemporaries than toward his parents. May experience some conflict between adult code and the code of his contemporaries.

Beginning of marked individual differences from child to child in all fields. Child's own individuality and personality making itself clearly apparent.

§2. SEX

18 MONTHS—*Sex interest and differentiation* Affectionate towards mother when tired, in trouble or when pants are wet.

Uses general term "baby" for both boys and girls.

2 YEARS—*Sex Interest and Differentiation* Shows strong affection toward parents: "My mommy," "My daddy." Kisses at bedtime.

Names genitals by word used for urination.

Distinguishes boys from girls by clothes and style of haircut.

Differentiates adults by general words, "lady" or "man," but continues to call children by specific names: "Jacky" or "Mary."

Babies Interest in the appurtenances of baby sibling: powder, soap, clothes, crib.

2½ YEARS—*Sex Interest and Differentiation* Conscious of own sex organs and may handle them when undressed.

Inquires about mother's breasts.

Knows that he is a boy like father and different from girls and mothers (and vice versa).

Non-verbalized generalization that boys and fathers have distinctive genitalia, and stand when they urinate; girls and mothers do not.

Shows interest in different postures of boys and girls when urinating.

Differentiates sex of children by general term "boy" and "girl."

If questioned about his sex, negates opposite sex, "I'm not a girl."

Beginning of interest in physiological differences between sexes.

Boys may prefer girls toys.

3 YEARS—*Sex Interest and Differentiation* Expresses affection by "I like" (3½ years—"I love").

Affirms own sex if questioned—"I am a boy."

Verbally expresses interest in physiological differences between sexes and in different posture for urinating. Girls attempt to urinate standing up.

Desire to look at or touch adults, especially mother's breasts.

Interest in marriage and marrying; proposes to either parent and others; thinks you can marry either sex.

No distinction between sexes in play.

Temporary and shifting attachment to some "friend" of the opposite sex (3½ years).

Babies Beginning of interest in babies, wants family to have one.

Asks questions: "What can the baby do when it comes?", "Where does it come from?"

Most do not understand mother when she answers that the baby grows inside of her.

4 YEARS—*Sex Interest and Differentiation* Extremely conscious of the navel.

Under social stress grasps genitals and may need to urinate.

May play the game of "show"; verbal play about eliminating and calling names relating to function.

Interest in other people's bathrooms; may demand privacy for himself, but extremely interested in bathroom activities of others.

Some segregation along sex lines.

Babies Questions about where babies come from. May believe mother's answer that the baby grows inside of the mother's "tummy," but may cling to the notion that the baby is purchased.

Questions about how the baby gets out of the mother's "tummy." May spontaneously think the baby is born through the navel.

5 YEARS—*Sex Interest and Differentiation* Familiar with, but not much interested in physical differences between the sexes.

Decrease in sex play and game of "show."

More modest and less exposing of themselves.

Less bathroom play, less interest in strange bathrooms than earlier.

Aware of sex organs when adult seen undressed and may wonder why father doesn't have breasts or sister a penis.

Boy may reject girls' toys such as dolls, although he may make a doll's bed in carpentry, or take part in house play.

Takes opposite sex largely for granted, little distinction between sexes in play. Frequent boy-girl pairs.

Babies Interest in baby and in having a baby of their own; may dramatize this.

Some boys as well as girls may relate back to when they were in mother's stomach, or to future when they will have a baby of their own.

Re-asks, "Where do babies come from?" and accepts "mother's stomach" as an answer.

Some cling to the idea that you buy the baby at a hospital.

Make little connection between size of pregnant woman and presence of a baby.

6 YEARS—*Sex Interest and Differentiation* Marked awareness of and interest in differences in body structure between sexes. Questioning.

Mutual investigation by both sexes reveals practical answers to questions about sex differences.

Mild sex play or exhibitionism in play or in school toilets. Game of "show."

Some children are subjected to sex play by older children.

May play hospital and take rectal temperatures.

Calling names, remarking or giggling involving words dealing with elimination functions.

Some confusion in differentiation of male and female. May dress in attire of opposite sex.

Interest in marriage to someone of opposite sex, often to a relative.

Strong interest of older boy for younger girl.

Babies Interest in origin of babies, pregnancy and birth.

Vague idea that babies follow marriage.

Interest in how baby comes out of mother and if it hurts.

Some interest in knowing how baby started. Accepts idea that baby grows in mother's stomach and started from a seed.

If told of intercourse by older playmates, child may be disturbed and usually questions mother.

Wants a new baby in the family.

Wants to hold baby after it is born.

7 YEARS—*Sex Interest and Differentiation* The child has long since satisfied interest in differences in physique between the sexes. Less interest in sex.

Some mutual exploration, experimentation and sex play, but less than earlier.

Interest in sex role and characteristics of boys and girls.

May be last age when boys and girls play together regardless of sex lines.

Strong and persistent boy-girl love affairs with the idea of marriage usually strong.

Babies Intense longing for a new baby in family usually of own sex.

Knows that having babies can be repeated and that older women do not have them.

Interested in mother's pregnancy. Excited about baby's growth. Wants to know how it is fed, how big it is, how much it costs.

Interest in literature, such as *The Story of a Baby*, by Marie Ets.

Associates size of pregnant woman with presence of baby.

Satisfied to know that baby came from two seeds (or eggs), one from mother and one from father.

May ask details of birth. Just where mother will be, how baby will get out.

8 YEARS—*Sex Interest and Differentiation* Interest in sex rather high, though sex exploration and play less common than at six. Girls may be unusually responsive to touch and rough play with boys.

Interest in peeping, smutty jokes, provocative giggling; whisper, write or spell "elimination" and "sex" words.

Girls begin to question about menstruation.

Boys recognize pretty girls and girls, handsome boys.

A boy may have several girls but he knows he is going to marry only one of them. But fewer boy-girl twosomes.

Plan to have own home when married.

Sexes begin spontaneously to draw apart in play.

Babies Warm and loving interest in babies.

Understands slow process of growth of baby within mother; connects appearance of pregnant woman with a baby.

Wants more exact information as to where baby is in mother's abdomen. Confused by use of word "stomach."

Some girls may ask about father's part in procreation.

9 YEARS—*Sex Interest and Differentiation* May talk about sex information with friends of same sex.

Interest in details of own organs and function; seeks pictorial information in books.

May be self-conscious of exposing body.

May not wish parent of opposite sex to see him nude.

Sex swearing; sex poems.

Division of sexes in play; if mixed, may stimulate kissing games; teasing about "girl" or "boy" friends.

Babies May relate selves to process of reproduction, "Have I a seed in me?"

Some NINES may still think that baby is born by Caesarian section.

16

INTERPERSONAL RELATIONS

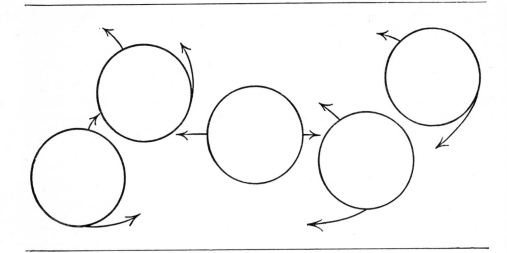

THE roots of the growth of a child's personality reach into other personalities. The detailed make-up of his personality depends upon the interpersonal relationships which he experiences from day to day, from age to age. If he did not come into contact with other human beings from the moment of birth, he could scarcely acquire a distinctive personality recognizable either to himself or to others.

His personal self, however, as shown in the previous chapter, is subject to the laws of growth. These laws place limitations on the *kinds* of contacts and the *depth* and *scope* of the contacts which he can make with other persons, young or old. Even a cursory reading of the growth gradients at the end of this chapter will demonstrate the presence of maturity factors and the resulting involvedness of the "anatomy" of the child's personality.

We need not fear the connotations of the word "anatomy," because the child's personality assuredly is a living structure, made up of attitudes, predispositions and potentialities. His personality is not a pure essence which in some obscure way absorbs the influences of abstract good and evil. It is a patterned and a patterning fabric which takes form and gives form within countless interpersonal relationships.

These relationships are so diversified that it will be useful to draw a map indicating their field of operation. The accompanying chart is, of course, highly diagrammatic. It represents the child in the midst of interpersonal forces which impinge upon him at home, at school and in the community.

HOME includes father, mother, grandparents, sibs, kin, visitors and guests (young and old). SCHOOL includes teachers, classmates, principal, janitor, supervisors, playmates and pupils from the various grades. COMMUNITY includes a host of persons and institutions, regularly or occasionally encountered on street, road and byways: in shops, at church or theatre, in clubroom, park and public places. The community includes also the intangible and yet personal forces which are embodied in laws, manners and customs, the local mores and the prevailing attitudes toward racial and minority groups.

Our schematic map pictures the child in a kind of electronic vortex symbolized by lines and arrows! These electronic arrows fly shuttle-like to emphasize that the interpersonal relation between the child and all his associates is truly a two-way interaction. Other persons react upon the child; but the child also reacts upon the other persons. The gradients which follow show the growth trends of these interactions. The diagram indicates that the child's personal world is a kind of web which he himself has helped to weave. Just as in Nature the circle of one creature's life cuts into the circles of many other

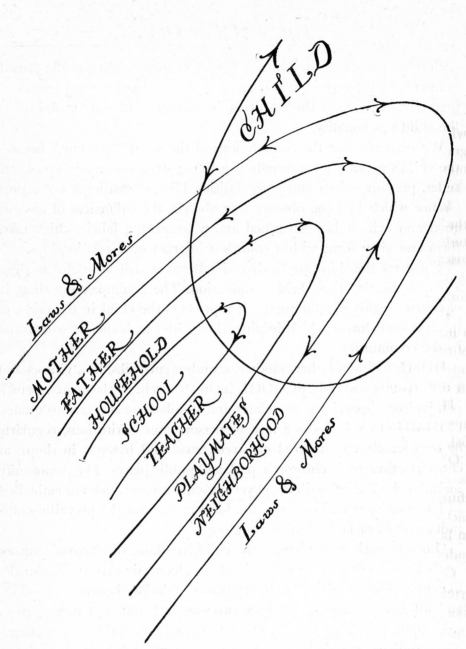

CHILD

Laws & Mores

MOTHER

FATHER

HOUSEHOLD

SCHOOL

TEACHER

PLAYMATES

NEIGHBORHOOD

Laws & Mores

SCHEMATIC MAP OF INTERPERSONAL RELATIONS

creatures, so in the psychological development of a child we glimpse the strands of a "web of life,"—a ceaseless process of adaptation to other individuals which registers itself in the tissue of the child's personality. Even the tensions and the maladjustments between parent and child are efforts at mutual adaptation. A knowledge of the ways of growth makes for improved adaptations. Anatomically regarded the child's personality consists of an indescribably intricate web of interpersonal relationships.

The detailed gradients of these relationships show how unprofitable it is to consider the social nature of the child in generalized terms. His social characteristics consist of concrete tendencies and orientations; far from remaining static these orientations are constantly changing. In a general way we may say that he loves his parents and likes his teacher; but this does not tell us much about the actual pattern or trend of his relationships. Sometimes his affection fastens more strongly on his mother, sometimes on the father. It is not a fixed quantity and parents should not expect an unvarying level of attachment. Each parent may anticipate temporary periods when the child shows relative indifference.

HOME

At the age of two years the child may actually be overtaxed when both parents are present at the same time; he can adjust to each one individually, but not to both simultaneously. At later ages he has comparable difficulties in apportioning his affection evenly. Parents will find it wise to shift their roles from time to time. When necessary they may even permit unilateral confidences, if the child so demands. At the ages of six and eight, children are rather deeply embroiled with their mothers. The 8-year-old is often so deeply sensitive toward his mother that he betrays impatience if she deviates even a moment from the consuming demands he makes upon her. This intensity can show itself in qualms of jealousy when mother and father are together. At the age of six the same child may have expressed both deep affection and contradictory hate. At seven his relations, though still variable, tended to be more smooth and companionable. At six he probably feared and admired his father more than his mother. At nine the father-child bonds strengthen, particularly if the father is companionable and respects the child's increased maturity. The child has reached the age when he is beginning to evaluate (intellectually and morally) his parents' actions and standards of conduct.

It is idle, of course, to exact affection, or to stipulate its occasions. Parents and their children must grow up together, and work out their several compatibilities in terms of temperament and maturity. Parents are likely to overlook the maturity factors and to be unduly sensitive in regard to the unforeseen fluctuations in the child's attitudes. Many of these fluctuations have a natural developmental basis. One need not worry. When the child himself reaches maturity his fundamental regard for his parents will prove to be the summation of an overall trend of development throughout a long stretch of years.

During the years from five to ten the parent-child relationship demands a high degree of flexibility. If there is more than one child in the family the principle of impartiality should not be applied too artificially. Each relationship is unique, and parents need not treat all children alike. With varying accent a child may display several stages of response: dependence, demandingness, indifference, worship and companionship. Comparable developmental variations reveal themselves in the relationships between siblings, even when every effort is made to avoid envy and jealousy. Oftentimes the frictions are temporary; many could be avoided if the household permitted the children to spend more time apart. The amicability span, like the attention span, tends to be shorter for younger children.

The family unit is a complex institution.* It needs more planning and deliberate self-appraisal than it ordinarily receives. This is particularly true when the household has to reckon not only with children,

---

* This is reflected in the increasing emphasis placed on the family as the basic unit in social welfare. *The National Conference on Family Relations* has been organized in recent years (Chicago) to serve as a clearing house for informed and advanced thinking on marriage and family living.

but with uncles, aunts, grandmothers and grandfathers. Inasmuch as we cannot cover the whole gamut of these complications, let us venture a few comments concerning grandparents!

The recording angel alone can do justice to the many practical services and to the words of counsel which an understanding grandmother supplies in a busy household. Her presence and contacts greatly enrich the experiences of her growing grandchildren. The 5-year-old is usually very fond of his grandparents. The 7-year-olds and 8-year-olds find a special pleasure in playing games with grandmother. She may have a special brand of patience or insight that they do not find elsewhere. The emotional bond with relatives is naturally different from the parent-child relationship and these extra bonds may exert a broadening beneficial influence on the developing personality of the child.

But there are hazards in this very relationship if the grandparents, unwittingly or otherwise, overstep their prerogatives. For better or for worse, the *mother and father* should be responsible for the government and management of the home. *They*, as parents (and not as children of their own parents!) should determine the goals of the family life. On matters of so-called discipline the judgment of the parents ought to prevail. Grandmother can claim no natural authority in these matters, although her consultative wisdom may often prove invaluable.

If she becomes too exacting, her misplaced strictness can easily disturb the domestic tranquillity. Perhaps she becomes too severe with the 9-year-old who is growing up, and who has a symptomatic aversion to being "treated like a little child." She may grievously misunderstand the 6-year-old when he bursts out with one of his aggressive verbal threats. Granted that a 6-year-old can, on occasion, be very "rude," his shocking behavior must be philosophically managed. He has even been heard to say, with probably more echo than comprehension: "If Grandma wants to be a burden, let her be a burden!"

The family is evidently a closely knit body-politic. Psychologically it consists of a veritable network of interpersonal relationships, subject to normal tensions and sometimes to abnormal frictions. The child's

developing image of family life is chiefly the outgrowth of the experiences which he undergoes in his own home-circle. If harmony prevails
it will help to integrate his orientations and to direct his affections. No
disquisition is necessary to show that maladjustment between husband
and wife has far-reaching effects upon the emotional life of perceptive
children. Marital divorce, therefore, can at times do deep psychological
damage to a child.

Perceptiveness, of course, varies with maturity as well as inborn
sensitiveness. It is interesting to note the stages by which the ordinary
child achieves a progressive insight into the meaning of family life. At
18 months he likes the run of the house, is interested in household
activities such as sweeping and dusting, and will soon participate in
putting away the groceries. By three years he is helpful in little tasks
and errands. By four years his identification with his home has become
personal and self-conscious, even to the extent of boastfulness. At five
years he may use the word "family" in a manner that suggests that he
has attained an elementary concept of the family as a social group.

During the sixth year he gives many evidences of forging to a higher
level of relationships, even though he, at times, seems self-centered,
resistant, or overly mother-centered. He takes a new kind of interest
in family outings, family secrets, and paternal and maternal relatives.
SEVEN in his little serious way has a deepened sense of the family as an
institution; he is proud of his home and family possessions; even his
negative behavior betrays an emotional strengthening of the family ties.
EIGHT is somewhat less subjective; he is interested in the family as a
going concern, and at a festival gathering he is especially anxious that
everyone should be having a full share in the good time. NINE likes to
be on his own, likes to be with his friends and away from his family. It
gives him a growing sense of self-sufficiency. But at the same time he
shows increased awareness of family standards and of differences between
his family and that of his friends. His greater sensitivity denotes a
deepening personal identification with his family. The steady processes
of growth have wrought extraordinary changes in his family relationships since the innocence of age five. During the teens there will be

another series of significant transformations; but the basic orientations are well-nigh complete by the age of ten.

SCHOOL

The school is a larger social unit than the home; but it is much less complex, and in many ways less decisive in the organization of the child's personality. It brings about, however, important extensions in the network of his interpersonal relationships.

The school-beginner is confronted with a whole host of problems of social adjustment. Even if he has acquired some background wisdom as a member of a nursery-school, he is obliged to make many readjustments; moreover, he is no longer a nursery-school child. He has the new impulses and the new uncertainties which come with being six years old. The smoothness of his school entrance will hinge largely upon his emotional maturity. The school world may seem so different from his home world that he will tend to retreat into the latter. In cases of acute conflict he may even react with a temporary stomach ache, or other symptoms of immature morale.

Usually, however, he weathers his transitional difficulties, and will soon regard that strange new adult, called a teacher, with various degrees of tolerance, awe and affection. He comes to consider her word law. He likes to please her, likes to be commended by her, but he is related to her not so much in emotional terms as through the activities and physical materials of the school program. When these activities appeal to him he makes a so-called good adjustment to the first grade. At seven years the teacher-child interdependence is more personal; and his adjustment to school is more dependent on an interpersonal relationship.

The pattern of that relationship, however, is, or should be, different from that between parent and child. Teachers should not take over the mother role, and parents, for similar reasons, should give all possible support to the role of the teacher. The amount of interplay of these two roles will vary enormously with the age of the child and other factors. In complex situations the aid of a third intermediary in the form of a visiting teacher or educational guidance worker is very beneficial. Parent-teacher complications are avoided if the psychological needs of the child are always considered paramount.

The teacher-child relationship undergoes natural developmental changes as the child progresses through the elementary grades. In the kindergarten he responds best to a homey, friendly teacher who is chiefly concerned with releasing the spontaneous interests of the children. The successful first grade teacher typically likes to work with materials herself; she manages a fluent group as a whole, through skillful manipulation of her activity program. The second grade teacher depends rather more on perceptive personal contacts with individual children. The third grade children like a comradely, factual, business-like teacher, who, in their eyes, can be a good sport and keep the show running. Personality factors continue to count in the fourth and fifth grades; but the pupils are now less submerged by the school group. The 9-year-old and the 10-year-old have attained a measure of detachment. They understand themselves better; and they have some capacity to step aside and make an objective appraisal of the teacher. They respect a teacher who knows, and who can satisfy their critical interest in Why? and How? They are anxious to perfect their skills in the tool subjects, so they can launch out into the new fields which they are eager to conquer. If now and then they play a mild practical joke on the teacher, it is probably because they are sensing a new kind of confidence in themselves. An understanding teacher will know what it is all about in terms of social psychology, to say nothing of the psychology of her own self.

Social mechanisms are at work. School life is beginning more and more to pre-figure and to forecast sociological and even political end results. The child from five to ten is indeed an embryo citizen, if we recognize the embryological processes which are shaping his attitudes toward his fellow man in the schoolroom, on the playground and in his neighborhood. This leads to a brief consideration of the child's interpersonal relationships in terms of the larger community of which home and school are a part.

THE COMMUNITY

It is difficult to draw any sharp precinct lines separating various areas of the community. Electrons keep to their orbits, but in the vast domain of interpersonal relationships, private, domestic and public circles are forever cutting across and into each other. When we say that radio and television have brought the outside world into the home (and the school!) we are scarcely using a metaphor; because the essence of the community is a psychological compound of awarenesses, ideas and attitudes. Developmentally, therefore, we can see the sketchy beginnings of the "community" in the early experiences which take the child beyond the confines of the family. Visitors from the outside come into the home; he greets the postman or the grocery boy; he takes a trip to the market; he joins a playgroup in the neighbor's yard.

It takes him many years to master the elementary structures of the community. He must become acquainted with it in terms of time and space, and its physical technology. Step by step he becomes aware of houses other than his own, of doors, windows, streets, curbstones, elevators, traffic lights, automobiles, airplanes. As physical phenomena these multitudinous impacts come without much order or sequence; but he assimilates them in terms of his interpersonal experiences. His social self alone can give meaning and order to the physical community. He becomes community-wise through other persons, particularly his playmates.

He has to adapt to them. Thereby he learns what a community is, both in peace and war. At 18 months he has scarcely made a distinction between persons and things; at 21 months he hits or hugs a playmate without discretion, without modulation; at two years his constant refrain is "Its mine." But at three years, as noted before, he shows a germinating capacity for cooperative play and can even wait his turn. This capacity increases through the years that follow. But the complexity

[335]

of the social situations also increases. Accordingly there are many manifestations of self-assertion and self-aggrandizement along the way. Normally the social and the selfish forces counterpoise each other so that the overall trend is favorable in spite of tattling, exclusions, cheating, sulking, ganging up, secret pass-words, wrangling, and combat. However, if the adverse behavior is not kept in bounds, and if it is not resolved *in its immediate contexts* by the child with the legitimate help of an adult, the overall trend can be decidedly unfavorable. The years from five to ten can breed delinquency and can lay the foundations for poor citizenship.

All interpersonal conflicts are specific; they have pattern and concrete context. When they are serious enough to demand adult intervention, they should not be handled too impersonally, or too intellectually. Appeals to virtue in the abstract are rather futile. The child is entangled in a specific situation, and *this* is the situation in which he needs assistance so concrete that his specific feelings and insight will be modified. It is a present incident, and the less said about the past or future the better.

The spontaneous groupings which take place on the playground are primarily determined by maturity factors. In the pre-school years there is a discernible progression from solitary to parallel, to sporadic cooperation, and to sustained cooperation and imaginative play. At seven there is an interesting developmental phase in which group and individual tendencies oscillate as though competing for dominance. The 8-year-old has a keen zest for group activity. At nine years his group consciousness is so strong that he likes to organize and to belong to a club, to accept a role in a group, to contend as a member of a group. The group solidarity is so strong that if a feud starts on the playground it is likely to carry over into the schoolroom,—an early example of how group loyalties overlap, even in juvenile years.

The spontaneous sex groupings likewise reveal the presence of innate maturity factors. The 3-year-old can affirm his sex; but he makes no sex distinctions in his playmates until about a year later. At four years there is a tendency toward division along sex lines in group play. At seven years a boy and girl may pair off as playmates for a period of weeks or months, but the larger play groupings generally ignore sex lines. In another year boys and girls begin to separate in their play; and from nine years to the teens there is a definite period of segregation. The segregation is marked variably by self-consciousness, sexual modesty, shyness, passing hostilities, giggling, teasing, spying, feuds and derisions. However temporary these diverse manifestations prove to be, they indicate the complexity of the growth processes which underlie the social nature of man.

The culture attempts to bring the social and anti-social impulses of the child under control through morals, mores, and many minor conventions including manners. Such controls are indispensable; they become most effective in practical application when we recognize the developmental stage at which the child is functioning in a given situation. We cannot justly appraise the ability of the child to meet an interpersonal situation unless we make allowance for his temperament and estimate the difficulty of the demands made upon him.

RACIAL ATTITUDES

The problem of racial antagonisms has become so important in our American culture that it deserves consideration in the present chapter. Inter-racial tensions involve complex political, economic and religious factors, but for children the problems are mainly psychological and concern interpersonal adjustments.

Strictly speaking, a race or a racial group is based on community ancestry. Every true race doubtless has certain innate physical and mental characteristics which distinguish it. Races, like individuals, are not born alike. Many so-called racial differences, however, are not due to ancestry or heredity, but to cultural differences,—differences of language, nationality, tradition, manners and customs. In the last analysis we have to reckon with problems of individual and group behavior; that is, with interpersonal relationships.

Prior to the teens children tend to be catholic and cosmopolitan in their inter-racial contacts. A pre-school child may be as fond of a black doll as of a white. Most three-year-old children are scarcely aware of differences of color, or for that matter of sex and other individualizing characteristics. Polyglot groups fraternize and intermingle harmoniously.

At about four years of age an exclusive *in-group* feeling definitely asserts itself. Children still play together cooperatively; but every once in a while several children will separate and organize into an in-group which actively and noisily excludes the other children. The exclusion is more likely to be on sex lines than color lines. The seceding group, for example, sets up a post-office and with brave words ("You can't play with us!") repels the minority group. The exclusion is temporary. It may last for fifteen minutes or a forenoon. Then it vanishes. But it may recur on a morrow in new circumstances and with new groupings.

It recurs because it is a mechanism of development. The exclusions may seem very arbitrary, but they have a developmental logic. By banding themselves together for negative as well as positive reasons, the children spontaneously practice group action and intensify group consciousness. They are exercising their powers of social behavior. The behavior is relatively innocent. We do not need to take these transient bravadoes and intolerances too seriously.

In moments of verbal aggressiveness the 6-year-old may indulge in vigorous anthropological name callings; at seven he may shout a folk rhyme derision and even gang up on a "racial" victim. At eight and nine years clubs may be organized with exclusion as their primary purpose. The exclusion occasionally follows racial lines. Under normal conditions these racial discriminations are neither deep seated nor persistent. Under unfavorable environmental conditions they may prepare the way for unintelligent and stereotyped racial attitudes. Left to themselves ordinary American children are not inclined to develop serious interracial tensions and conflicts. But children, of course, are not left to themselves. They are constantly subject to the attitudes, the preferences and the antipathies of their elders. Through deliberate imitation, and still more, through subconscious suggestion the children acquire the likes and dislikes expressed by their elders.

This suggests how cultural controls can be strengthened. Home, school and community should avoid the contagion of prejudice which comes from slighting remarks and uncritical generalizations. *Races and nations should not be slurred as groups. All persons should be appraised in terms of their merits as individuals.*

A sociologist recognizes a legitimate kind of attitude which is not colored by prejudice or antagonism, but which can be called a race feeling, namely "the ancient and deep seated preference of practically every individual for his own kind of people." Individuals then adjudge each other as individuals on the basis of proven and potential qualities. Justice between persons becomes a more significant and difficult virtue than undiscriminating benevolence in the planning and practice of social living.

An attitude is an habitual tendency to react in a characteristic manner in a given situation. The refinement of interpersonal attitudes accordingly constitutes one of the major tasks of elementary education. We know that adolescence is the period when all social attitudes, racial and otherwise, come to their final stages of development. This is the optimal period for educational control; but the basic groundwork should be prepared in the first decade of life. Children from five to ten have more insight into their mental processes than we give them credit for. We do not listen closely enough to what they say and how they say it. With shrewd suggestion and skillful spot guidance, while the occasion still tingles with its emotional realities, it is possible to help children toward more concrete self-control. We rely too much on abstract, remote, idealistic goals. Fortunately we improve our own interpersonal relationships when we become more perceptive and alert to the concrete interpersonal relations of our children.

GROWTH GRADIENTS

§1 . MOTHER-CHILD

4 WEEKS—Cries for social attention; quiets if picked up.

8 WEEKS—Social smile at sight of a person's face.

16 WEEKS—"Recognizes" his mother.
Notices sounds, especially voices.

20 WEEKS—May cry when people leave.

28 WEEKS—Enjoys people. Demands more of the one who feeds him.

40 WEEKS—Enjoys family group.
Continues to demand more of mother but also a special positive response to her.
Smiles at mother when urinating.
May be best alone with one person.

1 YEAR—Very social.
Enjoys kissing.

18 MONTHS—Affectionate with mother when tired, in trouble, or if pants are wet.
May refuse to be toileted by anyone except mother.

21 MONTHS—More responsive to mother but also more demanding of her than formerly.
Calls mother back at bedtime for an extra goodnight.
Has definite demands as to how mother shall speak and act.

2 YEARS—More affectionate with mother and more dependent on mother.
Kisses and clings to mother at bedtime. Not only kisses but may verbalize affection.
Will now willingly sit on lap and accept affection from mother.
Begins to demand that mother do certain things: leave room and come back only when he finishes with toileting; go out of room while he feeds himself. Very insistent about such demands.

2½ YEARS—Child is at his best and at his worst with his mother. Most tantrums with mother but most loving with her.
The great number of mother-child difficulties occur as mother attempts to administer simple daily routines. Child squirms out of mother's hands when being ministered to and may slip under the bed. Actual physical restraint often necessary. Child makes two-way response ("I don't want to—I do want to") to nearly every situation.

Long bedtime rituals and much calling back for kiss, drink, to tell that he loves mother etc.

May want mother if in trouble at night, though quiets more quickly for father.

Domineering with mother. Orders her around. Insists that she behave in certain ways.

Less clinging and less direct dependence on mother.

3 YEARS—Gets on well with mother. Mother usually the favored parent at this age.

Child may be of real help to mother around the house.

Child relives babyhood, talking it over with mother.

May want to get into parents' bed during the night.

4 YEARS—Great pride in mother. Boasts about her away from home, and quotes her as an authority.

Frequently resists mother's authority, both physically and verbally.

May threaten mother with: "Wait till I'm your mother."

5 YEARS—Mother seems to be center of the child's world. Relationship smooth, pleasant and not over-intense.

Likes to do things correctly, as mother desires. Likes to obey.

Likes to help mother, be near her, play or work near her. Tells her what he is doing.

Does not require all mother's attention though he likes her presence.

Expresses affection for mother: "I like you, mummy."

Sympathetic and helpful if mother is ill.

Likes to have mother at home when he returns home from school. Is disturbed if she is not there.

Accepts punishment from mother though it glides right off.

May say "You're a mean mommie." Blames mother, saying, "Look at what you made me do."

May talk of marrying mother (boys).

Again relives babyhood and likes to hear of mother's babyhood.

Needs, invites and accepts mother's supervision in learning.

6 YEARS—Mother no longer center of child's world; child himself now holds this position.

This shift, and separation of child from mother has not yet been achieved; is merely being achieved. Leads to much difficulty and dissension. Child and mother are embroiled.

As at 2½ years, child is at his best and at his worst with mother.

Very sensitive to mother's moods, emotions and tensions.

Contradictory responses toward mother: says he loves her, then says he hates her; says he wishes she were dead, but worries that she may die.

Unwilling to accept help which he needs from mother.

Child is rude, resistant, and argumentative toward mother. Speaks rudely to her; says "No I won't," "Try and make me." Strikes her.

What mother does is important, not, as later, what she thinks.

Not good about accepting directions, and is hard to punish.

Tantrum response.

Child "takes things out" on mother. Threatens: "I'll get another mother."

7 YEARS—On the whole child gets on well with mother, likes to do things with her at times. A "we" age for mother and child.

Relationship more companionable and less intense than earlier.

Variable in this as in other things: may become moody and sulky, "mad" at mother.

Likes to argue with mother: "But mommie . . ." However you can begin to reason with him and appeal to him ethically.

Easier to discipline as he is sensitive to praise and blame. Obeys mother quite well *if* he hears what she says.

May be extremely proud of his mother and self-conscious about her in public.

Occasional strong battle of wills between child and mother.

8 YEARS—Child "all mixed up" with mother; haunts her; wants all her attention.

Strong physical and verbal expressions of admiration and affection for mother.

Tries to live up to what he believes is mother's standard for him; often feels that he fails.

Child has definite standards of how mother shall speak and act (almost like 21 months). Unhappy if she fails to respond in the expected manner.

What mother thinks as well as what she does about child is important to him.

Obeys mother if she words direction in way which pleases him.

Very sensitive toward mother: tears likely to well up. May be sensitive even to a change in facial expression. An emotional relationship.

Likes to please mother and very responsive to praise.

May be jealous of mother and father when they are together.

9 YEARS—Child wants to be on his own and makes less demand of time and attention from mother because he is busy and self-centered. The relation smoother, provided that mother treats child with respect for his increased maturity.

Child may be demonstrative, affectionate and anxious to please, at times.

Boys especially react against mother's demands that they be neat and clean. They are becoming more independent about large matters: mothers react by exercising authority in little matters.

Some are quite indifferent to mother's directions, admonitions, scoldings. They have a "deaf ear" at home.

Some are sulky, "growling," fault-finding with mother. Others are bold and argumentative.

Best relation with parent in regard to some activity which really interests both: girls and mothers share interest in cooking, clothes etc.

He does not like to be reminded, by mother, of himself as a young child. Some boys may be embarrassed at being bathed by mother.

Beginning to "put things over" on mother.

Opinion of contemporaries may be much more important than that of parents.

§2. FATHER-CHILD

8 Weeks—Social smile at sight of person's face.

12 Weeks—Enjoys evening play with father.

28 Weeks—Enjoys people but demands more of mother than of father.

40 Weeks—Enjoys social play with family group.
  Vocalizes "dada" and "mama."

52 Weeks—Likes reciprocal social games with any member of family.

18 Months—May enjoy moderate rough-housing with father.
  May refuse toileting or other routines administered by father.

21 Months—Father coming in unexpectedly at mealtime may be disturbing.
  Any change in routine may be disturbing and father often unwittingly causes such changes.
  Father likely to step in firmly with rigid requirements: "Time my son stayed dry" etc. when child is not quite ready for them.

2 Years—Father often a great favorite but child may demand mother if in trouble or if tired.
  Child may find it difficult to be with both parents simultaneously.

2½ Years—Very definite ideas of which person he wants to have do things for him. "Mummy do" or "Daddy do." Varies from day to day or week to week.
  May ask for mother at night though may quiet more quickly for father.
  Domineering with father as with mother.
  Going to extremes, the child may be very demonstrative toward father at one time, and at another may say "I don't like you." Father usually surprised and hurt by this sudden "dislike."

3 Years—Mother commonly the favored parent at this age, but father can take over in many situations.
  Child clings less at bedtime and may go to sleep more quickly for father.
  Each parent should have authority over certain *kinds* of situations; should not try to divide authority or child will play one against the other.

3½ Years—Girls propose to fathers. Say "I love."

4 Years—Child boasts about father outside of home. Quotes him as an authority.
  Excursions and times alone with father greatly prized, though father may need to use techniques.
  Some, however, say they hate father, especially if his being at home cuts them off from mother.

[343]

5 YEARS—Some now for first time accept father when mother is ill.

> Relations with father smooth, pleasant, undisturbed.
> Enjoys special occasions (excursions) with father.
> Boys, especially, may prefer father to mother, but this is **exceptional.**
> Takes punishment better from mother than from father.
> Fond and proud of father, and may obey father better than mother.

6 YEARS—Both fears and admires father more than mother.

> Usually respects father's word as law and does not question it.
> Is not rude and resistant to father as to mother.
> Feelings hurt by a cross word from father.
> Child may believe that father—in his office—knows everything that happens.
> Many situations can be carried through more successfully and with less friction by father.
> Child enjoys playtime with father and may demand every minute of father's time while he is in the house.

7 YEARS—Variable from child to child and from time to time.

> Father's role may be slight at this age as child is occupied with his own activities.
> Some, especially boys, "worship" father, think he is wonderful. Have long, confidential talks with him. Confide their worries, troubles and even sometimes their misdeeds.
> Girls are more sensitive to any reprimand from father and may be jealous of his attention to mother.

8 YEARS—Relationship with father less intense but smoother than that with mother.

> Less ardent expressions of affection toward father but less demanding of him. Can allow him to make a mistake.
> Likes father's company but does not insist on his complete attention.
> Respects father's opinion and authority and (usually) obeys his commands.
> Father frequently needs to step in to settle disputes between mother and child.
> Child's best responses may come with his father at this age.

9 YEARS—Relationship smooth when father respects child's increased maturity.

> Boys often come into new relationship with fathers, sharing real interests. Child shows respect for father's technical knowledge. Father-son may group together against female interference.
> Very sensitive of criticism from father. Thinks highly of his good regard.
> Relationship with father largely through things they *do* together.
> Most "approve" of father except for occasional specific criticism of his actions, as that he drives too fast—or too slowly.
> May feel superiority in pride over father's occupation.

§3. SIBLINGS

18 Months—Calls all other children "baby," but treats them as objects rather than as persons and no marked interest in them.

May like to look at new sibling, but does not wish to play with him.

May accept attention from older sibling, but more responsive to adult than to children.

2 Years—Not much interest in siblings. Takes them for granted. Allows older siblings to play with him on occasion. May give and accept affectionate advances.

2½ Years—Difficulty with siblings as with adults.

Cannot share or wait a turn; cannot do things someone else's "way."

Over-rigid in demands; tantrums if things go wrong.

May express jealousy of younger siblings.

3 Years—Part of the time may get on well with older or younger siblings.

May tease older siblings, break or spoil their "things"; cry if older siblings retaliate.

May accept new baby and take a moderate interest or even pride in him; or may show jealousy.

May accept mothering from older siblings.

4 Years—Not very good. Out of bounds with siblings as with other people.

Old enough now to be a definite nuisance to older siblings.

Likely to be selfish, rough and impatient with younger siblings.

Much quarrelling over toys and physical fighting.

5 Years—Usually good with younger siblings. Girls especially are protective and kind, like to take care of them. Helpful rather than domineering.

May be good when someone else is present, but when alone with younger sibling may take things from him or tease him. May be better outdoors than indoors.

Should not be given too much responsibility over younger siblings as not dependable.

Often plays well with older siblings, accepting the "baby" role in domestic play.

6 Years—Not usually as good with siblings as at five.

Likes to teach younger siblings, but also may "egg them on"; likes to see them scolded; bosses them, hurts them, fights with them, tattles on them.

Gets on better with siblings outdoors than indoors.

Some are good with siblings except for the "usual spats."

Much quarrelling with older siblings.

7 Years—Chiefly good with siblings.

Plays "big brother" (or sister) to younger siblings and likes to protect them.

Boasts about older siblings and is proud of them.

Variable, however, from time to time: "Bickers with sister but thinks she's cute"; "Protects sister but teases her." A few are consistently bad: "fight like cats and dogs."

Frequently jealous: wants to do things which siblings cannot or are not allowed to do; fears that sibling will "put something over on him."

8 YEARS—Less good with siblings.

Some are consistently bad, teasing and being selfish and quarrelsome about possessions.

Others are variable: sometimes protective and thoughtful; at other times getting down to sibling's level and teasing and fighting.

Some are "kind, though they scrap around."

9 YEARS—Frequently get on well with siblings. May be thoughtful and protective if siblings are younger; proud of and try to emulate older siblings.

Some trouble if near same age: may argue, fight, compete, accuse. But often show considerable loyalty to siblings, uphold them.

May in presence of contemporaries be much embarrassed or disgusted by actions of siblings. May dislike their "messiness."

Boys often wrestle and "fool around" with siblings.

§4. FAMILY

16 WEEKS—Social play with one parent or the other.
Differentiate mother and father from other people.

28 WEEKS—Likes attention from parents or sibs.

40 WEEKS—Likes to be with the family group especially in morning or late afternoon.

52 WEEKS—The height of social give and take and imitation games with family.

18 MONTHS—Likes to have run of the house.
Interested in activities of the household such as sweeping, dusting, etc.
Likes to bring "daddy's slippers," etc.
Expects certain ministrations from certain members of family.

21 MONTHS—Knows which objects belong to each member of the family and can verbalize "This is mummy's," "This is daddy's."
Likes to have his own places for things.
Likes to participate in household activities, as putting away groceries.

2 YEARS—Is quite an acceptable member of the household: does not get into things as much as formerly, helps make beds, puts away silver, brings ashtrays.
Family is nearly the child's whole world though no verbal concept beyond the words "Mummy," "Daddy" and names of sibs.

Likes birthday party with just the family or perhaps one other child, though the party is the food, to him.

2½ YEARS—Very strong ritualistic sense of having everything at home in its usual place and done in its usual way.

May rule the household with an iron hand with his ritualistic demands.

Is building up his sense of home and family in a practical way.

Strong insistence on "Mummy do," or "Daddy do." Each one to his own role.

Can use the word "home" if asked "Where is mummy?" Will reply, "She's home."

3 YEARS—Fewer ideas and demands about the way the home should be run.

Really helpful in little household tasks: wiping dishes, running household errands.

Likes to go to market with mother, or to follow her about the house.

Likes the party aspect of family holidays.

Likes to go visiting, as lunch or afternoon with grandmother; visit to another child.

Likes to visit relatives.

4 YEARS—Is developing a strong sense of family and home.

Quotes parents as authorities; boasts about them.

Compares the outside world to his home, to his home's advantage. His family's way of doing things is for him the right and only way.

Family, as earlier, continues to be all important in fact, even though he has not too clear a structured concept of family.

Likes family picnics and other outings.

Looks forward to visiting relatives; to trips on train or by car.

Likes to be taken on nature trips. Excursions alone with father especially prized.

5 YEARS—May have strong feeling for family. Likes the idea of the "family," likes to talk about it, to use the word.

Enjoys family picnics and other outings.

Likes the details of family celebration of holidays.

May be very proud of his mother and of his father.

Likes to hang around mother and to help her around the house, to go downtown with her.

Boys want to be mother's husband. Interest in idea of marrying.

Seems to assume that he and parents are eternal and that parents are also omniscient and all powerful.

Usually very fond of grandparents at this age. Likes to visit them. Likes to hear grandmother's stories of his or his parent's babyhood.

Some interest in the fact of grandparents, two on each side of the family.

6 YEARS—Not much thought about, or emphasis on the concept of the family. Child is too egocentric at this age. However, school brings to him some experience with other children's families who may have different standards and ways of doing things. Some comparison.

Likes family outings though his behavior frequently does not hold up well. He teases for things he cannot have, is restless to get home, gets into trouble.

Enjoys family secrets, as about Christmas presents.

May cooperate in family matters, but not as naturally as at five.

Boasts about his home.

Likes to go downtown with mother to make some small purchase for himself.

Child begins to suspect that mother will one day die and thus destroy present family setup and someone else will have to take care of him. He thinks about what might happen in this case. May think in a long, orderly succession of ancestors and parents dying, then he will grow up and reproduce.

Likes to have mother at home when he gets home from school.

Argues with parents and likes to prove them wrong.

Wants to hear about parents' babyhood.

Interest in relatives expanding: way back in the line, also spreads to cousins, uncles and aunts.

Likes to talk about attributes, activities and possessions of aunts, uncles, cousins.

May be very rude ("bratty") to grandparents, especially to grandmother, and may act badly if he visits grandparents, although he might be better if his own parents are not there.

7 YEARS—Interest in and feeling for family very strong at this age.

Serious about such concepts as "home," "family," "government."

Very proud of home and family possessions. May think his family is rich because they have such nice things.

Compares own home and family to others, to the detriment of others. (One child loved home so much she hoped that mother and father would move out when she married so that she could have their home.)

Proud of family, parents, and especially of older siblings.

Is strengthening feeling about family even in negative ways. Thus may threaten to run away "from this family." May think that family does not like him. Or may believe that he is merely adopted, (and is actually of more rich and powerful parentage). May say he doesn't want to be "a member of this family."

Is interested in his place in the family, and in relation to all members of the family.

Interested in his own and everyone's "place" at the table, in the car, etc.

With characteristic variability fluctuates between love for family and anxiety that he does not belong.

May prefer to stay at home and play rather than go outdoors.

Variable about helping: may be very sweet and helpful and then very disobedient. May inquire *why* he should help parents.

May like to have house orderly and attractive but does not contribute much toward this.

May be interested in doing his *share* of the work: "That's my job."

Enjoys family outings. More interested in what goes on and behaves better than he did at earlier ages.

Likes to have mother or grandmother play games with him.

Wants the "family" to have a baby.

May realize that oldest die first and that just as grandparents may have died, later parents will die and then he himself will one day die.

8 YEARS—Interest at this age seems to be more for mother than for family as a whole. Relationship with mother very close and exacting. Child "haunts" mother.

Very insistent about both parents doing and saying things "just so." Quick to point out a fault or error on part of parents.

At seven, was building up a concept of family. Now tries to make it really work. Is very much aware of people's reactions and is very anxious to have things "go right" in family, as at festival like Christmas, wants everyone to get gifts and be pleased.

Until this age seems to assume, unless there is overt evidence to contrary, that all is well between mother and father. Now worries about this relationship along with other relationships. May express some jealousy of mother and father's being together.

May be very curious about telephone calls, mail, people's conversation.

Through this age may think own home is perfect.

May be the last age for whole-hearted enthusiasm about family outings.

Wants to have house neat and tidy though he does not keep own room neat.

May do home tasks if rewarded or some goal or prize offered, but not anxious to help around home for the sake of helping or for the sake of the home.

Interest in family background, relatives on both sides.

As at six, may be rude and impatient with grandmother, but may greatly enjoy long play periods with grandmother who may have more patience for the absorbing detailed play which the child requires, than does his mother.

Very strong demand for mother's time and attention. Likes to have her with him when he practices his music lesson. Likes to have her play games with him. Wants her there when he gets home from school, as at six.

9 YEARS—Concept of family important to most, even though in practice they like to be away from family, on their own, with own friends.

May be very sensitive as to how family and family possessions compare with those of others. May want a better house. But some still feel that anything of their own (city, house, father's occupation) is superior.

May be shamed in public by behavior of siblings or even of parents.

Some are indifferent, self-centered, irresponsible so far as family life is concerned. "Taking part in the home" doesn't mean a thing to them. Prefer not to go on family excursions.

Others have "strong feeling for family." Feel need of parents' care and happy to be cared for.

Many are more helpful than formerly with younger siblings.

§5. MANNERS

18 Months—Child says "Tata" which means "take it" or "give it to me." Probably does *not* mean "thank you."

2 Years—Child may enjoy saying "Bye-bye" or "Goodbye." May even greet an arriving visitor with this phrase.

If parent directs, "Say Goodbye to Mrs. X," child may parrot, "Goodbye to Mrs. X."

2½ Years—Child may use "Good morning," "Goodbye," "Please," "Thank you," appropriately if he has heard them used. Parents are proud of this accomplishment. It usually drops out after the novelty has worn off.

3 Years—Parent or teacher may suggest to child, "It sounds better when you say 'please.' " Child may or may not respond positively to this.

A few children respond reciprocally to the phrase "Good morning."

Less likely to respond to "Goodbye" as they are usually in a hurry on leaving.

4 Years—Very little spontaneous and unprompted use of conventional phrases of politeness.

Shows off and acts very badly before company.

5 Years—Some are able to greet contemporary age friends, let them into the house, etc. A few, if reminded, can say "Please" and "Thank you."

Some may be able to shake hands with adults and say "How do you do," but this is a learned response and does not seem natural to the child. Many are unable to make a conventional social greeting without undue embarrassment.

Usually docile before company though may retreat to 4-year-old showing off and noisy, conspicuous behavior. Likes to be present.

5½ Years—A verbal child may be able to say that you should keep quiet, answer people when they are talking to you, always say "Please" and "Thank you," always remember to say "Good morning," "Good afternoon," "Good evening." This knowledge may exceed the child's ability of performance.

6 Years—Marked difficulty in formal social situations, though with people he knows and likes he can open the door and with enthusiasm say, "Come on in."

Not yet good at shaking hands with strangers and saying "How do you do," or "Goodbye." Has difficulty in responding to the query, "How are you?"

Forgets to say "Please" and "Thank you." "Goodbye, I had a nice time" is especially difficult.

Most can at least look squarely at people who greet them. No longer hang their heads.

May behave very badly before company, though some are better away from home than at home. Very bad, however, at social gatherings such as birthday parties.

May be very rude in company without meaning to be: "Oh this soup is terrible!"

Many can entertain contemporaries (if not too many at a time), offering and receiving hospitality.

Uses telephone. Some can dial.

If parent gives exact words to use in social situation, child may be able to repeat them.

7 YEARS—Many can greet people with "Hello," looking straight at them, better than saying "Good-bye."

Very likely to rush in front of others to secure his "place."

Behaves quite well in the presence of company for a while, then withdraws to own activity.

Considers it important to say "Excuse me," or "I didn't mean to," if things go wrong.

Social telephoning to friends.

Can listen courteously in an audience situation for short periods (about 20 minutes).

Can talk about experiences in a pleasant manner.

May shake hands responsively though not with ease.

8 YEARS—Can verbalize "proper" greetings and "proper" goodbyes.

Some carry on real social conversation with adult.

May monopolize mother's attention if company is present.

May be very rude, as to grandparents.

Table "manners" now considerably improving in a new situation.

Many have excellent company manners away from home.

Marked individual differences between those who love formalized things and those for whom artificial steps are difficult.

Much social telephoning to friends.

9 YEARS—May be ready to shake hands spontaneously and with ease. May enjoy this formality. Can manage adequate formalized greetings if he takes time for them.

"Manners not deliberately bad, just never thinks. No consideration for others, no gracious courtesies." Child often simply ignores adults.

Marked individual differences here: some are "naturally polite," with others manners do not "come natural."

May behave with extremely good manners in public, as at a restaurant.

§6. TEACHER-CHILD

18 MONTHS—Child needs close and constant physical supervision of teacher.

Relation with teacher effected through objects, physical orientations and gestures rather than through words.

Teacher's chief role is protecting and supplementing.

2 YEARS—Child adjusts to school through one special teacher who greets him, stays near him, and helps him to initiate activity.

Usually knows teacher's name and responds to one teacher in preference to others. May form a close attachment for this teacher.

Child most likely to address teacher if he wants something from another child.

May not ask for help, therefore teacher must note when he needs it.

Teacher can direct child through words or can pick him up bodily.

2½ YEARS—May need considerable adult direction in his play.

Teacher needs to give herself and child leeway so as not to lose "face" in situations.

Teacher must not take over too much. Child says, and means, "Me do it myself."

Can use language in handling child since his comprehension is greater.

Teacher needs a wealth of techniques to draw on to prevent children's disputes.

3 YEARS—Child likes to talk to teacher conversationally. However can now address other children directly and does not need to approach teacher first.

Likes to help teacher, as in setting table.

Likes to listen to teacher read stories.

May listen to reason and modify his behavior.

Responds to whispering, to idea that he is sharing a secret with teacher.

Seldom asks teacher for help in solving his difficulties, though teacher may need to step in.

4 YEARS—Greets teacher, but now more interested in talking to other children.

Responsive to verbal suggestion or direction from teacher.

Teacher has less need of techniques.

Teacher needs to provide ahead plenty of play materials.

Teacher needs a wealth of information at her fingertips to answer questions.

Child can often be handled through silly language which he enjoys.

Child himself enjoys taking on a teacher or mother role with new or shy children.

5 YEARS—Child likes teacher. Relationship is matter of fact and pleasant.

Child obeys teacher as a matter of course. Quotes her as an authority.

Relationship less personal than it will be later.

Child may complain, "the teacher makes me do things," "the teacher makes me stay in line."

Needs immediate attention from teacher.

Refers to teacher for materials, to tell experiences, and to show his products.

Seeks teacher for approval and for affection.

6 YEARS—Child related to teacher through materials and activities.

Likes to conform to teacher's demands. May even like discipline.

Usually likes teacher, and likes to please her.

Wants and likes to be commended. Wants praise, attention and help from teacher.

In awe of teacher. Her word is law.

May need teacher to sit next to him and to work closely with him for a period.

Apt not to know when to ask for help from teacher.

Likes teacher to talk with him about what he is doing.

Looks for teacher immediately on arrival, wants to be assured that she is there. Brings things to school for her.

Does not like to have teacher laugh *at* him.

7 YEARS—More personal relationship. Crushes. Boys especially like to stand by teacher and hold her hand; to bring her presents.

Teacher really paramount in school. Child depends on her. If teacher holds up child's behavior, all goes well.

Because of personal relationship, child, girls especially, may think teacher is mean and unfair, or may act silly toward teacher.

Poor transitioners may remain loyal to first grade teacher and prefer her.

Child depends on a word from teacher often to start the simplest task.

May be interested in doing something forbidden when teacher is out of room.

Wants own teacher and does not like a substitute. Likes to be with her, to sit with her.

Makes an impatient demand for teacher's attention and assistance.

Asks teacher, "Who did the best drawing?" "Did I get 100?"

May be concerned that teacher does not like him.

8 YEARS—Teacher less personally important. Child wants her to be a part of group.

Child usually likes teacher. May evaluate: "She looks sour but she isn't."

Fewer complaints about teacher as well as less ardent liking.

Children like a teacher who is factual, business-like, comradely and a good sport.

Pleased at idea of teacher making a mistake.

Likes to have some individual contact with teacher relative to tasks to be done, but better able to wait for teacher's attention than at seven.

May be concerned about how teacher treats a friend.

Likes to help teacher, to pass papers, etc.

Likes to do things in order, in certain ways, and tells teacher if she deviates.

Wants teacher to enjoy activity with him, to have a turn.

Tells teacher what another child is doing.

Teacher can handle with humor and can control by her silence.

9 YEARS—Most seem to like teacher well or even be devoted to her.

Often a very strong feeling one way or other: teacher is "terrible" or "wonderful."

Great stress on whether teacher is fair or unfair.

Tendency toward crushes and this makes child shy with teacher.

Perhaps less talk at home about teacher than earlier.

Teacher needs to be aware of individual intellectual difference in children, and to help them perfect their individual intellectual implements for later use.

Child wants to be independent of teacher both in work and in play.

Still prefers teacher's assistance when needed in work.

Critical of teacher in relation to a specific subject. May blame her for a lowered grade.

Wants teacher to be reasonable.

May report on her mannerisms or conduct in a specific situation.

§7. CHILD-CHILD

18 MONTHS—Treats other children as objects rather than as persons: pokes, pulls, pinches, pushes.

21 MONTHS—Active but unmodified approach to other children: pulls hair, knocks them on head, hugs too tightly.

2 YEARS—Parallel play, which needs close supervision.
>   Like to watch each other at play.
>   May hug and kiss each other.
>   Cannot share though may, at adult suggestion, be able to give other child a substitute toy. "It's mine" is a constant refrain.

2½ YEARS—Quarrelling, arguing and physical combat over materials.
>   Cannot share; wants what others have.
>   Can sometimes give or accept substitute toys.

3 YEARS—Cooperative play beginning to replace parallel play.
>   Beginning of ability to share.
>   Can sometimes settle own disputes verbally or by giving other child a substitute toy.
>   Beginning to take turns.
>   Conversational approach to others.
>   Has preferred friends. Use of word "friend."
>   At teacher's suggestion may take charge of younger or shy child.

3½ YEARS—Cooperative play, two children or more than two.
>   Gets on well with preferred friends but excludes, hits or pushes others.
>   Play may be stormy and quarrelsome.
>   Beginning of temporary attachments to some one companion, often of opposite sex. Girls often initiate these attachments.

4 YEARS—Will share or play cooperatively with special friends.
>   Very conversational with friends. Good imaginative play.
>   But *much* excluding, tattling, disputing, quarreling, verbal and physical.
>   More interested in children than in adults.
>   May spontaneously take charge of younger or shy child.
>   May have special friends of same sex.

5 YEARS—Plays well with other children especially if groups are kept small.
>   Does not insist on having his own way and does not worry about behavior of others.
>   Prefers playmates of his own age.

Some are too rough, too bossy, or cry too readily to get on well in unsupervised play.

May play better with another child outside, rather than indoors.

6 YEARS—Marked interest in making friends, having friends, being with friends. Uses term "school friend" or "playmate."

Seems able to get along with friends but play does not hold up long if unsupervised. Quarreling, physical combat. Each wants his own way.

A good deal of tattle-taling.

May be very dominating and bossy with some playmates.

Much exclusion of a third child: "Are you playing with so and so? Then I'm **not** playing with you."

Cannot bear to lose at games and will cheat if necessary to win. Also thinks friends cheat or do things the wrong way.

Many are said to be a "bad influence" on playmates or are thought to play with someone who is a "bad influence."

May prefer slightly older playmates.

7 YEARS—Much fighting with playmates though less than at six. May leave the scene if things go wrong.

Less domineering, less set on having own way, less worry about how others do things.

Tattle-taling and some worry about goodness and badness in others.

Learning to lose but must win in the end.

Begins to be aware of friends' attitudes as well as of their actions.

Needs to be happy himself in a two-way relationship but does not worry much about friend.

Prefers older playmates.

Boys may have trouble with older boys who are bullies.

8 YEARS—Group play better: more cooperation, less insistence on having own way, less worry about behavior of others. But any unsupervised period of play may end in dissension.

With "best friend" an effort to work out a relationship. Friend's attitudes important. Child wants to be happy and wants friend also to be happy. Much arguing, disputing, getting "mad" caused by this.

Can take part in competitive games and can sometimes lose with grace.

"Enemy" is a word frequently used.

May again prefer same-age friends.

Sub-verbal appraisal of selves and others; controlled somewhat by criticism of others.

9 YEARS—Most have a special friend of same age and sex, as well as a group of friends.

Gets on well with playmates in spite of some quarrelling and disagreement. Interested less in relationship with friend and more in what they do together. The activity or goal is important. Real cooperative activity.

The gang or club is important. May subordinate own interests and demands to getting along in the group. Try to live up to group standards and criticize those who do not.

Girls beginning to like to spend the night with each other.

Beginning of crushes on older child or adult.

Evaluation—not just judging, behavior of others.

Much good-natured rough-housing and wrestling among boys. Boys have considerable trouble with "bullies" of own age or older.

Boys dash about shouting; girls giggle and whisper.

§8. GROUPINGS IN PLAY

1 YEAR—Social with family group. Shy with strangers.

18 MONTHS—Solitary play. Not ready for play with other children.

2 YEARS—Likes to be with other children. Parallel play.
Not ready for cooperative play or for extensive group activity.
No sex preference in play.

2½ YEARS—Beginnings of cooperative play together in small groups. Several may sit together on a block train.
Chiefly parallel play and imitation. Little real cooperation or sharing.
No sex preferences in play.

3 YEARS—Some spontaneous group play, taking different roles, i.e. one conductor and several passengers in train play.
Group play may be quite harmonious.
No distinction between sexes in play.
Racial attitudes   Child not aware of racial differences. May fear person of different color.

3½ YEARS—Group activity, but some of group may discriminate against others, and forcibly exclude them.
Beginning of temporary and shifting attachments to some one child of opposite sex. Girls often initiate these attachments. Strong feeling for "friend" of opposite sex.
Pairings in same sex not as characteristic.
Racial attitudes   Discrimination in group play may or may not be along sex lines; usually not on race lines.

4 YEARS—Cooperative and imaginative group play—sustained dramatic or imaginative play.
Tendency in group play for division along sex lines. Play groupings fluid. Some chanting at other sex, in an excluding way.
Some have special friends of same sex.

[356]

Racial attitudes Exclusion from play groups may be along sex lines; usually not along race lines.

5 YEARS—Children mostly play in groups of two: seldom more than five in a group.

Personnel of any group is rapidly shifting.

Little solitary play, but often parallel play.

Imaginative play gives appearance of being cooperative though actually involves little real cooperation. Each child carries out his individual ends and has little concern for the group as a whole.

Children symmetrically organized in play, ready for all relationships. Largely ignore sex in choosing a playmate or a group of playmates.

Most frequent grouping is of two children of same sex. These pairs of friends may be shifting.

Racial attitudes Usually no concern about racial differences.

6 YEARS—Much group play, especially in imaginative play of house, store. Groupings so flexible that any one child may leave or join the group without being noticed

Little organization to group play, though he can choose sides and may accept direction of a domineering older child or teacher.

Little concern for welfare of group; interest still primarily self-expressive.

Leaders are leaders of small group only (in school).

Little solitary play.

Considerable time spent in play with constant friend.

As at five, may group for games ignoring sex lines.

Some constant friendships begin to persist.

Parties: behavior diffuse, child is "all over the place," all want to have presents and win prizes.

Racial attitudes There may be benign verbalization of racial differences but usually no exclusion in play. In anger, some name calling stressing any distinctive characteristic, race among others. Child himself is beginning to be aware of his own race.

7 YEARS—Play in pairs (same or opposite sex); but also much group play.

Group play not well organized and still primarily for individual ends. But beginning of real cooperation.

Several children "gang up" against some other child.

Child worries about his place in the group, afraid he will not hold his own.

Girls are eligible for Brownies (preceding Girl Scouts), or Bluebirds (preceding Campfire Girls). Boys are eligible for Cub Scouts.

Largely ignore sex lines in play groupings. But if by chance children have separated along sex lines they may verbalize this in exclusion chanting.

8 YEARS—Child enjoys group activity. Accepts fact that his role in group is to some extent determined by his abilities and limitations.

Real cooperative play and carrying out of simple projects.

Not ready for complex rules, but can accept very simple ones, or directions.

Organization of simple same-sex clubs with names and passwords, of temporary duration.

Beginning to have a "best friend" of same sex.

Boys and girls separate off in play. Prefer play with same sex. Girls conscious of this sooner, but boys probably the first to actively *exclude* child of other sex from play.

Children will not play long in a group in which they are only one of their sex.

Racial attitudes Ganging up against some one child may be along race lines. Calling names may stress race differences.

9 YEARS—Informal clubs, still short-lived and very varied though a little longer duration and more structure than earlier. May be for some definite purpose: paper club, press club, scrapbook club, sewing club.

Clubs are mostly secret with passwords, initiations, hide-aways, codes, secret language, dues, club bulletins. Rigid exclusion of non-members. But clubs "don't last."

More formal clubs under adult leadership: Cubs or Brownies.

Children like to act as a group and compete as a group. Accept own role in group and can evaluate contributions of others. May be more interested in success of groups than in own individual enjoyment. In games or for projects, organization is complex and detailed, cooperation is excellent.

Birthday parties: usually own sex only. Rather complex entertainment as magician, treasure hunt, athletic event and refreshments.

Racial attitudes Very little interest or comment. May say that Japanese and Chinese are both yellow, but Japanese are horrible and Chinese nice.

17

PLAY AND PASTIMES

CHILDREN reveal themselves most transparently in their play life. They play not from outer compulsion, but from inner necessity,—the same kind of necessity which causes a kitten to chase a rolling ball, and to play cat and mouse with it. The kitten is not a cat, and the ball is not a mouse; but in all this playful pouncing we see a preliminary exercise of serious adult activities. The kitten's play is also reminiscent because it involves a rehearsal of activities inherited from the ancestral generations. It is indeed a zestful merging of past, present and future.

A child's play possesses similar qualities. It rises spontaneously out of instinctive promptings which represent developmental needs. It prepares for maturity. It is a natural enjoyable exercise of growing powers.

No one needs to teach a child to play. Even a young infant knows how. What does a 12-week-old baby do with his "idle" time? He practices all his budding abilities in the four major fields of human behavior, namely, motor, adaptive, language and personal-social behavior. He flings his arms and flexes his legs (motor); he fixates his eyes regardfully upon his fisted hand (adaptive); he coos and chuckles (language); he vocalizes on his mother's approach (personal-social). He is ceaselessly active during his waking hours, playing in one form or another. Play is his work, his business.

Play never ceases to be a major business throughout childhood. Nature plants strong play propensities in every normal child to make sure that certain basic needs of development will be satisfied. The culture directs, restrains and redirects these play impulses into approved channels, but always at the risk that the child will not get an optimal measure of the kind of play life which is best suited to his stage of maturity. All things considered the modern child has too many set tasks, and not a sufficient amount of untrammelled leisure and self-activity.

Needless to say, a child does not play because he is too lazy to work. Often he puts forth his most strenuous energies in moments of play. He concentrates with his whole being and acquires emotional satisfactions which he cannot get from other forms of activity. Deeply absorbing play seems to be essential for full mental growth. Children who are capable of such intense play are most likely to give a good account of themselves when they are grown up.

The gradations of play interest are part and parcel of the very process of growing up. Take for example such ancient play materials as sand and mud. They must have figured very early in the playful manipulations and workmanship of our remote ancestors while idling at a sea or lake shore. Sand appeals even to the 18-month-old. Although he is naturally a run-about he is so intrigued by the tractability of sand that he will sit for a long period filling and dumping, refilling and redumping endlessly. In this self-perpetuated play he is getting a delectable mixture of visual, tactile, and motor experience, and a sense of mastery which feeds his mental growth. His later exploitations will be more sophisticated but they will have a similar developmental function.

Already at two years his play is more elaborate; he mixes stones with his sand; he fills a pail and lugs it back and forth; he plays with water too, filling and emptying dishes. In another year he makes mud, combining the basic elements of earth and water. He even fashions them to his devices, moulding, patting and smoothing his plastic mud into cakes and pies.

By five years he does not like to be confined by the sand box; he prefers a generous heap of sand which he can dramatically use as a stock pile for filling his truck which will transport and retransport its load to distant points. The 6-year-old operates on a more imaginative scale; and combines sand and water to build definite structures. The 7-year-old elaborates still further. He likes to combine phantasy-play with his digging and construction. He builds streets and houses, lakes and river beds out of sand and mud; and as he builds he chatters, soliloquizes or ruminates. And so he weaves new threads into his growing mental structures. Perhaps he is already preparing to become an engineer. There is an element of anticipation in all play; and if he is by inborn aptitude an engineer, he may already be revealing talent in the accents of his play.

By eight years the sand box has graduated from the back yard into the schoolroom. Here, under the influence of curriculum and culture the desert sand may blossom into an Indian village, or an Arab camp. The distinction between play and work dissolves into an educational project. And the project in turn is reinforced by the pressure of the schoolroom group and by the teacher. The child's play impulses thus are socialized.

But there still is scope for the more aboriginal type of undirected play, and we hope that the 8-year-old boy will not be prevented from going to some hillside to dig himself a cave, or erect himself a hut planted upon the mother earth. These private ventures and contacts with Nature go deeper than a schoolroom project.

What a 9- or 10-year-old will do in this particular gradient of play cannot be predicted. As a child grows older, the Culture tends more and more to intervene, and determines even his extra-curricular activities. He may dig a tunnel, a fox hole, or a canal. He still likes to dig and to feel the earth yield to his hands. With his like-minded companions he builds a well-drilling machine,—a wooden derrick, a pulley, a sash cord and iron weight, and perhaps a wheel and axle to operate the rhythmic drop of the drill. With what triumph he sinks a shaft and pulls up the moistened earth in his tomato-can bucket! The play sequence of sand and mud and water which began before the age of two has come to higher issues.

In many fields of play, one could trace a similar developmental sequence, the patterns of play always conforming to the advancing patterns of maturity. A child's play often appears to casual observation to be so haphazard, so determined by chance environmental factors—what playmates are available, what toys are at hand, what play space is provided —that it is easy to underestimate the strong developmental factors which underlie his choice of activity. Closer observation will disclose that deeply determined developmental trends often underlie this choice. Again and again, from child to child, do we find the same sequence repeated with increasing maturity: sand and water; doll and teddy bear; cars and wagons; tricycle and domestic doll play; dramatic play of store, hospital and school; reading; games; radio; bicycle; paper dolls; funny books.

There are variations based on individual and sex differences, and on cultural influences, but age is the basic factor. Children of high intelligence, accelerated beyond their years as measured by an intelligence quotient, nevertheless tend to remain true to their chronological age in many of their spontaneous play interests. This fact, itself, testifies to the basic significance of play in the dynamics of development.

In a more Utopian child-world we would doubtless make more room for free, unregimented play activities. There would also be more organized outdoor play, in which children might make spirited and rhythmical use of their large, fundamental muscles, through the medium of folk games, dancing, music, pantomime and dramatic games. Such group activity taps the deeper springs of personality which are not reached by sedentary and restricted indoor schooling. Such expressional play can bring about much needed improvements in body posture and motor control. It would have a beneficial effect upon the organization of the emotions. It surely would be preferable to the aimless physical activities of unsupervised and chaotic recess periods.

As our culture becomes more technological the psychological health and growth of children need increased protection. This protection requires a deeper understanding of the play interests of children, particularly in the age period from five to ten. For this is the period when we are in danger of introducing children too rapidly into our adult culture. We should have more faith in the simple, unsophisticated forms of play life, which keep the child closer to nature. Technology tends to use more and more technology in order to catch up with the pace which technology itself sets. Hence radio, comics, movies, and television for children. These devices have come to play a tremendous role in the recreation and pastime of the school child. They do indeed induct him into the civilization into which he is born, and they inevitably stir his elemental emotions as well as his phantasy. To that extent they serve the true functions of play. But they are a poor substitute for the more basic types of play which come from inner urges and which express the initiative and resourcefulness of the growing mind. Carried to excess at the expense of natural, oldfashioned (!) play, these recreational facilities lead to superficiality. Television will aggravate the present imbalance in play diet, if not offset by more active forms of self-expression.

So much for the general philosophy of play and its underlying principles. These principles suggest that we should give considerable scope to the child's own spontaneous play enterprises. His play has a developmental logic which does not necessarily fit into our preconceptions. We must be tolerant toward some of his apparently illogical reactions. For example, you may enthusiastically give your boy a new and shining toy. There are so many different things that he could do with it. You can think of all of them; but if the timing of your gift was poor he may disappoint you with a very meager response. It may, however, be just the response that befits him and his maturity. Perhaps if the toy is put aside, he will come back to it with a wider range of response when he is older. Children themselves like to come back for a new contact with previously discarded play things, when they can use them again at a higher level. The sand-mill toy which had superficial attention at three or four years may be revived at six years with a mounting of new interest. Then there is the common error of giving too many toys all on one occasion, when spacing would work to everyone's advantage. With pets as with toys, good timing is important. Many a child has been given a dog when he was scarcely ready to take care of a goldfish, and might in fact, have had more pleasure in the latter.

Parents are sometimes worried about obsessive preoccupation with a single toy or with one kind of play, to the exclusion of others. Such obsessive interest is more common in boys. Girls are more balanced and diversified in their play preferences. At the age of five-and-a-half years a boy may be obsessed with the motion of his toy trains. At six years he may be obsessed with climbing. At seven years, characteristically enough, he shows a succession of intensified interests. At nine years he can hardly wait for school to close, so he may get back to his erector set. These obsessions have their own logic in the scheme of development. They are benign and probably beneficial seizures.

At another extreme a child's play is sketchy rather than obsessive; and exploratory rather than conclusive. He starts something,—a lemonade stand, a postal card collection, or a play hut; but he does not carry through and finish the job. A father, unfamiliar with the ways of child development, detects a weakness in such behavior; and sternly expresses his disapproval. It is usually wiser to be patient with such beginnings. They are embryonic. They will come to fuller fruition at a later stage. One must also be patient with a certain amount of disorderliness. Unaided, the child may not be interested in completing what he has begun; he does not have the maturity of perception to see the whole. We can make concessions to his request that we do not molest his unfinished construction.

We can also make concessions to his so-called destructiveness, which may well be a form of constructiveness in reverse. Oftentimes a child shows interest in taking a toy apart long before he is able to put the toy together. A baby spills the contents of a waste basket before he is able to replace them. He delights in demolishing a tower of blocks before he can re-erect the tower himself. An older child may show a readiness to dismantle an erector construction well before he has the capacity to reassemble its parts. A wise father or older brother will encourage this kind of mechanical interest, because it actually represents a positive as well as negative form of workmanship. It is a preparatory stage.

When destructiveness becomes violent, and emotionally charged, it means that the child is not ready for the play materials with which he is confronted. He probably will adapt to more simplified situations. There may be personality or maturity factors which need consideration.

However, his unreasonable behavior does not necessarily denote either sadism or an incest complex. Even when he jabs a rubber doll in the stomach and tears out the rubber eyes, it does not automatically follow that these acts are symbolic. Among normal and relatively normal children play tends to be practical and experimental in its essence. Even in the play of phantasy, the child projects his private mental images in a practical spirit. He manipulates them in order to organize his concepts of reality, and not to deepen his self-illusion. Even his imaginary companions are amazingly serviceable devices, and so he uses them pragmatically,—until he is old enough to dispense with them. This is one more evidence that play has a positive role in the drama of development.

The role is many sided. Play is an outlet for obstructed and over-flowing energy. It manifests exuberance in laughter, rollic and euphoria. Play is imitative, repetitive, or rhythmical in skipping, dancing, and dramatic expression. Play is psycho-motor exercise in running, jumping, tossing, hustling, balancing, and a host of gross and fine muscular activities. Play harks back to the past, in the emotional stirrings that accompany games of hunt, hide-and-seek, combat and chase, and in the quieter pastimes of exploring, collecting, hoarding, camping and caring for flowers, plants and animals. Play penetrates into the future, spurred by impulses of curiosity, experimentation, exploitiveness and workmanship. In highly gifted children this workmanship declares itself in re-sourcefulness, originality or even in genius. In all children play has a creative function. It serves to organize the abilities with which the child is endowed. In its supreme moments it reveals his individuality and his potentialities.

GROWTH GRADIENTS

§1. GENERAL INTERESTS

1 YEAR—Reciprocal nursery games as, "Where is baby?"
  Gross motor activity.
  Putting objects in and out of other objects.
  Play with buttons attached to a garment.

18 MONTHS—Climbs; moves furniture.
  Plays with pull toys, dolls, teddy bears, pots and pans, balls, hammer toy.
  Plays with sand, fills and empties containers, likes to pour it.
  Blocks: carries around room, pounds together, builds tower of three or four.

2 YEARS—Feeds and toilets doll, teddy bear; takes them for rides in carriage.
  Plays with sand and/or water, filling dishes and then emptying them.
  Pushes wagon or carriage.
  Plays with little cars, screw driver, egg beater, little objects (pebbles, beads, bottles).
  Some painting, finger painting, play with clay.
  Blocks: lines them up or uses them manipulatively to fill wagons. Likes colored blocks or blocks which fit into each other.
  Christmas: chiefly the tree is important. Some interest in presents.

2½ YEARS—Domestic play with doll or teddy bear and housekeeping toys.

Plays with cars or wagons.

Sand and water play, makes pies and cakes with sand or mud. Tea parties with mud cakes and water tea. Soap bubble play.

Paints with some design. Finger paints.

Makes pies or cakes of clay.

Blocks: vertical and horizontal building; names structures; may use large blocks as coal and lumber.

3 YEARS—Rides tricycle; pushes wagon, fire-engine or train.

Swings, plays on jungle gym.

Domestic play (both girls and boys) with doll, teddy bear and household equipment.

Plays with imaginary playmates.

Plays house, store, train with other children and simple equipment.

Colors with crayons as well as paints. May draw simple figures.

Plays in mud or sand: makes cakes, pies, roads, tunnels. Combines with other materials.

Blocks: builds structures, using a diversity of shapes and sizes. May combine blocks and train. Enjoys construction more than play with finished product.

Christmas: interest in Santa Claus; in presents he receives.

4 YEARS—Prefers to play with other children. Dramatic play of house, store, train, hospital involves costumes and "props." Combination of real and imaginative.

Rides tricycle; climbs, does "tricks."

Plays with imaginary companions.

Draws, paints, colors.

Admires own products whether of clay, paint, paper, blocks.

Blocks: makes detailed constructions. Combines with furniture for dramatic play. Builds cooperatively with others.

Christmas: asks for specific presents, then brags about size and amount. Strong interest in Santa Claus.

5 YEARS—More independent play and likes to play indoors or out according to season or weather. Likes to have an adult nearby.

Much play centers around a house. Builds house with large blocks or with draped furniture. Plays house imitating adult activities.

Plays with dolls using them as babies.

Child runs, climbs, swings, skips, jumps, dances.

Rides tricycle, pushes cart.

Tries roller skates, jump rope, even stilts.

Uses sand in making roads, transporting it in cars.

Imitative play: house, store, hospital.

Paints, draws, colors, cuts, and pastes, and does puzzles.

Copies letters and numbers.

Games of matching pictures and forms.

[367]

Builds with blocks, large and small. Likes to copy designs with blocks.

Christmas: asks for specific presents. May request things by letter to Santa Claus. Anxious to tell what he has received. Strong belief and interest in details about Santa Claus and in visiting him.

Girls Doll play, playing house, dressing up.

Boys Blocks, tools, cars and trucks, war games, mechanical toys.

6 YEARS—Elaborates and expands five-year play interests.

Mud, sand and water play.

Games of tag, hide-and-seek; stunts on trapeze, on rope and on tricycle.

Ball play: tossing, bouncing throwing.

Rough and tumble play, climbing, swinging.

Interest in roller skates, double runner ice skates.

Simple carpentry: hammering, sawing.

Table games with cards ("Go Fish"), anagrams, dominoes, and puzzles.

Paints, colors, draws and uses clay. Cuts and pastes.

Collecting odds and ends.

Printing letters to spell real words.

Games of oral spelling or oral numbers.

Imaginative play: pretending to be a horse; pretending furniture is a boat, etc.

Blocks used imaginatively and constructively.

Christmas: may want specific toy (doll or train) and be disappointed if it is not received, but also wants *many* presents. Boasts and brags about how many received. Strong interest and belief in Santa Claus.

Girls Doll play elaborated with dolls' accessories: clothes, suitcase, furniture.

Dressing up in adult clothes.

Playing school, house, library.

Boys Tinker toys and simple erector sets.

War games, cowboys, cops and robbers.

Digging holes and tunnels and simple activity in garden.

Interest in transportation using wagon, trains, trucks, airplanes and boats.

7 YEARS—More intense interest in some activities, fewer new ventures.

Has "mania" for certain activities: guns, funny books or coloring.

More solitary play.

Some play with mud, and digging, and some interest in garden tools.

Tricycle usually discarded; some ride bicycles.

Magic and tricks. Jigsaw puzzles.

Collecting and swapping cards, bottle tops, and stowing away stones and bits of this and that.

Interest in swimming often strong.

Plays library, train, post office with elaborate paraphernalia.

Rudiments of ball play: "catch," batting with soft ball.

Christmas: very great disappointment now if does not receive a requested toy. Writes letter to Santa Claus with list of desired toys.

Girls Cutting out paper dolls and their clothes. Doll play may decrease. May "invent" dresses for dolls.

Playing house which includes dressing up in elaborate adult costumes.

Playing school with emphasis on teacher role.

Hop scotch and jump rope, roller skating, ball bouncing.

Boys Active outdoor play of running, wrestling, climbing trees.

Carpentry, especially sawing. Like to make Christmas presents.

Rigging things from cereal boxes, etc.

Make paper planes and shoot them; make model airplanes.

Cops and robbers, commandos, gun play, war play.

Building and playing in tree houses, forts, huts and tents.

Beginning interest in chemistry, telegraphy, navigation.

8 YEARS—Variety of play interests. Prefer companionship in play (adult or child)

Games of all kinds played indoors or out. Differentiate work from play.

Table games of parchesi, checkers, dominoes, card games. Jigsaw puzzles and map puzzles. Scorns too simple games. May make up own game with own rules.

Dramatic play of giving shows. Arranges and produces these shows.

"Gadget" age. Likes to have variety of things and tries to make something of them.

Collecting, and arranging of collections.

Beginning interest in group games such as soccer or baseball with supervision.

Unorganized group play of wild running, chasing, wrestling.

Beginning of secret clubs, usually short-lived.

Seasonal interests: rowing and swimming in summer; skating, sliding, skiing in winter; playing with marbles, kites and tops in spring.

Boys and girls beginning to separate in play.

Christmas: has innumerable ideas of what would like for Christmas and wants are now intense. Interest in how *many* presents received. Do not want useful things. More interest than earlier in giving presents.

Girls Doll play and playing house, stressing more complex adult relationships.

In make-believe play, child requires complete attention of companion.

Paper doll play: collects large number of dolls and doll clothes. Cuts out and tries on dresses. Likes to have them admired. Simple dramatic play with dolls involving much verbalization. Likes books with many different dolls.

Boys Beginning to utilize tools to fix things around house; make mixtures with chemistry set. Use telegraph to communicate.

Continue to work with airplane, train and boat models.

War games, cops and robbers, commandos.

Electric trains and movie projectors.

9 YEARS—Plays and works hard and is apt to overdo to point of fatigue.

Busy with own activities. Plans what he is going to do.

Individual differences stronger: some read and listen to radio more; others play outdoors more.

Some former interests may be dropped while others are intensified.

Coasting a favorite outdoor sport, but also marked interest in baseball, skating, swimming and other sports.

Interest in organized clubs such as Cubs and Brownies.

Spontaneous clubs are short-lived. Stress special interest in club house or hide-away.

Collecting of stamps, minerals, etc.

Hikes and goes for walks in woods.

Drawing maps, making lists of collections. Writing "business" letters in response to radio advertisements or from catalogues.

Playing more complicated table games.

Some have animals which they are supposed to care for.

Christmas: makes long lists of presents, not expecting to receive all. May understand that cost of presents may be too high or that they may not be procurable. Interest in number of presents and may classify them by size or type.

Interest in trimming own tree and in making ornaments for it. May do own Christmas shopping, buying presents for family and friends. Interest in what they give others and how much they spend for each.

Girls Paper dolls used in dramatic play. Identify themselves with dolls, playing out elaborate dramas. Like books with fewer dolls and more different costumes. Or may enact entire day's routine in doll play.

May show interest in manipulating puppets.

Put simple abilities in sewing and cooking to practical use.

Boys Constructing with mechano and erector sets and in work shop. May work with material for long period on a planned project.

Rough-housing and wrestling. Some are interested in boxing or gym lessons.

Beginning interest in bowling and horseshoes.

§2. READING

18 MONTHS—Turns pages of a book.

2 YEARS—Likes to hear rhymes.
Likes tactile books.
Looks at pictures.

2½ YEARS—Likes to look at books alone; or to fill in last word as adult reads.
Likes rhymes or short stories about familiar subjects.
Enjoys books about transportation or animals: *Saturday Walk, Ask Mr. Bear.*

3 YEARS—Longer listening span.
Likes repetitive stories of familiar experiences, or imaginative books based on people and animals: *Caps for Sale, Little Black Sambo.*
Likes riddles and guessing games.
Stories must be re-read and re-told word for word.
Looks at books and may "read" to others or explain pictures.
Likes to look at colored advertisements of familiar objects in magazines.

4 YEARS—Listens to long stories and poems.

Likes nonsense rhymes—*Nonsense ABC*; humorous stories—*Junket is Nice*; exaggeration—*Millions of Cats*; alphabet books—*The Jingling ABC's;* stories of function or growth of things—*Mike Mulligan and his Steam Shovel*, or *Tim Tadpole and the Great Bullfrog*; or information books.

5 YEARS—"Loves" to be read to and shows preference for certain stories which he likes to hear over and over.

Likes poetry, stories of animals who behave like human beings, holiday and seasonal stories. (E.g. *Winnie the Pooh; The Country Bunny.*)

Likes to have first grade primer about children in play activities read to him.

Comics May puzzle out pictures in newspaper comics. May like to have some comics read to him. Slight interest in "funny books."

6 YEARS—Likes to be read to. May read familiar stories from memory. Likes to hear stories about himself.

Beginning to recognize words.

Less selective in choice of stories and may be disturbed by unpleasant event in story.

Likes poetry (as of A. A. Milne), stories about activities of children.

Comics Rudimentary interest in comics and comic books. Likes to try to read or to have them read to him. Interest general, but some have particular favorites.

7 YEARS—Some become inveterate readers and even want to bring books to the table and read as they eat. Others like to be read to while at play.

More individual reading interests: books about children, animals, nature, the elements. Boys like books about the army and navy, airplanes, and electricity.

Likes fairy tales, myths and legends, poetry. (E.g. *Alice in Wonderland; The Hobbit.*)

An interest in going to the library for books.

May enjoy a children's magazine which suggests activities which they may carry out.

Comics Much interest in comic books. Reads these himself. These books become a "passion" with some. Child buys, collects, barters them. Has definite favorites: daily adventures of animals, of ordinary people or adventures of supermen.

8 YEARS—Variable enjoyment in reading. Girls may read more than boys.

Interest in reading stories such as childhood classics. Books of travel, adventure, geography, primitive times and Bible stories.

Still enjoys books about children, animals, the elements, fairies.

Expanding interest in books about far-away or long-ago people.

Delights in the humor in stories—people put in the wrong position. (E.g. *Mary Poppins.*)

Enjoys looking at catalogues and at adult magazines as well as own literature.

Comics Continued interest; now buys, collects, barters, borrows, hoards. Likes animal, adventure and some "blood and thunder" comics.

9 YEARS—Individual differences: some are omnivorous readers who secure books from the library weekly; others do not read at all.

Reads Junior classics. Re-reads favorite books.

Many like a book with several stories in it. Likes mysteries and biographies.

Increasing interest in magazines.

May still enjoy being read to on occasion.

Comics Interest reaches a peak with some, beginning to wane in some. Some have a "passion" for funny books. Reads "any kind." Buys, swaps, borrows and hoards them.

§3. MUSIC, RADIO AND CINEMA

18 MONTHS—Listens to radio music; dances to it.

Turns knob of radio himself.

2 YEARS—Dances to radio or phonograph music.

Prefers phonograph to radio because it repeats and he can watch it turn.

2½ YEARS—Continues to prefer phonograph to radio. Likes to watch and to repeat some one piece.

Likes to run, gallop, or swing to music.

3 YEARS—Likes to watch and listen to phonograph. Little interest in radio. Can recognize several melodies. May have favorites.

Gallops, jumps, walks, runs in time to music.

4 YEARS—Still prefers phonograph to radio. Some can run phonograph themselves.

Likes to experiment with the piano.

A few can sing songs correctly; can identify simple melodies.

Likes to dramatize songs.

Occasionally listens to children's programs on radio and may be susceptible to admonitions delivered on these programs.

5 YEARS—May pick out tunes on the piano and learn to play a few familiar, simple melodies.

Prefers phonograph records to radio. Likes to play them over and over and to sing or dance to them.

Some listen to scattered radio programs. Like a combination of music and talking.

May like the advertising jingles on the radio which are repetitive.

A few listen to one or two special programs, favoring those directed to very young children.

Some have attended an occasional child's movie.

6 YEARS—Enjoys own phonograph records.

Radio becoming a great favorite with most. Spends several hours a week listening.

Likes talking programs with some music.

Most have one or two preferred programs to which they listen regularly; prefer adventure stories of children.

Anxious not to miss his particular programs. Asks, "Is it time for my program?"

Likes short home movies about nature, animals or his own early life.

Attends cinema occasionally. May become restless, close eyes or cry.

7 YEARS—Craving for piano or dancing lessons. Likes to use various percussion instruments.

Radio now a part of daily diet. Dislikes to miss set programs.

Many listen to late afternoon programs of adventure and shooting. Beginning of interest in Westerns. Likes to have radio turned on loud.

Slight interest in news broadcasts; little in music.

Some attend cinema weekly. Others occasionally.

Likes musicals, dancing, singing and animal pictures. Some like adventure movies while others are disturbed by them. Dislikes love stories.

8 YEARS—Less desire to practice on piano. May like to change a passage in a piece to one of own invention. Likes to have an audience as he plays. Also enjoys duets.

Marked interest in radio programs. Most listen to several regular programs each day and do not like to miss these.

Likes late afternoon adventure stories, slap-stick comedies, mysteries, quiz programs and dramas of domestic life.

Frightening programs may influence dreams. Can turn radio off if it becomes too frightening.

Great interest in cinema. Most attend weekly, usually on Saturday.

Boys like action pictures: Westerns, baseball, war. Girls like musicals.

Both like animal and adventure stories and those about children. All dislike love stories.

If movie is too exciting, close eyes, hide heads or go to back of theatre.

9 YEARS—Really applies himself in practicing music. Touch is lighter with girls but surer with boys. Enjoys executing staccato or legato notes.

Beginning to be interested in composers.

Listening to radio is constant from late afternoon to bedtime with some.

Knows time and station for programs. Likes teen age serials; detective, mystery, quiz, information, and adult comic programs.

Individual differences with cinema. Some go to weekly cinema, others go on occasion. May want to see one picture several times.

Girls like musicals. Boys like action, war, cowboy, Indian pictures.

Both sexes like animal stories and dislike love stories.

18

SCHOOL LIFE

WHY do children go to school? Because our civilization has grown so complex that the home alone can not transmit to the child the culture which the race has prepared for him. The home is still the primary cultural workshop in which he learns the alphabet of civilized living; it remains an extremely important workshop even in the years from five to ten. But the accumulated inheritance from past and present is so vast that teachers and schools and pencils and books have become a social necessity.

SCHOOLS ARE FOR ACCULTURATION

A universal public school system, as ideal and as fact, is the most significant achievement of our democratic culture.

And of what does this culture consist? It consists of ways of life (manners, customs, rules and rites); of things material (houses, roads, farms, factories, markets); of property (real and personal, moneys and certificates); of laws and governments; of arts of communication, and self-expression; and endless records,—printed, graphic and otherwise of the accomplishments of mankind.

Schools are devices and teachers are agents designed to induct the growing child into this immense, moulding heritage. But this heritage is no mere hand-me-down from the past. It is something organic which must be lived into. The school is itself a product of culture, and a workshop in which the child should find himself and enjoy himself. It is easy to overstress the idea that the child is a "candidate" for our culture. He is in truth a *member* of the culture. And the school should grant him full membership in terms of *his* developmental past and *his* developmental present. If we think too much of future values we shall squander the ever-present present. Children wisely hold the present dear.

For this reason we have labelled this chapter *School Life*. We believe that the child is entitled to a generous measure of life, liberty and the pursuit of happiness during the very years in which he is in school,— the years from five to ten.

Our task, then, as adults, is to interpret school going children, not only in terms of the official course of study, but in terms of their psychological natures and their growth needs. How do the children themselves react to the school curriculum, to the school day, and to the teaching methods? That is the crucial consideration. The curriculum should not be envisaged as blocks of academic requirements, but as areas of educational opportunity corresponding to the major facets of our culture. These facets correspond to three culture areas. We may well think in terms of these three Culture Areas rather than in terms of the time honored 3 R's.

THREE CULTURE AREAS

1. *Language Arts* (conversation; drawing; writing; spelling; reading; listening; looking).
2. *The Sciences* (mathematics; natural science—physics, chemistry, biology; social science—geography, history, civics).
3. *Personal-Social Participation* (creative self-expression; arts and crafts; dancing, poetry, inventon, technology, engineering; pre-vocational skills; social cooperation and leadership; aesthetic, ethical and spiritual appreciations).

These three cultural areas are more comprehensive than the 3 R's to which the old fashioned red schoolhouse was so exclusively dedicated. The culture of today comprises a vast array of interrelated knowledge, skills, attitudes, values, goals. It cannot be conveyed in neat bundles of subject matter; it must be assimilated in organic bits of experience which correspond to the maturity traits of the individual child. We can, if we wish, dispense even with the noble word education; *for education in these modern days must be reconverted into a process of acculturation.* The child must learn to carry the culture into which he is born.

The schools are his second birthright. He comes into his biological endowment, that is, his ancestral inheritance, through the processes of maturation. He comes into the social heritage of culture through the process of acculturation. The two processes interact and interfuse, but maturation is fundamental.

A sketchy outline of the progressive maturational steps by which the child from five to ten enters the three major cultural areas should furnish us with a better understanding of his characteristics, both as a novice and as an enrolled member of his culture. A year by year summary of the advancing school grades will serve our purpose.

The child of five has already had a vast amount of cultural experience and participation. A companion volume (*Infant and Child in the Culture of Today*) was necessary to describe his development during those first four formative years. His acculturation began at his mother's

[376]

breast. In quick succession he advances to her lap, to crib, high chair and pen; to porch, perambulator and play yard; to the junior, middle and senior grades of the nursery-school. He has assimilated many of the folk-ways, manners and customs of civilization. He is toilet trained, he wields a spoon and even a tooth brush, he washes himself, he goes on simple errands; he talks freely; he can count to one, two or three; he makes many a foray into his widening world. In the next five years he makes deep penetrations into the fundamental cultural areas. At age five he is ready for kindergarten.

THE SCHOOL GRADES IN DEVELOPMENTAL SEQUENCE

KINDERGARTEN. FIVE is a kind of finishing age which brings to a conclusion the pre-school years. We do not think of the 5-year-old as a school-beginner, but rather as a completed pre-school child, who is well organized within his limits, without, however, being maturationally ready for the first grade. Unemotionally he tolerates separation from home, and easily re-adapts his home behavior to the simple demands of the kindergarten. He interprets these demands in terms of his own home life. Kindergarten is a kind of extra-mural home. School does not yet mean the novel and exciting transition to a new world, as it will a year later.

Nor is the kindergarten truly a preparatory course for the first grade. Successful adaptation to the kindergarten does not always augur a comparable adjustment to the first grade. Discontent in the kindergarten may denote a rapidly maturing pupil who will make a successful adjustment at school entrance. Occasionally a child adjusts better at kindergarten than at home and vice versa. But generally the children enjoy their kindergarten life.

The child likes his teacher, obeys her as a matter of course, and quotes her as an authority. His relationship is matter of fact and pleasant, and much less personal than it will be later.

In the *language arts*, the 5-year-old is relatively facile and well balanced. He not only likes to talk, he likes to listen; and loves to be read to time and time again. He also looks at books alone and may pretend to read. He may recognize some of the capital letters, pick out familiar words on a page or placard and indulge in a little simple spelling. But he is probably more alert with his ears than with his eyes.

He is beginning to use his hands languagewise, to delineate figures and simple dramatic episodes, to trace, to paint at an easel, to underline and to draw capital letters, and perhaps, to print his own name.

In the *sciences*, he shows a dawning interest in meanings. He has reached that stage of human culture when digits meant digits; and so he counts the five digits on his hand. He may count to ten; but his concepts are typically within the domain of five. Finger counting should not be denied him now or later. It is as natural as finger feeding once was.

His intellectual interests are varied rather than inquisitive and critical. He does not distinguish readily between fantasy and reality. He accepts "magic" as an explanation. He is fond of stories in which animals act like human beings. Nevertheless as a constant talker and listener he accumulates abundant simple information in the areas of natural and social science.

His *personal-social participations* reflect the organization of previous experience somewhat more than adventurous expansion into the unknown. He foregathers in fluid groups of two, three or four in his kindergarten play; he dramatizes familiar events; he dresses up in adult clothes. He works creatively with paint, clay and blocks, usually starting with a goal idea and finishing with a recognizable product. Socially he shows an inclination to establish friendships; and he can carry through on a group project from one day to the next. He takes an interpersonal as well as personal pride in achievement; for he likes to take home his kindergarten handiwork, and to keep the things that he has made out of his own spontaneity in response to the pressures of culture.

FIRST GRADE. The psychological climate changes when the child becomes truly a school-beginner; when he crosses that threshold which leads to books, blackboards, attendance records, classrooms, rules and regulations! The transition is bound to produce stimulating tensions and thrills; and also confusions; because the organism itself is undergoing transformation. Often the methods of acculturation, which the school awkwardly attempts, come into conflict with the maturational changes. When both school and child are awkward, the end results are awkward. Many concessions should be made to the school-beginner.

He is a poor subject for regimentation. His whole growth complex is "loosening," groping and thrusting to make new contacts with the multifarious world. He has lost some of the solidarity and assurance which he displayed at five. In his eagerness he copies new capital letters and also small letters; and he makes more reversals than he did formerly! This does not mean that he is slipping, or that he is fundamentally more unstable. But he learns to detect his errors and his reversals. Many children learn best through their errors. This then is no time for rigid insistence on accuracy. Errors can be good because they are approximations. Even in arithmetic we should be more lenient with such good errors. And because the 6-year-old is in such a promising state of many-sided ferment we should not put all our pedagogical eggs in one basket.

There is no single method of learning or teaching reading. There are multiple methods,—visual, auditory, manual and phonetic, which should be used freely and variously and separately and in combination to suit the fluid psychology of this school-beginner, and to do justice to the individual differences which prevail among all school-beginners.

It is not surprising then that the first-grader works in spontaneous spurts and in short shifts, that he is somewhat expansive and diffuse, that he intermixes impulsive play and earnest learning. He also intermixes home and school loyalties and attachments. By the same token teachers and parents intermix their tensions and blame each the other for shortcomings. How tranquil and beneficent in comparison was the kindergarten where work was play and play was work, and school was home.

Parents who would now insist on systematic thorough drill in fundamentals (with discipline and no nonsense), might easily disturb the process of acculturation in the name of downright education. The child is not ready for such rigorousness. He is ready for the kaleidescopic activity programs which progressive teachers have found suitable to his transitional stage of growth.

The various behavior patterns which he displays in the three cultural areas reflect his distinctive psychology. A few will be mentioned by way of illustration.

There is a burst of activity in the *language arts*. The school-beginner often speaks with vehemence and aggressiveness. He may temporarily stutter at six, although he did not do so at five. He likes to use big words; and he is a spontaneous commentator on his own activities and those of others· ("Oh, I'm going to go ahead and draw." "John, what are you making,—gosh!")

His drawings and picture writing are becoming more realistic. He renders the leg of a man in two strokes rather than one, to represent a second dimension. He can usually print most of the alphabet. He writes numbers from 1 to 12 or to 20, with frequent reversals and irregularities. He picks out single words or combinations of words, and is beginning to master the mechanics of holding a book and turning a page. A few children can read sentences. Abilities, of course, vary with individuality and social pressure. The most natural and universal reading interest is that of listening. The first-grader likes to be read to. He also likes to read pictures and labels; he is beginning to explore comics and illustrated books.

The Sciences. The first-grader is advancing in his mathematics. He is interested to make simple measurements using ruler, tape, yardstick, quart, spoonful, etc. He is beginning to label quantities and series with numbers: 2 of this, 4 of that, etc. He reads as well as writes numbers up to twenty; adds within the range of ten, and subtracts within the range of five.

Through care of school pets, plants and flowers, he acquires elementary notions of natural science,—growth, nutrition, cleanliness, weather, seasons, etc. Through the everyday experiences of school going, he becomes acquainted with social relationship between home, school and community; between parents, teachers, sibs, strangers, friends, neigh-bors, etc. This elementary social science is too complex for lessons and curriculum; it comes through actual life situations, informally and in-cidentally. In life-centered schools, such acculturation is more funda-mental than the academic fundamentals.

Personal-social participation lies at the basis of activity programs, and schoolroom projects. The 6-year-old is at once an eager ego, and a med-dling, social thruster. He cannot be organized by lesson setting instruc-tion. But given opportunities for creative self-expression and apprecia-tion, given a diversified menu of brief tasks which call for skill, given liberal opportunity to fumble, stumble and make errors, he will, in a social milieu, find the cues that will set him on true course.

SECOND GRADE. The first-grader is a school-beginner,—eager, spon-taneous, expansive. The second-grader,—to draw a contrast, is a school going pupil, earnest, assiduous and somewhat channelized. He has a new holding-on quality. Whereas a year ago he worked in short, shifting spurts, he now selects a groove within which he exercises a special skill. He even tends to overdo his practicing, as though he did not know how to stop once started. With the teacher's help he is diverted to something else where he again displays a characteristic repetitiousness. This trait is so marked that he is generally reputed to be a good learner.

There are, of course, individual differences, but the mechanical, learning attitudes are so prevailing that a volatile and highly spon-taneous type of child is likely to be more conspicuous than he would be in the first or third grade. Within limits the second-grader takes kindly to drill as an individual and in small groups.

He wants to be correct. This is why he consumes so much rubber, erasing what is wrong, or what he thinks he might improve. He likes ruled paper to write on, which is further evidence of a growing interest in form and performance. However, he works best in delimited areas. He does better with single sheet work than with a more elaborate work-book. He functions best when the environment is suited to his limitations. At nine years he will be able to make more adjustments by drawing on his own resources. At seven years he accepts, likes to know in advance what comes next, and does not readily make transitions from one activity to another.

This lack of pliancy may make him seem humorless, and leads to hackneyed jokes. It also makes it difficult for him to take compliments in praise of his school work. He identifies himself in a primitively grave manner with his printed name, and is much impressed by mail addressed to him. His orientation to school life is greatly influenced by the teacher-child relationship.

These emotional characteristics combined with his bent toward mechanical learning reflect themselves in the general atmosphere of the second grade schoolroom. A definite advance in intellectual maturity is reflected in the achievements in the three cultural areas.

The *language arts* show a marked increase in the capacity to communicate. The second-grader uses a telephone for social conversation. His sentences are more thoughtful and reflect a growing degree of abstraction expressed in analogies, opposites and similarities. He is beginning to use a child's dictionary.

Writing lags behind speech. It is ordinarily large, awkward and uneven in size and irregular in position. It is in a labored label stage rather than at a fluent, cursive stage. Half the children may prefer printing to script. Many can write their signature; they are beginning to use a small pencil.

Reading is in advance of writing. Single words are recognized rapidly and accurately. Familiar sentences are read with ease and new words are mastered through context. But language is still primarily assimilated through ears rather than eyes; and true to his mechanical learning tendencies, he often reads mechanically with only secondary regard for meaning. This pleases him; perhaps it should please us, for the time being.

Some children, however, are "great readers," and read to themselves for an hour or more at a time.

In the area of *the sciences*, the second-grader reveals a more discriminating interest in measurements and values. He identifies and comprehends the values of the common coins. He is beginning to tell time to the minute. He counts to a hundred, by ones, fives or tens. He adds within twenty, subtracts within ten, and uses a few very simple fractions.

Natural and social science information is acquired incidentally to projects, excursions and the celebration of holidays. The aquarium, the pet turtle, the weather calendar and an ever changing schoolroom museum become centers of interest which organize knowledge in fields of nutrition, biology, geography. These interest centers are still more important for the organization of attitudes toward nature and man's relations to nature.

Attitudes also are organized (often unconsciously) through the *personal-social participations* which the informal and planned activity programs entail. The life situations call forth latent abilities of leadership, of cooperation and inventing, of creative self-expression and group-expression in the arts. Even though this expression may have the crudeness of immaturity, clever teachers will manage to relate the personal-social behavior of the children to the culture of today,—to the conditions of the children's own homes and life interests. Through personal experience, rather than rote learning, the child is acculturated.

THE THIRD GRADE. Speaking comparatively, and one cannot do otherwise when dealing with growing school children, the third-grader is less channelized and more expansive than the second-grader. He is less mechanically concerned with practice for its own sake; he is also interested in associated meanings. Being less deeply immersed in himself and in the immediate environment, he gives more attention to relationships of cause and effect. He is more aware of his school mates both as individuals and as members of the same school grade.

These new maturity traits reflect themselves in the attitude of the third grade teacher and the atmosphere of the schoolroom. She is able to manage the grade as a total group, because the children enjoy working together as a whole group. They make little distinction between work and play, and are adaptable to shifting demands. They generally like all subjects of the curriculum equally well. They bring home good tidings about their life at school. Parents are gratified to see them so well adjusted.

Third-graders are more articulate with reference to their experiences and to their own mental processes. The teacher is more aware of how their minds operate, which eases the tasks of teaching.

The *language arts* reflect this increased articulateness. The third-grader converses almost as freely as the adult, not eschewing some slang (or mild profanity), exaggeration, and elevation of voice to suit emotional tensions. Good pronunciation and good grammar usually have been achieved.

The art of fluent penmanship, as a motor skill, is far from mastered, but the intellect may be equal to the use of punctuation marks, capitals and the composition of a simple letter. Reversals in writing are rare; but neatness, modulation of size, spacing and alignment do not measure up to good intentions. Great variations in style of writing are to be expected from child to child. Some children, especially girls, request to write cursively at seven. Some, especially boys, prefer a manuscript style.

Spoken language is far more fundamental than written language. With the great increase in powers of speech, it is not surprising that the third-grader enjoys oral reading, that he can tackle new words by phonetics as well as context. He may also be so interested in reading as a form of communication *to him*, that he takes new pleasure in silent reading.

The greater fluidity in the mental processes of the third-grader manifests itself in *the sciences*. His arithmetical sense is less stereotyped; he can break up quantities and series into fractions and simple proportions. This leads to the elementary insights of multiplication and short division. (The younger child's mind may be too "mechanical" for such insight.)

[384]

Measurement means more. He can lay ruler and tape against the four walls of his schoolroom. He can keep a weather calendar and note the effects of weather and season upon plants, animals, and men. He distinguishes between the passive movements of things inanimate, and the spontaneous movements of things living.

He makes a more rational approach to nature, to foreign peoples and strange lands. He differentiates with increased awareness between fantasy and reality, and begins to verbalize ideas and to formulate problems. All this is done at a very elementary level, but it denotes a real advance in the academic career of our school child. He is acquiring a modern scientific outlook.

It will be a socialized outlook if linked with *personal-social participations.* The third-grader is in an expansive phase of development, when his intellectual nature seeks knowledge and when his emotional nature seeks rapport with the widening world. As always, attitudes are organized through personal experience, which can come only through concrete extensions into community life,—through drama and creative art, through puppetry, field trips, radio and screen. Indeed a roomful of lively third-graders are none too young to tackle as a group project the writing of a motion picture script which will document or interpret some phase of the culture in which they live.

FOURTH AND FIFTH GRADES. As the kindergarten child epitomizes the mental growth of the first five years of life, so the fifth-grader consolidates the development of the years from five to ten. He has himself well in hand for one so young. The maturity traits of self-dependence and of *savoir-faire* are especially marked in well organized girls. Girls of this age are nearer to adolescence than are boys, and nearer to the wisdom of adult years. In the interests of brevity we shall characterize the fourth and fifth grades in general terms; but it should be noted that sex differences now begin to count heavily, and make themselves increasingly felt in the reactions to school life.

The fourth-grader is no longer a mere novice at school work. He can set his mind to a school task, and he can take a school task home. This is the grade when home work begins to be effective and meaningful.

The fourth-grader works well as an individual. He rather likes written work; and once embarked on a school exercise he tends to practice and repeat in a manner somewhat reminiscent of the second-grader. At a higher level he is perfecting the school skills which will be so important in the next grade. He takes readily to school methods which put a premium on efficiency and preparation for promotion.

The typical fifth-grader is less concerned with training for skill than with application of skill in the solution of problems. He likes to use his intelligence. Having mastered his intellectual tools he is more interested to put them to use. He seems less driven by time and the urgencies of school. He shows a better command of time and space; knows where he is at; makes more modulated adjustments to imposed demands. Even his voice is more modulated and he shows a capacity for self-criticism which makes for a realistic and factual approach to school tasks. He is ready to work by the clock.

The *language arts* reflect in the fourth and fifth grades a more subtle use of words. Vocabulary grows not only in size but in discriminativeness. Fine distinctions are made in characterizing emotional as well as physical qualities. Language is used as a tool, and somewhat consciously when he voices criticism of the actions of others.

The printed word is also used more as a tool and a device. In the fourth and fifth grades the child learns to use the dictionary more systematically, to recognize diacritical marks, to make simple outlines and to consult index, glossary and table of contents. He also learns how to skim for thought and to search for the main idea of a story.

Writing, as a motor skill, is under relatively good control. Penmanship becomes smaller and uniform. It begins to take on a mature aspect and individuality of style. The elegances of calligraphy will come with adolescence.

Writing as a means of communication comes into its own. In the fourth and fifth grades children develop a sentence sense, and to some extent a sense of paragraph as well. They develop ability to write brief stories, letters, thank-you notes, invitations, notices and advertisements. The language arts enable them to penetrate more deeply into community life.

The sciences assume an increasingly important role. The child extends his arithmetic skills and computations in common fractions, decimals and long division. He puts his skills to increasing use. Arithmetic becomes truly mathematics, which he applies to practical problems. He builds up tables of measure,—liquid and dry, linear and avoirdupois, time and money.

In the fourth and fifth grades there is a definite advance in critical and abstract thinking. The child is able to define abstract words like pity and curiosity. He acknowledges natural origins and natural processes in the physical and organic world. He is likewise more reasonable in the interpretation of social relationships. He worships heroes, but he acquires through history and geography a dawning sense of social evolution, and of the inter-dependence of peoples.

Information and attitudes are kept in good balance through *personal-social participations* and applications. When he utilizes his mathematics to keep accounts, to record the height of a growing bean stalk, to graph changes in temperature, and to chart the course of a shadow, he brings himself into social relationship with the life of the community as well as of the school.

Through field trips, through a collecting hobby, by neighborhood surveys, and by studies of plant and animal life, he begins to sense something of natural laws and their effect upon his own life. Similarly he learns about our technological culture, through more or less direct contacts with industry, aviation, transportation. During the fourth and fifth grades, the creative arts and crafts continue to serve a high social function. Through drawing, design, decoration, painting, modelling, mechanical contrivance, etc., the pupil not only clarifies his own ideas and feelings, but relates them to the social order. The complex process of acculturation depends upon a progressive organization of factual information and of attitudes formed through actual experience.

During the high school years the child, now youth, makes idealistic projections to encompass the culture which presses upon him more closely than ever before. The prerequisites for a favorable orientation are laid down during the elementary grades, in the years from five to ten.

HOME AND SCHOOL RELATIONSHIPS

To see the school grades in developmental sequence is to see them in perspective. Perspective relaxes tensions; it reduces crises. Teacher and parents alike are so absorbed by their immediate responsibilities that they lose sight of the overall, self-corrective trends of child development. A "failure" in spelling, a "careless" arithmetic paper, an inverted figure five, a lapse in obedience,—are magnified all out of true proportion. Report cards are read, and often they are filled out, with excessive gravity. They subject school, child and parent to unnecessary misjudgments and emotional reactions. The whole procedure of classification and promotion rests too heavily on the idea of competition. We can not fully humanize elementary education unless we consistently adopt a developmental point of view, which clarifies the relativities of failure and success. Time and again we must ask the simple question, *"Why does the child go to school?"*

When we view the school child in developmental perspective, we realize at once, that his whole school life is affected by his maturity level and by his individual growth pattern. The fact that he was born in December rather than June may have a decisive effect on his status in kindergarten. A difference of six months in chronological age or of developmental age may radically change his adjustment to the first grade. Obscure, but none the less real, retardations in the maturity of his eyes and his oculo-motor muscles, may account for his reading difficulties. The unreasonable exactions of the curriculum may be the source of his attitude toward arithmetic. The fatigue of a double ses-

[388]

sion, or the teasing of a bully on the way home from school may bring about amazing personality reactions. School life is beset with innumerable and not always preventable contingencies. Minor emergencies constantly arise, but are readily managed or carried if regarded in terms of the total sweep of development. The long range view makes many worries unnecessary both for parents and teacher.

Consider the matter of neatness and accuracy in written work. High standards of excellence may be commendable as absolute standards; but not as relative norms suitable to the immaturity of the child. Writing, reading and arithmetic alike depend upon motor skills, which are subject to the same laws of growth which govern creeping, walking, grasping. They are subject to physiological awkwardness. A child falls down in the motor aspect of his school tasks for the same reason that he falls down in his early efforts to stand and to toddle. This simple fact is often sadly overlooked both by teachers and parents.

When the school child was a baby the adult attitudes tended to be more reasonable. One did not say he should walk at this or that age. Feeling confident that he would walk at the most seasonable time, one was more interested to observe the stage and degree of his preliminary development. If reading readiness and walking readiness are appraised on similar grounds, more justice is done to the child.

Maturity traits determine the general patterns of adjustment to the successive school grades, to teachers and to schoolmates. The kindergarten child, typically, is well adjusted to his home, and is equally at home when at school. The first-grader is likely to stand in pleasant awe of his teacher; the second-grader has a very personal relationship; the third-grader has a less emotional regard; the fourth- and fifth-graders may establish business-like working relationships.

Sex differences also determine patterns of adjustment. Girls may be more neat, slightly precocious in reading and penmanship, and may advance more rapidly in the early grades.

Individual differences should not be underestimated. They would be much more freely acknowledged if we did not make a fetish of uniform standards during these years when the varying tempos and patterns of individual development declare themselves so strongly. It is contrary to the laws of nature that children should advance lock step through the grades. Individual variations in the development of speech are the rule and they are wide in range. Similar variations should be recognized in the closely related art of reading, and allowances should be made accordingly. A culture-conscious school, being democratically interested in all individual differences, would place a premium on non-verbal as well as verbal abilities.

Reading deserves special comment here because it is often made the basic factor in determining promotion. The school system places excessive emphasis on the importance of the printed word. An experienced high school principal has recently reminded us in forcible terms that at least a third of the entire secondary school population (grades nine to twelve) are "incapable of mastering the stock tools of learning (reading and writing) well enough to profit from text-book instruction." Not even attentive perusal of the pictorial comics has served to make these non-verbal millions of pupils masters of the printed page. The comics doubtless increase the reading vocabulary of the verbal multitude, but the non-verbal child suffers from limitations which are more or less constitutional.

This does not mean that he is backward or dull-witted. As a matter of fact he is frequently talented in less verbal directions, and is more than ordinarily wholesome in personality makeup. He may be able to "read" music, or physiognomy, or the contours of a landscape; or even the devious ways of his fellow men! In a word he may have excellent judgment; and a whole host of actual and latent skills, which will some day make of him a valuable citizen. In fact there are many potential leaders among the lower non-verbal third.

If our schools were less narrowly preoccupied with typographic reading, they would discover marked skills and potentialities early in life. We should not wait until the high school years before we discover our non-verbal pupils and burden them with the consequences of educational neglect. At the latest they should be recognized in the fourth grade. NINE is a somewhat critical age for these practical lads (and some lassies) who need above all an enrichment of opportunity in the creative arts, in the technologies of science, in manual skills and in personal-social participation.

Reading, writing and arithmetic are not only tool subjects; they are symptomatic indicators. A discerning school system would be less concerned to measure achievement as end product; and more concerned to use the measurements as indicators of the total psychological makeup of the child, including his true interests, his maturity status and growth trends. There need be no fear of "progressive education" when it deals positively and realistically with the assets and liabilities of the individual child. A child-centered school can promote maximal development without sacrificing minimal competence in the "fundamentals," and in the conventions of everyday life.

But a child-centered school will not ignore the home; rather it will work in partnership with it. Such a school will be concerned about the kind of home in which the child has been reared, will be interested in his past biography. Every child comes to school with a long developmental career behind him. Can the school afford to be altogether unaware of that past? Parents can be helpful both to teacher and child by bringing significant information to the attention of the school.

When classes are too large and when teachers have been too narrowly trained, a flexible partnership between home and school is impossible. But a spirit of mutual cooperation is in harmony with the democratic tradition. Even under unfavorable conditions, parent-teacher organizations working in harmony with school administrators can be more democratically utilized to determine educational procedure and policy. Should the session be shortened? Should there be two sessions when most of the parents are sure that the children are over-fatigued? Should the lavatory facilities be improved? Should the child be laden so heavily with formalized homework? Or should the home be encouraged to supply special learnings through games and informal approach? Etc.?

The total welfare of the child should determine the answers to such questions. Sometimes home and school can decide together; although there are many areas where the responsibilities of each are separate and defined. But who is responsible, after the child has crossed the threshold of the classroom and after he has crossed the school premises? The journey home is not without complications. There remain joint solicitudes and joint responsibilities to be shared by home and school.

If conflicts arise relative to the aims and methods of education, a developmental approach to the problems can have a solvent, clarifying effect. Most minor disputes can be adjusted by calmly asking, *"Why does the child from five to ten go to school?"* ... He goes because society should have something to offer which will enrich his life as an adult citizen in the culture of tomorrow, and which will also enrich his life in the culture of today.

GROWTH GRADIENTS

§1. ADJUSTMENT TO SCHOOL

5 YEARS—Adjusts to school with relative ease. May request to stay at home intermittently; shows fatigue occasionally.
> Mother or older child may need to accompany child to school for first few days or longer.
> Girls are more apt to like school than boys.
> May like to take a favorite toy to school.
> Sometimes takes his products home.
> Some children are better at home than at school and vice versa.
> Very little reporting at home about school activity.

5 YEARS—Anticipates first grade but may have difficulty with adjustment.
> May refuse to go to school because of some unpleasant experience.
> Fatigue, with or without two sessions and frequent colds are common.
> Brings, and may share toys, cookies or a book with classmates or teacher.
> Loves to take his products home to show his parents.
> There is little verbal reporting at home of his school activities but he may report about a "bad" child in the group.

7 YEARS—May not anticipate return to school in the Fall. May think it will be too hard. Some would prefer to remain in first grade.
> Relationship to teacher is important in his adjustment.

Likes to go to school with other children or alone rather than have his mother accompany him.

May show fear of being late to school. If he is to be late, would prefer to stay at home.

Shows fatigue, especially with two sessions.

Brings fewer things to school, though likes to display a new possession.

Now accumulates his products in his desk and takes home only occasionally.

8 YEARS—Enjoys school and even dislikes to stay at home, particularly if he will miss a special event.

Much less fatigue and fewer absences because of illness.

A few children are said to have an occasional "bad" day at school.

Some dawdle and have difficulty getting ready for school on time.

Now brings things to school which relate to his school work.

Some of his products may be taken home.

Many children now report on their school activities.

9 YEARS—On the whole likes school.

Takes responsibility for getting himself to school.

Apt to forget to take material to school unless reminded.

A few boys may take a gun or ball to school with them.

Reports some home and outside activities at school, usually in great detail. Talks at home about his standing in a school subject or about a special event.

§2. CLASSROOM DEMEANOR

5 YEARS—Needs some assistance from teacher with dressing and undressing.

Enjoys routine and adjusts to an activity program which allows freedom yet maintains control of the sequence of separate activities.

Changes from one activity to another with relative ease.

Likes to complete a task.

Some respond well to a rest period, others resist it.

Class can enjoy a directed activity for about twenty minutes.

"Reading" and "number" work closely associated with play.

Refers to teacher for materials, to tell experiences, and to show his products.

Child works in short bursts of energy.

Kindergarten activity is not highly social.

6 YEARS—Loves to be busy but will avoid things he cannot do.

Is in almost constant activity. Frequently stands to work at a desk or table.

Easily distractible as he watches others as well as within his own activity.

Does not know when to ask for help.

In attempting to form a group line, will push or lean on each other.

Can be given a choice of many things to do but may need suggestions from teacher to make his decision. Then may choose opposite.

Talks about what he is doing and what his neighbor is doing.

When working does not like interference until he needs help.

Tries to conform and to please teacher and himself.

Some children spoil games and need individual play activity. May do better with teacher close by or may need separation from the group.

Likes a "chart" of own successes but not ashamed of showing to others even if has only a few.

7 YEARS—Works quietly and with absorption for periods.

Noisy and explosive during transitions.

Is impatient in his demands for assistance from teacher.

May regard neighbor's work and copy from it.

May whistle and make different noises.

Accumulates all sorts of objects in his desk or pockets.

Becomes concerned if does not complete a task.

Wants to know what comes next, how far to go, etc.

Is anxious for his place in the group and does not like to be singled out for reprimand or praise before the group.

Does not like teacher to repeat instructions although he may need repetition.

When whole class gets out of order, necessary to shift to a different activity.

Class becomes disorganized and some do forbidden things, if teacher leaves the room.

8 YEARS—Eager to verbalize and to respond. Cannot wait for a slow child.

May dawdle and be slow during transitions.

Tackles work with speed. Even likes to be timed in a performance.

May interfere with others by his need to verbalize.

Likes and seeks praise both from teacher and from neighbor. "My drawing isn't good, is it?"

May work better with separation from the group within the room.

Wants to have his turn and wants each child to have a turn.

Some play with "gadgets."

Teacher more aware of child's process. Can explain in group how his mind is working.

9 YEARS—Individual behavior more noticeable.

Quieter while at work, but may make sudden noise such as banging desk top.

Competitive in work and in play, and is afraid of failure.

Wants to work independently of teacher. Refers to her for assistance.

May be self-conscious when reciting before the group.

Has better critical evaluation of how he can do things best.

Knows when he is "sure" or "not too sure."

Works for longer periods and may be unwilling to stop.

Likes now to be graded and to compare his grades with others.

Isolation to do his work is less effective than earlier.

Needs to know own process and to be given individual assistance apart from the class.

§3. READING

18 Months—Points to identified pictures in book.

2 Years—Names pictures in book.

2½ Years—Pretends to pick up objects from picture book.

3-3½ Years—May identify some capital letters in alphabet book or on blocks.
May select a letter by form, such as a circular or angular one, to identify. **May** learn to identify by association as "M for Mommy."
Enjoys song about ABC or *The Jingling ABC's.*
Wants to look at pictures in book when being read to.

4 Years—Identifies several capital letters. Some associate letter with the beginning letter of a familiar name: "S for Susan."
Enjoys having adult print his name on his products.
May identify a letter without naming. "That's in my name."

5 Years—May cease temporarily to identify letters formerly recognized, when attempting to print them.
Likes to identify repetitious phrases or words in familiar books such as exclamations or sounds that animals make. Also identifies word signs such as *stop, go,* or *hot* and *cold* on faucets, or words on cereal boxes.
Some like to underline letters or words in a familiar book.
May read letters in sequence and ask, "What does D-O-G spell, Mommy?" Likes to spell simple words as *cat, dog, yes, no,* and *mommy.*
In identifying letter or word, often selects first or last letter on a line and reads vertically from bottom up or from top to bottom.
Recognizes own first name.
May enjoy using wooden letters to represent names of people and may use these in combination with block building.
May recognize several or all numbers on the clock, or those related to certain routines. May identify some numbers on calendar, on telephone dial or on own house number plate.

5½ Years—More familiar with letters of the alphabet.
May translate a word into more familiar meaning: *"coffee"* for *cup,* etc. (similar to 2-year-old who names the picture of a cup "coffee").
May "read" pictures of a book.
Likes to listen to stories of children in action such as those in a First Grade primer.
May regard print as well as pictures when read to.

6 Years—Interest in small as well as capital letters.
Recognizes words and phrases, and perhaps sentences. Finds words related to picture or story. Matches words.

[395]

Likes to have material which relates to his own experiences.

Beginning to develop reading vocabulary. Beginning to recognize word out of context.

Gets clues from length of word, beginning sound or letter.

Uses marker or points with finger at words.

Some like to read nursery books. May now read though earlier may have memorized.

Some like to pick out letters on a typewriter and have mother spell words for them. May supply beginning letter but need help with rest.

Likes to listen to poems about letters such as found in *Sounds the Letters Make.*

When can read a book, apt to read and re-read it many times.

Typical errors of those who read: Words added to give balance (a king and *a* queen). May reverse meaning (*come* for *go*; *I* for *you*). Substitute words of same general appearance (*even* for *ever*; *saw* for *was*; *house* for *horse*). Add words (*little, very, y* at end). Tendency to carry down a word which was encountered on line above.

7 YEARS—Can now read sentences. Recognize familiar words easily and rapidly out of context.

Individual differences in reading rate are marked. In oral reading many try to maintain flow and prefer to have unfamiliar words supplied or they guess at them. Apt to repeat word or phrase to maintain speed. Some are excessively slow.

Likes to know how far to read. May use a marker.

In spelling may supply beginning and ending letters if cannot spell the whole word. May enjoy game of spelling words at home during routines.

Enjoys finding familiar words in a child's dictionary.

Typical reading errors: Omissions of short familiar words (and, he, had, but, and final s or y). Some similar additions (the, a, but, little). Substitutions are the most common error (*the* or *some* for *a, come* for *go, was* for *lived, a* for *the*). One letter substituted: (*pass* for *puss, some* for *same, they* for *then*). Changed order of letters: (*saw* for *was, three* for *there*). Letters added at beginnings or end: (*the* for *he, y* at end). Words of similar form: (*green* for *queen, bed* for *bird*).

8 YEARS—Masters new words through context, division into syllables, initial consonants, prefixes and suffixes.

Mechanics and reading for meaning now in better balance.

Begins to be able to stop and discuss what he is reading.

Reads easy material with exaggerated expression. Considers it "babyish."

Uses table of contents and index.

Book usually held easily on lap with some little shifting of head distance. Seldom needs to point to maintain place. May point or bring head closer for a new difficult word.

Reads more rapidly in silent reading, and usually prefers silent reading. Also enjoys taking turns in reading a story orally.

Typical reading errors: Greater variety of errors but they interfere less with mechanics and meaning. More omissions than additions, chiefly: *the, little, and, in, then.* May read words in a phrase in wrong order.

9 YEARS—Reading now more related to various subjects.

Individual differences in abilities and interest. Now some who have been slow have a real spurt.

Utilize dictionary.

May do better in silent reading but need to be checked by oral reading.

Many prefer silent reading but when reading for facts and information retain reading matter better when read orally.

Typical reading errors: Repetitions are frequent, usually one or two words at a time. Substitutions of meaning as: (*house* for *room, she* for *mother, beautiful* for *wonderful*).

§4. WRITING

3½ YEARS—Makes controlled lines, then scribbles.

In copying a cross, may split the horizontal line.

Likes to put a "frame" around paper.

4 YEARS—*Letters* Prints a few capital letters, large and irregular. Prefers circular letters as C, G, O, Q; or angular letters as E, H, I, L, T, A.

Selects first letters usually of familiar names as own name or of a member of family: T for Tommy, C for Charles.

Letters are often made with many parts (four parts to E).

Prints on page at random. Variable positions of letters and may lie flat in horizontal position. Seldom reverses.

Name May attempt to print own name (girls especially). Some print first few letters and mark for remaining ones. May split name in middle and continue on next line.

5 YEARS—*Letters* Prints some letters of varying sizes, in various positions and usually large. May be vertically reversed.

Letters formerly made in three parts are now made in two parts.

Asks help in forming or identifying letters already drawn. "How do you make F?" "That isn't any (letter) is it?"

May recognize a letter that is in own name without identifying it.

May write from right to left without reversing any letters.

Some like to copy letters and frequently do so from right to left.

Name Prints first name, or nickname, large and irregular. Printing gets larger toward end of name.

Numbers May print certain numbers which have significance. (5 for own age; 12 for 12 o'clock.)

May copy from the clock or calendar.

Some draw on a page from right to left without reversing. Some draw in a confused manner or reverse.

Marked variation in ability to write numbers. Some can write into teens and usually reverse the position of the separate digits (*31* for *13*). Frequently omit a number.

6 YEARS—*Letters* Prints most of the capital letters with several reversals (usually horizontal, fewer vertical).

Prints some words. May use all capitals and may use a mixture of capitals and small letters without differentiating their size.

Letters are now more apt to be drawn with a continuous stroke.

Prints large and increasingly larger letters as proceeds across page. Certain letters may be consistently drawn larger.

Beginning to recognize reversals but may not change.

Likes to use variety of materials: Writes on blackboard with chalk, or on large paper with crayon. Later able to handle writing at desk with a pencil.

Name Prints first or both names and may add middle name or add Junior at end usually in all capital letters.

Letters large and uneven. May reverse a letter (especially S). May not separate names, or may write one under the other.

Some print increasingly larger; some increase, decrease and then increase; others maintain fairly uniform size and write with an undulating line.

Numbers Many can write from 1-20. Print numbers large in horizontal rows.

May reverse order of digits in teens either in final product, or in execution (writes end digit first and places one in front of it).

Reverses one or two digits (*3, 7* or *9* more usual).

7 YEARS—*Words* Prints or writes words and sentences, in capital and small letters.

Beginning to differentiate height of capital and small letters, but may make about the same height. Capital may be substituted for a small letter.

Writing is somewhat smaller and in a few it is greatly reduced in size.

Corrects letter reversals (usually 6½ years), but still makes an occasional letter in reversed position. May place letters in reversed order or omit a letter.

Beginning to separate words but sentences usually run together.

Tends to reduce letters in size as writes across page.

Prefers ruled paper. Some want large space, some small.

Likes to copy sentences.

Pencil grasp is tight with the forefinger caved in and the shoulder is tensed. Now prefers pencil rather than crayon for writing.

Likes to write correctly and erases a good deal.

Numbers Writes 1-20 or higher usually without error. May still reverse one, sometimes two numbers. The same number may be reversed as a single digit and not when it appears in the teens or vice versa. (*6* and *9* most frequent; also *4* or *7*)

Figures are smaller, and considerably smaller with a few children.

Usually place numbers in one horizontal row at top of page, but some write in vertical column at this age.

8 YEARS—*Words* Can write several sentences.

Considerable variation in writing. Many now do cursive writing instead of printing. Write fairly large and rather "squarely" usually with slight slant. A few still write large and very irregularly. Some write a medium size and somewhat evenly though still quite straight. Letters may be wider. IF writing is becoming smaller, then capitals and looped letters tend to be disproportionately tall.

Reversals are now rare.

Now beginning to space words, sentences and paragraphs.

Tries to write neatly although sometimes hurries and does not care.

Still may not be able to write down all the ideas he has for a story.

Name Writes both names with good spacing and correct use of capital and small letters. Considerable discrepancy in size between capitals and small letters.

Great variation from child to child in size and style of writing.

Numbers In writing 1-20 does not reverse single digit. May reverse order in number 20 (*02*).

In written number work may still have an occasional reversal of a digit especially when making a double number.

9 YEARS—No longer prints, unless manuscript is to be continued form of writing.

Handwriting is now a tool. Writes for extended periods.

Writing is smaller, neater, more even, and slanted. The pressure is lighter (especially in girls). Some write with upward slant and some make letters irregularly.

Letters are in good proportion.

Some now have a skillful "style."

Now use finger movements with tension in the forearm.

Increase in speed and in volume of writing.

Occasional error when copying or in recording dictated numbers.

§5. ARITHMETIC

1 YEAR—"One-by-one" pattern of manipulating one object after another consecutively, the rudiment of counting.

Can release one cube into a cup.

18 MONTHS—Can build a tower of 3-4 cubes.

Ten cubes into cup.

Uses the word "more."

2 YEARS—Distinguishes between one and many, but usually does not count objects. Says "anudder." Idea of one more.

Says "two balls" when handed a second ball. Can say "big ball" if big and little are presented.

Can build a tower of 6-7 cubes.

2½ YEARS—Can give "just one" cube on request.
May count by rote: one, two, lots.

3 YEARS—Can usually count two objects. May or may not start with "one" when counting.
Is reported to count to five.
Can give "just one" or "two" cubes on request.
Activities may be influenced by numbers. May demand "three" or "four" of everything.

4 YEARS—Counts with correct pointing three objects.
Is reported to count to ten. May start with a number higher than one. Verbal counting without objects definitely exceeds counting of objects.

4½ YEARS—Can give "just one," "two" or "three" cubes on request.
Counts with correct pointing four objects and answers "how many?" Some can count ten objects.
Understands the terms "most" "both" and "biggest" but not the terms "same" and "equal."

5 YEARS—Counting by ones: Usually stops just before a decile (*19, 29*). May jump from 29 to 40, or go back to a smaller number.
Counting objects: Can count and point to thirteen objects. Some difficulty maintaining regard and pointing and if loses sequence is apt to go back to beginning again. May need two or three trials.
Naming coins: Names a penny. Likes to take from adult to give storekeeper for a purchase.
Writing numbers: May write some numbers from dictation. Names and verbalizes as writes. "I don't know what 7 looks like." Usually writes in confused manner (*2, 5* and *8*) or reverses (*3, 7, 9* and *teens*). Omits *6* and *9*.
May write in horizontal line across top of paper or vertical line at left of paper. Many place anywhere on page.
Some like to copy numbers from clock. May know numbers such as *7, 3* or *12* associated with time of events in daily schedule.
May not be able to identify the number made. Asks, "What does it look like?"
Addition and subtraction: Some enjoy oral figuring and can add within five. May use objects or fingers and count by ones. Errors are usually one number more or less than correct answer. In attempts to subtract within five, counts forward from one to larger number using fingers, then counts backward to answer.

5½ YEARS—Counting by ones: Error at decile or at *17* or *27* or omit 7.
Counting objects: Can count to twenty, pointing correctly and giving total on one or two trials.
Writing numbers: Writes from 1 to 10 or higher with many reversals, or in teens wrong order (*71* for *17*) and/or reversal. Writes in confused manner: *2, 5* and *6*.

Reverses: *3, 4, 7* and *9*. May omit *9*. Writes horizontally across top of page. Many turn paper sideways and then write horizontally across width of paper. Verbalizes: "I can't make it." "Down like that and over like that." "My hand gets kinda tired."

Addition: Adds correctly within five. Counts on fingers or counts in mind, starting with the smaller of the two numbers.

Subtraction: Subtracts correctly within five.

6 YEARS—Counting by ones: Counts to 30 or more. May over estimate how high he can count: to "million" "dillion."

Counting by tens: To 100 or to 90 and then says "20."

Counting by fives: To about 50.

Names coins and knows number of pennies in nickel and dime.

Counting pennies: Counts twenty with correct pointing and gives total.

Writing numbers: Recognizes and may write numbers to 12 or 20. Writes large, with some numbers (especially *5*) larger than others. Reverses especially *3, 7* and *9*. Rarely omits a figure. Usually writes horizontally across top of paper.

Verbalizes: "Can't too well because I mess them up." "I'm tired. I'm hot, too." "I wonder if I'm making them backward."

Addition: Many add correctly within ten. Count starting with larger number or at the one following this: (3 + 7: 7, 8, 9, 10 or 8, 9, 10). Errors are usually one number more or less than correct answer. A few guess. Some know small combinations, especially balanced numbers as 3+3 by heart.

Subtraction: Correct within 5. Counts from one to larger number and then back. May add instead of subtract. A few use balanced numbers to figure from.

Likes to group objects: 4 of this, etc.

Interest in balanced numbers: 2 and 2, 3 and 3, etc.

Uses simple measurements: pint and quart.

7 YEARS—Counting: Can count to 100 by 1's, 5's, 10's and by 2's to 20.

Naming coins: Can name penny, nickel, dime, quarter, half-dollar and tell how many pennies in each.

Writing numbers: From 1 to 20 or higher. Fewer errors. Some reversals especially *4, 7* and *9* or reverses position in teens especially *12, 17, 19, 20.* May write horizontally or vertically on page. Little verbalization while writing, though small mouth movements indicate silent counting.

Addition: Correct within twenty. A few make errors of+or— one, suggesting that they are still counting. Others know combinations, especially even combinations, (3+3) by heart, and break harder ones down into known combinations and figure from there. Thus 18+5: 18+2=20+3=23. In the teens may add the right hand figures and then precede answer by one, thus 14+3: 4+3=7, preceded by 1=17.

Subtraction: Subtracts correctly within ten. Counts backward from larger number: uses balanced number (10−4: 5+5=10, 5−1=4, so 5+1=6, therefore 10−4=6); changes to addition (6−4=2 because 4+2=6). Knows many combinations by heart.

When doing written work, does not shift easily from addition to subtraction on same paper.

Likes to write a number of many digits.

Learning to use fraction of one-half of a unit or a group.

8 YEARS—Counting: Counts by 3's to 30 and 4's to 40.

Writing numbers: Rarely makes an error in writing numbers through 20 or higher. Spaces correctly and may put dots and dashes between. Figures are more uniform and smaller.

Addition: Knows many combinations by heart. Some count by ones from larger number; some rearrange in combinations which they know by heart ($8+5$: $7+5=12+1=13$). Occasional error of $+$ or $-$ one.

Subtraction: Knows some combinations by heart. In teens may subtract the right hand figures and then precede this answer by one. Errors mostly $+$ or $-$ one but a few "wild" answers suggest that they are no longer counting by ones.

Learning to add and subtract one to three digit numbers requiring borrowing and carrying.

Multiplication: Through 4 or 6 table. Knows some low combinations by heart, especially 3×3, 4×4. May add ($3+3+3=9$), or say table.

Division: Uses simple facts of short division. Errors mostly $+$ or $-$ one of a single digit in the answer.

Can measure distances in room in terms of feet.

Fractions: Uses fractions of one-half and one-quarter.

Interest in weights of people and things.

Interest in money and relative value of coins.

Shifts process frequently. Suddenly shifts to adding when multiplying. May be aware of it and say, "I always do that!"

9 YEARS—Writing numbers: Writes numbers accurately though may make occasional error when dictated to or when copying from the board. Prefers to figure by writing numbers down. Does not verbalize while writing but may not do neatly and says: "My worst numbers," "My most careless thing." May now prefer to write a vertical column.

Addition and subtraction: Knows all simple combinations by heart. May select certain combinations when adding a column.

Can tell own process. Knows what combinations has most trouble with and may write them on a card or desk until knows by heart. Wants to analyze errors with teacher. Likes to differentiate between "good" errors and "bad" errors.

Multiplication: Through the 9 table. Errors are mostly with 7 or 9. A typical error is to substitute 6 or 8 for 7, or 8 or 10 for 9 ($\pm$ one shift). Most now multiply instead of adding. May change 8×3 to 3×8. May start from even numbers 6×7: $6 \times 6 = 36 + 6 = 42$; or from one he knows by heart and adds or subtracts from this.

Fractions: Learning to use fractions and measurement.

Division: Can, on paper, use 2 to 5 digit dividends and 1 digit divisors, using the method of long division.

Can keep accounts and records.

19

THE ETHICAL SENSE

THIS chapter deals with a prickly theme. Any discussion of morals, whether it be the morals of children or of adults, inevitably invites confusing emotions and conflicting concepts. It is almost impossible to set aside adult preconceptions of what a child *ought* to do; and so we fail to understand what the child *does*, and what he actually *is*.

Our culture is surcharged with moral directives and with ethical norms which must be preserved if civilization is to survive. Generation after generation the wisest of men have argued the age-old questions of Right and Wrong. The literatures of the race are laden with writings on virtue and sin, duty, discipline, punishment, justice, mercy, guilt, expiation, retribution, salvation and transgression. Not so long ago there were sober disquisitions on inborn child depravity. Nor have all the ghosts of the past yet been laid.

As adults we inherit a culture of long lineage in which time tested wisdom is intricately mixed with persisting error. We cling to arbitrary absolutes which prevent us from seeing the true and ever-changing nature of the growing child. Although this chapter concerns morals, we shall not subject the reader to any further preachment. Our purpose is to describe objectively the growth of the art of good conduct in the child from five to ten. This is a complex art which depends upon the development of an ethical sense,—a sense which matures by natural progressions.

What are these progressions? The growth gradients which follow indicate that the underlying growth mechanisms begin to operate in early infancy. At the age of ten years these same mechanisms are still operating. They continue throughout adolescence. When, indeed, *do* morals mature? And if we compare the tremendous moral growth of the first decade with the relative increments of the second decade, does not the child give an amazingly good account of himself? To what extent has the adult transcended the gradients of infancy and childhood?

The ethical sense defies definition, unless we resort to oversimplified absolutes, and merely say that it consists in the capacity to distinguish right and wrong in thought and conduct. But such a definition is not very useful. What we are really interested in is the development of that capacity, as manifested in patterns of behavior.

A child is not born with a weak ethical sense which becomes stronger as he grows older. He is born with certain dispositions and potentialities, which undergo progressive organization from day to day, and from month to month. As early as the age of 6 weeks the child smiles by himself. An egocentric smile! At 8 weeks he smiles back at the beaming face of his mother,—a responsive social smile, which relates to some one else! At 12 weeks he spontaneously initiates a similar smile,—a reciprocal social smile, which has a double origin, a two-way implication! In this simple sequence we already glimpse the dynamic which governs the growth of the ethical sense. There are three phases to this fundamental dynamic which repeats itself again and again with ever widening elaborations as the spirals of development ascend: (a) intrinsic-self phase (b) social-reference phase (c) a reciprocal self-and-social phase. We need not burden our discussion with these designations; we simply mention them at the outset to suggest how the "moral fibers" of infancy and childhood are gradually interwoven into patterned textures and how the shuttle weaves back and forth between the central self and the selves of others.

Already the infant is sensitive to smiles of approval. Soon he will be sensitive also to frowns. Very early (about the age of 36 weeks) he heeds a monitory "No! No!" as a nursery game, and also as a serious command. Here we glimpse the germs of self-inhibition and of social disapproval. At one year the baby is so highly socialized that he likes to please others. At any rate, he greatly enjoys repeating performances that are laughed at by others. So far as the culture is concerned, he is already caught in a complex web of smiles and frowns,—of approbation and disapprobation. His moral welfare would appear to be assured.

But, behold, at the age of 15 months he has a will of his own, so strong that he no longer heeds "No! No!". His conduct becomes self-assertive. He insists on doing things for himself. Sometimes he seems to carry this insistence to excess. He does not accept the kind of protectiveness which he welcomed at the age of one year. He casts his toys in a "self-willed" manner. But we do not make a moral issue of his obstreperous behavior. He is too young for that. Tolerantly we recognize the favorable and constructive significance of the growth changes that are taking place before our very eyes.

All too soon, however, his behavior is misconstrued through over rigid application of standards of right and wrong. As he approaches his second birthday, more and more is expected of him. His toilet behavior may be made the object of emphatic approbation and disapprobation. At 18 months he may hang his head in shame if he is adjudged "guilty" of the puddle for which he is "responsible." He counters by blaming the misdeed on some one else, as though groping for an alibi.

Does all this mean that the young pre-school child is in possession of an ethical sense and that he can be credited with self-reproach and a consciousness of guilt? And having credited him with these capacities, shall we hold him unwaveringly to exacting standards? If the ethical sense were a special distinctive faculty of the mind, our reply would be affirmative. But the ethical sense is not such a faculty. The mind is an enormously complex system from which the ethical attributes cannot be separated. To evaluate the moral significance of the conduct of an 18 months child we must consider the total child in all his attributes rather than his conscience per se.

We doubt that his feeling of guilt is profound, or that it encompasses his whole personality. He is probably incapable of blushing; although in another year or two a sensitive child may indeed blush when reproved for a fault. Darwin, by the way, regarded blushing as the most human of all emotional expressions.

The primitive shamefacedness of the 18-month-old denotes a simple form of shyness and withdrawal, linked in the present instance with the function of elimination, which is closely bound up with his emotional life. Nevertheless, this disgrace gesture with its projective reference to some one else, reveals that the personal ego is elaborating, and has even attained a measure of detachment, in its capacity to set up a flimsy alibi.

This capacity has far-reaching import for future developments, but we must emphasize that the ethical sense, as a psychological structure is still extremely meager. It will take years of structural growth and of patterning experience before the individual is capable of the higher forms of moral judgment. As adults we are too prone to think of the ultimate forms, rather than of the gradients which lead to them.

Fortunately, the gradients have a forward reference, and even undesirable behavior sometimes signalizes a growth process which becomes constructive under skilled guidance. The 2½-year-old, for example, when confronted by two alternatives has a way of trying out both. Opposites seem to have equal appeal. But with experience and with help, he learns to choose *within the limits* of his maturing capacity. At the age of three, he actually likes to make choices and he likes to please. Within the limits of his maturity he is becoming a moral agent, who assumes, and who should assume, suitable responsibilities.

At four years, for developmental reasons, he is apparently less anxious to please. He is less sensitive to praise and blame, and he needs new kinds of motivation when questions of obedience arise. He tends to go out of bounds. Wisely managed, he usually proves to be conforming again at the age of five. Then he invites and accepts supervision. He likes to ask for permission, even of strangers. He likes to stand in well with people. His ready obedience has an attractive quality. He is very good!

But "obedience" is not an absolute trait, fixed once and for all. It is really only a general label for a diverse group of specific obedient acts of which a child happens to be capable. The patterns, the contexts and the occasions for obedience inevitably change with age. The wise parent never makes a fetish or even a goal of obedience for its own sake. As we have already noted in our behavior profiles the whole map of behavior undergoes deep changes in the second half of the fifth year and throughout the sixth. The psychological transformations involve the entire personality, creating new problems of conduct for the child, and new demands for guidance for his father and mother. At five his sense of goodness and his good conduct consisted largely of obedience to the commands of grownups. His ethical development between the years from five to ten is clearly traced in his expanding concepts of GOOD *and* BAD, particularly goodness in himself and badness in others. The two-way dynamic works like a weaver's shuttle, as he penetrates more deeply into his own ego and that of his coevals and elders. Observing others helps him to understand himself. And what he inwardly feels he also ascribes, more or less aptly, to others. A nicely balanced two-way appraisal is no mean feat. It takes skill. It takes maturity.

No wonder the 6-year-old is ethically inept when the tide of development brings him to a level where he yields to the temptation of cheating, a new form of behavior which he partly learned by being cheated! He has an acute sense of possession; but a very poorly organized relation to his belongings. He must also have an acute sense of self-status; for he cannot gracefully bear to lose a game. He will cheat on occasion. But to even the psychological score, he denies his guilt; and he displays an apparently altruistic worry about the cheating of others! Perhaps he worries most at the very time when he is himself most liable to cheat. And note, he does not dwell much on honesty as a positive excellence. He approaches that bright jewel by the indirection of its dark opposite. There is a negative corner to Robinson's barn, and it may well prove to be the nearest way home.

In the seventh year there is already a decline in the amount of cheating; and a more robust insistence on the part of the 7-year-old that there should be no cheating by others. Thus he adds his own weight to the social disapprobation of dishonesty. Thus the threads of the fabric of morals are minutely, ceaselessly woven; and the children themselves help to fashion the growing designs.

Pensive SEVEN has a new type of awareness of the GOOD *and* BAD. Home ties are loosening; he vaguely apprehends the community. He generalizes and abstracts to a degree far beyond conforming FIVE and sketchy SIX. He does not limit his thinking to specific acts. He is beginning to sense the *qualities* of goodness and badness, and to erect more universal standards of conduct to live by. He is getting a firmer grip on everyday honesty and truth. His blaming and alibiing have moral overtones, and he can even be appealed to on ethical grounds. All of which means that he is becoming more of an individual among individuals.

EIGHT with all his expansive and evaluative traits is yet more conscious both of himself and of the selves of others. His awareness of these others is more perceptive, and increasingly subtle. He shows an impressive catholicity of insight into the good characteristics as well as the shortcomings of his comrades. He grants that Boy X is the best athlete, that Girl Y is the most skillful artist in school, that Boy Z is not always fair, but that he is the most fun in this game or that, etc., etc. The widening range and refinement of his estimates lend substance to his ethical out-look. Vigorous morals are based on acquaintance with the world.

The evaluative tendencies of EIGHT do not exclude himself. He is vulnerable to criticism. He is contrite. He will *never*, no NEVER, do it again! All told, he has the essentials of an advanced ethical sense. He is sensitive; he is not over competitive; he has a fairly tolerant insight into the psychology of his associates; he shows a strong tendency to work out his relationships with them, unaided by interference from without. He may squabble in the process; but even so his collective behavior represents an embryonic forecast of a democratic culture.

The 10-year-old registers a further advance along these same promising developmental lines, when surrounding conditions are favorable. Cultural controls have become of increasing importance in moulding the resultant patterns of social behavior. A most important period for the prevention of juvenile delinquency embraces the years between seven and ten.

The normal, well rounded 10-year-old is already a law abiding citizen. He is able to organize and to conduct a club, with rules, regulations and referee. His bylaws, written or unwritten, ban lying and cheating. He is morally mature enough to sternly oppose black markets. He follows leadership, but he also participates in discussion, and he can wait his turn in the discussion, because he has outgrown the eight-year-squabble and the six-year-quarrel, and the five-year-compliance. Best of all he has a sense of humor. He is able to take a joke on himself,—a capacity which we would include as one of the metaphysical ingredients of the ethical sense.

In this narrative interpretation we have naturally stressed the constructive aspect of the developing ethical sense. There is such an aspect inherent in the process of maturation. It may be contended that there are also evil possibilities and eventualities in this same process; because the "normal" child is not uniformly "good." He is sometimes selfish, destructive, deceitful,—at least by dictionary definitions. Even the 10-year-old, whose virtues we have just proclaimed, can use his new found ethical abilities to spite his comrades, to gang up against them, and to disrupt their club activities.

In the shadow of world-wide wars, we may have to take a second look at the moral constitution of man as embodied in children. Here we get a first glimpse at the face of evil. It would, however, be gratuitous to assume that the failures of adult ways of life are due to the limitations of children. These limitations are relative, and in large measure manageable because they have a natural negative function in the economy of development.

This does not mean that we place a premium on "badness," or grant it license. Mere indulgence does not lead to constructive prevention and to control. But a knowledge of the developmental logic of misbehavior will enable parents and teachers to use enlightened methods of management. On many pages in this volume we indicate concretely how adults can use foresight to spare children from excessively difficult moral situations. Intelligent anticipation will avoid many an emotional crisis. A developmental interpretation will reduce the emotion if the crisis comes. In the first ten years of life, it is unwise, and usually unjust to impose standards of conduct *arbitrarily*. Arbitrariness leads to emotional conflicts and to intellectual confusions. Parents frequently become emotionally "burned up" by the child's poor manners,—a misplaced emphasis which suggests a confused scale of values. And manners, like morals are influenced by immaturity. They do not yield to arbitrary authority.

Harsh forms of punishment are, of course, automatically ruled out by a developmental approach to the problems of child conduct. When an adult pits himself against a child for the mere sake of preserving authority, no good follows. Care needs to be taken even in exacting apologies. Apology is a form of expiation, intended to set matters right between child and adult, or between child and child. But injudiciously demanded it leads to insincerity or resentment, or to a sit-down strike. Forceful physical punishment is so difficult to apply beneficially in times of crisis that it is the better part of wisdom to have recourse to more enlightened methods of control.

In all disciplinary situations the adult must keep an eye on himself as well as on the child. He should feel certain that he is not demanding too much in terms of the gradients of growth. He must be sure of steps 1, 2 and 3 before he exacts steps 4, 5 and 6. He will not knowingly confuse manners with morals and will keep his eye on the one long range goal: the mental health of the child. A sense of humor and a little skillful, face-saving banter, can work miracles in discharging emotional tensions, even in the moral realm.

And perhaps, we should think more in terms of emotional equilibrium, and less in the gloomier terms of expiatory punishment and of retributive justice. Because over the long pull which begins with birth, there is nothing more stabilizing than affection and mutual respect between adult and child. Morals are rooted in mutual respect, and in the reciprocity which comes with such respect. Reciprocity in turn leads to reason, and ultimately to the concepts of equity, which distinguish the mature ethical sense.

GROWTH GRADIENTS

§1. BLAMING AND ALIBIING

18 MONTHS—Blames "puddles" on others—cat, grandmother. Says "no" if asked if he made them.
Becomes angry if things do not work as he wishes.
If he takes something he shouldn't, may run away and drop object.

21-24 MONTHS—Becomes angry at inanimate object. Kicks and hits chair, etc.

4 YEARS—Blames inanimate objects. Some tattling on others.
Will sometimes admit own fault in a whisper: "An accident."

5 YEARS—Denies own fault if questioned directly.
Blames nearest person for his own misdeeds: "Look what you made me do."

6 YEARS—Usually denies own fault if questioned directly. May blame sibling, friend or mother.

If admits fault, alibis: "He made me do it," or "His fault," or "I didn't mean to."
Can be led into admitting fault by an indirectly worded question: "How did you do it?"
May blame inanimate objects for his mistakes in school.
Better at accepting blame for big things than for small.

7 YEARS—Directly accuses others: "He did it," or "His fault."
Alibiing takes form of self-justification: "I was just going to do it," "That was what I meant."
May throw book if cannot read; may throw game cards if loses game.

8 YEARS—More responsible for his acts. Usually some justification if blames another person.
May deny guilt, but not blame others.
Blames himself. Feels need to apologize. Says he will "Never do it again."
May evaluate own action and feel guilty about it.

9 YEARS—Wants blame apportioned fairly; much interest in who started any difficulty; tries to explain own behavior; reasons his way out.
Some can accept blame and say "I did it and I'm sorry"; may even feel ashamed of own wrong doing; upset if blamed for something he has not done.
Makes excuses when things go wrong (studying and practicing): "He was bothering me."
Considerable "taking it out on others," "picks at others"; if hurt kicks the next fellow who comes along.
Self-criticism implied in "I would do that!"

§2. RESPONSE TO DIRECTION, PUNISHMENT AND PRAISE

1 YEAR—Gives object on request.
Repeats performance laughed at.
Imitates simple behaviors.
May be inhibited by "No-no."

15 MONTHS—No longer enjoys game of "No-no" but demands his own way. Physical restriction and removal of breakable objects necessary.

18 MONTHS—Responds to verbal "No-no" but not consistently.
Knows where things belong and likes to put them in their places.
If fatigued, grabs things and resists physical inhibition.
Temper tantrum if cannot have own way.

21 MONTHS—Very insistent on having own way but cannot verbalize wants. Direction, praise or criticism have little effect in altering his demands.

2 YEARS—Demands strong at home though child may be meek and compliant away from home. Cannot share, but at adult suggestion can accept substitutes.

2½ YEARS—Opposites are of equal value (yes-no). Tries out both simultaneously, even in responding to directions.
   Verbal directions not enough. May need physical restraint.
   Tantrums and refusals to obey.
   Imperious, domineering, wants his own way.
   Neither praise nor blame very effective.
   Can sometimes accept substitutes when two children want same object.

3 YEARS—Responsive to directions. Tries to please and conform. "Do it dis way?"
   Attentive to spoken directions. Notes facial expressions.
   Can be bargained with; can be put off until "Later," or "When it's time."
   Begins to be able to share, to take turns.
   Fewer techniques and fewer environmental restrictions necessary.
   Takes routines more for granted.
   Responds best to specific suggestions, rather than general ones.
   Susceptible to praise, also to blame.

4 YEARS—Less anxious to please, obey, conform.
   Routines go smoothly and independently.
   Out of bounds, resistant response to many directions. But can understand that rules and restrictions are sometimes necessary. Likes to receive new privileges.
   Verbal restrictions now better than physical.
   Goals and competitions help motivate.
   Less sensitive to praise and blame.

5 YEARS—Needs, invites and accepts some supervision and direction.
   Asks permission. Asks, "Is this the way to do it?"
   Likes to help mother at home.
   Likes approval but does not demand praise. Likes to please and to do things right.
   May hesitate to carry out direction but usually does. May refuse because he can't do a task, or is too busy.
   Many are described as "angels" or "perfect."
   If corrected or reprimanded may become angry and cry.

6 YEARS—Responds slowly or negatively to demand, but in time may spontaneously carry out as though it were his own idea.
   If pressed, may be defiant: "No I won't," or "How are you going to make me?"
   An indirect approach is usually more effective: counting, magic word, a surprise. Needs extra chances.
   Needs clear simple directions in advance to get him started in the right direction.
   Vacillates with two choices and usually ends with wrong one.
   Loves praise and wants approval.
   Resists punishment physically and verbally. Punishment does not improve behavior.

[413]

If criticized or blamed may become saucy, rude, argumentative or have a temper tantrum.

May respond to isolation.

7 YEARS—Does not respond promptly; often does not hear directions. May forget easily.

May argue: "But mommie," or "Why do I have to?" Delays: "Just a minute" (which may be several).

May start to obey and then get into a detour on the way.

Wants to be warned ahead of time. Also likes to know what punishment will be. Can plan with him to avoid disaster.

Better at helping mother than at doing household tasks alone.

Is suggestible and sensitive. Cares what people think of him.

Many respond well to praise though it is less necessary than at some ages. May be embarrassed by praise.

If criticized or if feelings are hurt, may cry.

8 YEARS—Delays in carrying out a request; may argue and find excuses but finally obeys with "If you insist."

Demands to be treated as an adult. Wants cues, a hint, secret codes. Wants instructions worded just right.

Likes to work for an immediate reward, not just to help.

Responds to small deprivations for short periods. May say "I didn't care anyway."

Loves praise and to be reminded of his improvement.

May burst into tears if blamed or criticized, or may say "Who cares?"

Mere words or a look may suffice to help him to control his behavior.

Often cannot tolerate even a slight correction.

Feels guilty if he does wrong: "Never do it again."

Does not like to be teased or joked about.

Criticize and compliment each other.

9 YEARS—Can now interrupt own activity in response to a demand from adult. Securing his attention may depend upon his interest and willingness to carry out the request; may wish to postpone until later because so busy with his own interest and then may forget.

Needs to be given detailed directions and to be reminded.

Much less "arguing back" than earlier.

If does not like directions may look sulky, cross, truculent, but if no issue is made will usually obey eventually.

May go from extreme of taking over authority for himself (unexpectedly brings a child home to lunch) to asking permission for some small thing.

May prefer reasonable appraisal of his work rather than praise, though nearly all welcome praise.

A threat, or deprivation of some desired object or activity usually suffices to put him in line.

May be "sore" at punishment; "gyp," "not fair," "just my hard luck."

Takes criticism better than formerly, but it still needs to be carefully phrased.

Says he is sorry if he does wrong and may feel ashamed of himself.

Group standards may be more important in determining behavior than parental standards.

Begins to be able to take a joke on himself.

§3. RESPONSIVENESS TO REASON

2½ YEARS—Cannot make choices. Wants both extremes.

3 YEARS—Better at making choices. Likes to be confronted with a choice.
Adult can bargain with him.
Responds to reason. May do something he dislikes if given a good reason.

5 YEARS—Not much difficulty in making up mind. Decides quickly what he wants; does not present himself with too many alternatives.
Likes to do things his own way but also likes to conform and to please adult. Thus adult can change his mind. May refuse because he considers himself unequal to demand.

6 YEARS—Difficulty in making up his mind. Vacillates between two choices. Gets mixed up.
Will not change mind once it is made up.
If reasoned with, does not change mind, but explodes into temper.

7 YEARS—Transition stage. Somewhat easier to make up his mind, to make choices and simple decisions, especially if both alternatives appeal to him.
Still hard to change mind, but can occasionally listen to reason and change mind without exploding into temper.
Has standards and is trying to live up to them. Thus may be appealed to ethically.

8 YEARS—Makes up mind rather easily, though he has difficulty with little things of life. Knows what he wants.
Frequently can listen to reason and can change his mind with some ease.
However, does like to have his own way.

9 YEARS—Can make up mind easily and some can change it in response to reason, though this does not hold for all issues.

§4. SENSE OF GOOD AND BAD

1 YEAR—Repeats performance laughed at.
May be inhibited by "no no."

15 MONTHS—Wants own way. Not inhibited by "no no."

18 MONTHS—Shame at making puddles.
Runs away and drops object he has taken.

21 MONTHS—Conscious of adult approval or disapproval.

2 YEARS—Imitates phrases "good boy," "bad boy" in regard to toilet functions and other routines.

2½ YEARS—Opposite extremes appear to be of equal value—"good—bad."
Little influenced by adult approval or disapproval. Wants his own way.

3 YEARS—Tries to please and conform. "Do it dis way?"
Responds positively to question, "Have you been a good boy?"
May repeat prayers about "God make me a good boy."

4 YEARS—Begins to understand about *rules* and ways to do things.
Some interest in good and bad, but not much understanding.

5 YEARS—Child is "good" (from adult point of view) much of the time.
Sense of goodness and badness limited largely to things parents allow or forbid.
Child's "goodness" largely due to his interest in conforming and obeying. "Is this the way to do it?"
Likes to help mother and to do other things considered by adult as "good."
Likes to stand in well with people and to ask permission.
Understands and respects rules, that he must get to school on time, etc.
Knows when he has been good and may plan to be good next day.
Dislikes being called "bad." May play being "bad."

5½ YEARS—Little generalized sense of good and bad. Seems to keep in mind for each specific thing whether it is "good" or "bad," i.e. allowed or forbidden by parents.
Likes to be made to conform; but seems often to define what he must not do by doing it.
Much interest in behavior of playmates; whether it is good or bad, whether they do things in the right way.
May behave better away from home.

6 YEARS—Notion of good and bad still largely connected with specific activities allowed or disapproved of by parents.
Rudiments of a sense of good and bad, and may ask, "Was I good?" (Question usually asked after he has been bad.)
Very undifferentiated in ethical sense as in other fields.
Great interest in behavior of playmates: whether good or bad, whether they do things in right way. Especially report on bad behavior of playmates.
May think that other people are not fair.
Chief interest is in having own way.
Once he has started misbehaving, is not influenced by criticism of his behavior.

7 YEARS—Simple but generalized notions about goodness and badness. Knows that some kinds of behaviors (obeying, doing things willingly) are good and others bad.

Has standards of goodness for himself as well as for others, and means to live up to them.

Has a sense of fair play and can be appealed to ethically.

Thinks that things are "a gyp," "not fair" and that he too must be "fair."

Judges behavior of playmates as good or bad but not quite as verbal as at six.

His own behavior varies, sometimes quite good, sometimes not. May b· better away from home.

Concerned about being good. Proud of good days. Worries about bad ones.

Realizes that being "bad" spoils things.

8 YEARS—Aware of goodness and badness. May try to evaluate them.

Good and bad no longer just what parents permit or forbid.

Child wants and means to be "good." Wants to be appreciated.

Tries not only to live up to his own standards but to what he thinks are the adult's standards.

More evaluation may lead him to believe that he has been "bad," or has failed to live up to standard. Then may feel guilty.

Inwardly unhappy if he does wrong. Dislikes to admit wrong-doing.

If fails to live up to standard, wishes failure to be condoned: "Do you blame me?" "Could I help it?"

Thinks of things as "right and wrong," no longer simply as "good and bad."

9 YEARS—Less concern about good and bad; now thinks in terms of right and wrong.

Wants to do things the right way; may be ashamed of being wrong.

Interest in fairness of teacher, of others and of punishment.

Evaluates behavior of other children: "He's a good sport."

Standards are those of contemporary group; disgusted with others who do not live up to these standards.

§5. TRUTH AND PROPERTY

18 MONTHS—*Property* May have a special toy, blanket or other object to which he is attached. Unable to sleep without it.

Definite relationship of possessions to their owners—takes hat or pocketbook to its correct owner.

Knows where things belong and likes to put them in their places.

21 MONTHS—*Property* At home may know which objects belong to each person. In grocery store, etc., may walk off with merchandise unless prevented.

2 YEARS—*Property* Possesses as many things as possible. Strong feeling of ownership, especially in toys. "It's mine" is a constant refrain.

Great pride in clothes—especially in shoes, socks and handkerchief.

Interest in possession is one-way, an interest in his own things. Interest in possessions of others is merely verbal: he likes to name over what things belong to what people.

[417]

Hoards toys. Cannot share them.

May bring small token, such as a marble or orange section to school and hold onto it all morning, objecting to anyone's taking it.

Money   Names penny. Interest in money, but almost no understanding of its use. Likes to use it manipulatively and to carry it around.

2½ YEARS—*Property*   Child is "into everything" regardless of what or whose it is.

Objects which he is not to touch need to be removed from reach.

Interest in acquiring possessions of others, though seldom plays with them.

Brings a favorite toy to school to show others, but cannot share it. May bring same object every day.

Clings to favorite possessions when insecure.

Especially fond of hats and mittens. May cling to old clothes and dislike new ones.

May go through elaborate rituals with possessions, at home.

Money   Likes to have a few pennies in his pocketbook and is very possessive about them.

If asked "What is penny for?" (meaning what is its use) will answer, "For me."

3 YEARS—*Property*   Beginning to share toys; less hoarding.

Brings possessions (books for example) to school in order to share with others.

May enjoy exhibiting possessions, then forgets about them (at school). May bring a different object each day.

Enjoys new clothes and likes to exhibit them to others, especially to teacher.

Money   Likes to have pennies to put in the bank.

Knows that money is used in making purchases though has no idea of how much.

Play money is often a very satisfactory substitute for real money.

4 YEARS—*Property*   Much interest in possessions. Showing off and bragging about possessions: "Mine is bigger (better) than yours."

Especially proud of large possessions (big bed) of which he can boast.

Possesses parents and boasts about them.

Begins to possess his special friends.

Strong feeling for teddy bear. May treat him as a real person.

An age of bartering and swapping of possessions. Most apt to share with special friends.

Shows off new clothes.

Strong personal feeling for own products made at school. Wants to take them home.

Will help feed and care for pets under parents' direction, but not dependable.

Honesty   Expansiveness leads to taking of small objects (such as labels) from store, objects of little value to either store or child.

May take home school equipment as well as own school products.

Money   May know what penny will buy and may save several pennies to buy a more expensive object.

Can count three objects.

Objects to parting with money, even in purchase.

Truth   Tells very tall tales, often with little basis in fact.

The peak age for imaginative verbalization.

Often makes little distinction between fiction and fact.

5 YEARS—*Property*   Little trouble about possessions. Child does not seem to want more than he has.

May show pride in clothes but does not take good care of them, on or off.

Likes to take school products home; also likes to take own things to school.

Other people's possessions remind him of his possessions. "I have blocks."

Much less bragging about possessions than earlier.

Money   Interest in money not strong.

Knows that money is used in making purchases; likes to take penny from adult to give to store-man.

Can name penny. Can count ten objects.

Truth   Fanciful stories and exaggerations continue, but child begins to distinguish real from make-believe and may know when he is "fooling."

5½ YEARS—*Property*   Likes to have a great many possessions. Likes to have large quantities of objects.

May collect a few miscellaneous objects: toys, fancy paper, odds and ends.

Very poor at taking care of things: leaves them around, breaks them, loses them.

Takes poor care of his things, but objects to parting with them; unless he goes to opposite extreme and is over-generous.

Some are destructive and even like to break things.

Pride and interest in clothes, but do not take good care of them.

The phrase "Play with *my doll*" suggests strong feeling of possessiveness.

Likes to take things from school.

Honesty   May take toys or possessions of others. May also take gum or candy from stores. Now take things they really want.

Money   This is a "money for candy" age. Money is important not for itself but for what it will buy.

Many have an allowance of 5¢ or 10¢ a week. May do tasks, as clear off table, help with dishes, in return for this.

Little saving; mostly spend allowance.

Spend money slowly and carefully, taking much time to decide which object they will buy. This decision usually takes place at the counter and by means of picking up and handling many different objects.

Can name penny, nickel, dime.

Truth   Less exaggeration and untruthfulness. May tell fanciful stories but usually distinguishes fact from fancy.

Some said to be *very* truthful, their word "law."

6 YEARS—*Property*   Likes to take things to school to show and share; takes work home to show parents. Takes present to teacher.

Likes to have a great many possessions but does not take care of them or keep track of them. Scatters them around house or yard. Breaks them. Loses them.

Loses toys, clothes, pocketbook money. Cannot keep track of anything.

Miscellaneous collecting and accumulating.

Some have pride and interest in clothes, but do not take care of them.

Bargaining, but little sense of value so may make poor bargains.

Honesty His needs are strong. Sense of the limits of ownership is weak. Thus takes what he sees and wants, regardless of who owns it.

Conversely may give away his own most valuable possessions.

In collecting and accumulating, may accumulate belongings of others.

Cannot bear to lose. Will cheat if necessary to win.

Money Money still thought of in terms of what it will buy: "Good Humor money."

Interest in the object that money buys, not in the money. Careless with money; might "steal" objects that money buys; less likely to take money.

Spends money immediately and thoughtlessly. Little saving unless motivated by parent.

Many have a formal allowance, (5-10¢ per week). Most do some work at home in return for this: empty wastebaskets, take out milk bottles.

Can name penny, nickel, dime, quarter.

Truth Will deny fault if questioned directly. Falsehoods told often to evade blame.

Some are very "honest" verbally; but may cheat at games.

7 YEARS—*Property* Less taking things to school to show, but sometimes takes special things.

Becoming more interested in possessions and takes better care of certain things.

Some, especially girls, may take good care of clothes.

Much collecting: the goal being a large quantity.

Bartering: mostly on an "even swap" basis.

May give away own things.

Feeling of possession in relation to "school things": likes to have a school pouch or bag which contains his own pencils, eraser, etc.

Honesty Takes home school-pencils and school-erasers.

Girls may take attractive small belongings of mothers.

Money An increasing interest in money.

Most have an allowance and are interested in the fact of having it. Some earn this; others have a basic allowance and may supplement it with earnings.

Can name all coins and tell how many pennies in each.

Many are interested in saving: defense stamps or bank account.

May also save money toward some expensive purchase, as a bicycle.

Truth Less lying than at six.

Much concerned about wrongness of lying and cheating, especially in friends.

Quick to tattle of any breach of ethical code by others.

8 YEARS—*Property* Great interest in property and possessions.

Likes to acquire, own and barter objects: hoards, arranges, gloats over possessions.

Wants a place of his own in which to keep things.

Some take good care of things, but most continue to be very careless.

Room and clothes usually untidy, but keep some things neat: desk, books, certain toys.

Likes to bring to school objects related to the school subjects.

Takes short-cuts across property of others, often damaging property.

Honesty Child *needs* what he wants. If not provided for, may take money, which is now meaningful in terms of what it will buy.

May take household money to "treat" friends.

Money "Money mad," "just loves money."

Real interest in money and in acquiring a good deal of it. Likes to earn money at home.

Knows how much he has, how much is due him, what he wants to buy, what it will cost.

Plans ahead (in his mind or from catalogues) as to what he will buy.

Saves up for expensive things; little squandering of money on trivialities, except funny books.

A high age for bartering. Ability along this line improving.

Truth Expansiveness may lead to telling tall tales and to boasting. But distinguishes fact from fancy and may size up adult to see if adult believes his stories.

Many are truthful about matters which they consider really important.

9 YEARS—*Property* Beginning to be neater and does not lose things as much as he did.

Some effort (parent-instigated) at picking up room, but does not usually hang up clothes.

Usually "particular" about own things and may consider room and possessions "sacred."

Some boys interested in trading and barter.

Possessions quite numerous. Elaborate collections, carefully classified.

Honesty Has ethical standards and may be very exacting of self and of others.

May verbalize, "I'll have to be honest."

Only a few children deliberately take things not belonging to them.

If forbidden something such as comic books may read them in secret without parents' knowledge.

Many can lose in competitive games with fairly good grace.

Money Likes idea of having large amount of money to look at, to show, to count and to talk about.

Less interest in allowance. May forget to ask parent for it. Knows he can do chores to earn it, but may not care enough to, except on occasion. May be paid a certain amount for each chore.

Buys little needs (glue, crayons, clips, comics) and asks for money to pay for them.

Interest in how much different things cost.

Some can save up smaller sums to attain a more costly object.

Truth Becoming more truthful. Are "essentially" truthful, but there are definite exceptions. May exaggerate, may say have washed hands, etc., when they haven't, and may support friend or sibling in a lie.

20

PHILOSOPHIC OUTLOOK

Man has lived on this swirling globe for a million years. It has taken him a long time to get acquainted with himself and to become aware of the universe in which he has his being. Day before yesterday he discovered that the earth is but a speck in a vast cosmos. Only yesterday he discovered the cosmic energy contained in the atoms which constitute this planetary speck. Even with the help of Einstein he has not yet solved the riddles of Time and Space. Only a few hundred years ago America was unknown; and medieval Europe lived in a "dream of eternity," which, Mumford suggests, did not dissolve until the 13th century when campaniles and belfries were erected to announce the passing hours. This imparted a new sense of time and tempo.

There remained, however, many childlike beliefs about human fate and evil, life and death, nature and deity. Modern science and technology reconstructed these beliefs and is still reconstructing them. Copernicus revolutionized the naive ideas concerning the canopy of heaven. Darwin gave us a new outlook on the origins of plants, animals and mankind. The Encyclopaedia Britannica in 160 miles of linotype gives a large scale account of transformations of human thought and action which have taken place throughout the ages. And now a new atomic age is upon us. Never was philosophy more needed!

Man is continually engaged in the task of reconciling the known and the unknown. He is forever seeking orientation to the realities and the unrealities which surround him. If he is a professional philosopher he may formulate his outlook into weighty tomes and bring a conscious logic and science to bear upon thoughts. So he organizes his reflections and arranges them into an orderly system.

Needless to say, the child from five to ten is not a philosopher in this articulate sense. Nevertheless, the modern child spontaneously develops notions about natural phenomena which bear striking analogy to the concepts of the early philosophers of ancient Greece. He also has spontaneous ideas of physical causality which do him no little credit. And he, like his forebears, is continually engaged in reconciling the known and the unknown. Even in infancy, long before the age of five, he thinks thoughts which once constituted major achievements in the mental evolution of the race. For that matter, Einstein and Newton acquired their basic physics and geometry in the nursery.

The term philosophy can be variously defined. As systemized knowledge it is the general science which integrates all sciences. At its highest levels it is a codification of man's reflections on his relations to the universe. Now children do not deliberately codify their concepts; and yet they have characteristic modes of thinking and acting, which express their relations to the knowable universe. They have intellectual orientations and tendencies which constitute the essence of a philosophy in the making. It is difficult to draw a line between a complete and an incomplete philosophy, because even at adult levels no final philosophy has been achieved. We surely would not wish to say that the 5-year-old has no philosophy at all. His intellectual orientation to the world is already so advanced that we must trace the threads of development back to infancy to find the antecedents of his philosophical outlook.

The newborn baby is immersed in the cosmos from whence he came! But when he wakens from his natal sleep to search for the breast, and when he opens his eyes to look upon the world he is already at the threshold of the riddles of Time and Space. He promptly begins to solve these riddles at a pragmatic level. The ego which philosophers ascribe to him begins to expand; so that he steadily disengages himself from the cosmos which held him so intimately in its grasp at birth. Under the surge of growth he pushes frontiers toward the unknown. Whenever he is startled by a novelty or a surprise he reacts with a movement, a feeling, a shift of attention, an exclamation, a word, a sentence. And thereby he becomes an embryonic philosopher! We cannot begin to catalogue the cumulative conquests at his fast widening horizons; so we shall content ourselves with a condensed sketch of his intellectual progress in four classic areas of the philosophic domain: 1. *Time and Space* 2. *Ego and World Society* 3. *Life and Death* 4. *Cosmos and Deity.*

1. TIME AND SPACE

The eyes take the lead in making a pathway into cosmic space. On the very first day of life, an infant may incipiently fixate one of his open eyes upon an approaching object. During the first week he can sustain fixation on a *near* object. By the end of the first month he can fixate *far* as well as near objects. In another month he can co-ordinate both eyes to explore his surroundings with *roving inspection.* The conquest of space is well under way.

[424]

Having cleared a trail with his nimble eyes he must now use his hands to penetrate the spatial wilderness. Thereby he refines his estimates of near distances (and stops reaching for the moon, if he ever did!). When he gains better command of his legs, he will creep and walk, thereby refining his knowledge of far distances.

But practical (and philosophic) space is a manifold of many sectors, indicated by numerous prepositions and adjectives: on, under, in, above, in front of, behind, high, low, thin, thick, vertical, horizontal, oblique, etc. The infant invades and conquers these varied sectors of space through a joint use of eyes and hands, fine and gross muscles, postures and locomotion. He probes the third dimension with index finger. He learns the properties of container and contained in his poking, filling and pouring play at sand pile or seashore. He rediscovers the elementary architecture of space by building vertical towers, horizontal walls, lintels and arches with his blocks. These rediscoveries have a lawful developmental sequence, because they are inherent in the architecture of the nervous system itself.

"Nature geometrizeth," said the philosopher Plato. The infant confirms the philosopher by demonstrating a geometry of growth in the ontogenesis of geometry itself. Held in his mother's arms at the age of one year he wriggles to get *down*; he gestures to be taken *up*. At two years he has an expanding vocabulary of prepositions and place words. At three years he has a definite sense of destination. At five years he likes to make a simple map picturing a road which goes somewhere.

This is prophetic of an almost revolutionary reorientation which gets under way at six years. At that age he is still the center of the universe, but he is less space-bound, and takes a new and rangy interest in the sun, his own planet, and other heavenly bodies. At seven years he is interestedly aware that there are other places than those just "right here." At eight years he has a new awareness of foreign lands. By ten years he has a fairly comprehensive feeling of the earth as his home, the points of the compass, the significance of parallels of latitude and longitude. He has made immense strides since he first cast his eyes on a moving shadow on the ceiling above his crib. He is spatially oriented to the *basic* geography of his world. To that extent he has a philosophic outlook.

He becomes oriented in time in much the same manner. For time has much of the essence of space, and most of our time words are space words. Time is long and short, near and far, two part and three part, before long (soon), endless; it fills an interval. Here and now, and then and there are closely united in the psychology of growth. The calendar is a kind of space map of time.

Time, however, is in a sense more abstract and inflexible than space. It has only two sectors or dimensions (backward and forward). In an unsophisticated way the infant is aware of the flow of time; but not of the units of time. By association he learns to *place* events in his accustomed surroundings and his accustomed daily schedule. (Note that the word *place* has a spatial connotation.) By experiences of *place* expectancy, he identifies *times*. By deferments he learns to wait and to appreciate units of time. His capacity to expect punctual happenings, and to wait for deferred happenings determines his elementary sense of time. As he matures he is able to manipulate and to foresee potential time in the same way that he learns to manipulate plastic space. Some individuals are more adept than others in this manipulation of time; and this, by the way, fundamentally colors their philosophic outlook as children and as adults. Some of the most durable individual differences of childhood pertain to this very trait.

A glance at the growth gradients shows that the child progresses from appreciation of personal time to inter-personal and to more abstract non-personal time. At two years he comprehends the words "soon," "wait," and "pretty soon," particularly if the inflection is emotionally reassuring. It must be a tangible and prompt transaction. At three years there can be more interval in the bargain, and the child knows what he will do on the morrow. At four years he uses past, present and future time words with similar facility. At five years he is so symmetrically oriented in both time and space that he seems to live in a relatively stable world of *Here* and *Now*.

At six years he takes a new type of interest in the ages of young and old, and in the babyhood of his mother. This is more than a perception of *duration*. It is a beginning apprehension of a *time cycle*,—a higher order of insight, a more philosophic outlook. At seven years he not only tells time by the clock, but is interested in time schedules,—a cultural kind of time. At eight years he likes to consult the schedules as they are posted on the bulletin board. He is getting time bearings in a restricted province. But he is still color blind for historic time. For all he knows, George Washington is mentioned in the Bible.

At ten years, however, the child is better oriented with respect to historic time, and he is yet more precisely oriented to local community time, life cycle time, and personal time. He is at home with units of time. He knows the date; the day of the week; the exact minute of the next program on the radio. His timing and tempo are more highly geared than the bells of the medieval campanile. As he grows older he will move nearer to Emerson who enjoins us to have faith in the years and the centuries, so that we may restore the minutes to their proper perspective. Philosophy again!

2. EGO AND WORLD SOCIETY

Since the so-called ego and the social organizations of mankind have been a necessary theme for philosophers, we must bring this subject, briefly, into consideration. By the ego we mean the personal self,—and the non-personal,—the individual who by progressive detachment be-comes a partial entity in the vast human family.

The process of detachment is slow and also paradoxical; for the ego takes form only as the infant becomes more and more aware of other individuals. The process begins with the mother. We shall not repeat this oft told tale. The drama of reciprocal identification, projec-tion, and separation ordinarily takes place in a household. The presence of other persons helps the baby realize his own status. This psychological mechanism is a little like stereoscopic vision. The baby senses himself to be in others; but he also senses himself in his own physique; the two experiences offset each other; they are sufficiently different to build up a sharpening image of his own integral self.

As early as the age of 32 weeks he senses strangers as something different from familiars; although he does not recognize himself in the image which stares at him from a mirror. At two years, he has a heightened sense of self-identity. He calls himself by his own name; he calls all men and women "mommies" and "daddies"; he calls every child "baby." And he has taken one short step beyond the confining boundary of the household: he feeds and toilets a doll. Even if he prefers a teddy bear we may consider that he has begun to relate himself actively to other selves. He enjoys simple pictures of persons as well as of things. At three years he likes to hear stories about them,— a definite step beyond egocentrism.

The noteworthy bargaining ability of the 3-year-old must again be cited as a symptom of a changing (philosophic) outlook upon the world. At five years he likes to feel grownup, and significantly he asks "Could a baby do this?" meaning, of course, that a baby couldn't.

At six years the child is emotionally in a paradoxical, or shall we say a two-way state, so far as ego and the world are concerned. He is certainly the center of his universe, even though he is emotionally embroiled with his mother. And he is inordinately interested in himself; he is intrigued with his own babyhood, and inquisitive about his anatomical make-up. Notwithstanding, he is eager to participate in the world's work, and is earnestly concerned about his school work. From the latter standpoint he is not so egocentric after all.

The world is widening. At seven years he may be provincial enough to want his own set place at the table or in the automobile; but he is also seeking a place orientation in his school and community. He shows a dawning interest in government and in civilizations. In another year this interest comes to expansive expression. The 8-year-old, although his temperamental traits of individuality are now more marked than ever before, identifies himself with foreign peoples, and foreign cultures. He can hardly wait to grow up.

The 10-year-old has begun to read adult magazines, and is reflecting seriously on the vocation he will follow when *he* is grown up. Accordingly, he reads biography and history with deepened perspective. He listens to the radio for communications from the outer world. In time of World War he follows the news commentaries with a factual, almost adult interest. He consults maps. He makes surprisingly few aggressive remarks about the enemy; although, we know that the enemy successfully trained 10-year-old boys in the lethal techniques of war, including rifle, machine gun and grenade.

The American 10-year-old considers in his mind whether he would prefer Army, Navy, Marines, aviation, radar, etc. He helps in the civilian aspects of war work. But fundamentally his psychology is preparing a foundation for a potentially peaceful philosophic outlook on a world society.

He has made excellent progress since his earlier years.—"What do soldiers do?" At the age of three his answer was "Dey march!" At four he said "They fight with guns!" At five, he may have asked a thoughtful question about good Japs and bad Japs. At six, he takes a firmer stand: "Why, Hitler is so dumb, I bet he can't even spell cat."

Philosophic outlook in the making!

3. LIFE AND DEATH

The subject of war naturally brings us to another great theme in the domain of philosophy: the origin of life and the meaning of death. It took no little insight on the part of our racial forebears to make a biological distinction between life and death; and there is a period in the development of the child when he unites the two phenomena so closely that he believes in reversible death. This interesting notion rises in the mind of the 5-year-old child, at the very time when the distinction between the quick and the dead dawns upon him. He recognizes the immobility of the dead. His attitude is factual, unemotional. He may even do a little experimental killing of lower forms of life. But his concepts are vague. He does not think of himself or of the aged as dying. He has an inkling of finality, but does not sorrow. The idea of the reversibility of death is, of course, implicit in primitive and modern religions. Religious beliefs are akin to philosophies.

The 4-year-old has a very limited and almost purely verbal concept of death. The 3-year-old has little or no understanding of death; but he is making a definite approach to the problem of the origins of life. He does so through his interest in babies. He likes them; he wants the family to have one right away. He may ask groping questions: Where does the Baby come from? Where was it before it was born? What can the Baby do when it comes? The questions are not as profound as they seem to be on the surface; but they do denote an interest in origins. Mythologies which express the philosophic outlook of primitive peoples are replete with theories of origin and genesis. The 4-year-old, living in a commercial culture may cling to the idea that babies are purchasable; or in his more private thinking he often maintains that the baby is born through the navel. The 5-year-old is somewhat matter of fact about the birth of babies, as he also is about the finality of death. In a vague way he associates movement with life; and probably does not make a consistent distinction between animate and inanimate objects when the latter seem to have the power of movement.

But with the forward pulse of growth which comes at six years, the child has a new awareness both of life and death. An appreciation of the negation of death serves to sharpen his perception of manifestations of life. He shows a more concerned interest in babies and asks many questions about them. He makes general inquiries about the process of gestation and of birth. He may show a beginning interest in the reproduction of animals.

At seven his interest is less outspoken and more reflective. He does not need the concrete stimulus of an actual baby to start a short train of theoretical reflections. The mechanical aspects of birth may chiefly engage his attention.

The 8-year-old characteristically shows a definite expansion in the scope of his comprehension. He sees the necessity of a long uterine period of growth prior to birth; and he is beginning to understand that the father plays a part in procreation. His thinking, however, is relatively concrete and he may retain naive notions about the floating clouds, the current of rivers, the action of the wind and the movements of sun, moon and stars.

The 10-year-old is less naive. He still thinks vaguely of forces behind all movements; but he has grasped the significance of spontaneous movement so he arrives at the rationalistic conclusion that animals— and plants—are endowed with life. For all practical purposes he has made a distinction between animate and inanimate. The distinction cannot be final for even now scientists and philosophers are debating whether the protein molecule of a virus is animate or inanimate.

Death poses the distinction in new forms. As already suggested, the 6-year-old is becoming more aware of the meaning of death, emotionally as well as intellectually. Self- and mother-centered as he is, he begins to worry about his mother's dying and about the separation which will result. In an aggressive mood he may invoke death upon parent, or playmate. His vehemence may astound; but often it is purely verbal. However, he feels the passing shadow of the curse of Cain; for he is acquiring the idea of death by violence,—death as a condition which results from killing! (The war has not delayed this insight.)

For the 7-year-old the death idea becomes somewhat more personal. He suspects that he himself will some day die; but since this suspicion is in tender and timid beginnings he also denies that he will die. While Six might verbally visit death upon another, SEVEN, true to his inwardizing psychology, may verbally complain, "I wish I were dead." But even more than Six he has a realistic curiosity about the objective appurtenances of death: coffin, burial and cemetery.

The 8-year-old progresses from an interest in graves and funerals to an interest in what happens after death. His comprehension is more general, and he acknowledges that "All men must die."

The 10-year-old accepts this philosophic dictum more completely. He confronts the fact of death as a natural phenomenon; he does not limit his interest to its appurtenances and consequences. He thinks of life as having a physiological basis in nutrition, growth, blood and breathing. Death comes when these essentials fail. Death is a negation of life, a biological process. True to his maturity traits, the 10-year-old again approximates and foreshadows the outlook of the adult.

4. COSMOS AND DEITY

The newborn infant, as already suggested, is immersed in the cosmos. Perhaps that is the reason he has about him an "air of infinite wisdom" which tends to vanish when mere mortal intelligence develops.

Thoreau hints as much: "In a sense the babe takes its departure from Nature as the grown man his departure out of her, and so during its nonage is at one with her, and as a part of herself."

Our growth gradients attempt to tell something about how this generic Babe disengages himself and makes the developmental departures toward a state of maturity where he can contemplate the cosmos which gave him birth! It is a long journey which begins with his first steps in the early conquests of time and space; which continues in his endless questions: What's that? Why? How?; and which ultimately brings him to the sacred and the secular literatures that deal with Nature and with God. The culture answers his childhood and adult questions through sciences and religions.

The cosmology of the infant is delimited by the nursery. His world system consists of furniture, feeding utensils, crib, clothes and domestic trappings. In his perambulator he may note the waving trees against the horizon; he glimpses the come and go of other vehicles; he senses vast masses of houses against the sky; but, as yet, he is scarcely conscious of either earth or sky for he makes no distinction between the two. He is space-bound by what immediately impinges on his needs, his economy.

With increasing powers of locomotion his hitherto constricted world system enlarges and takes on structure. He walks on curbs and walls with a thrilling sense of distance and destination. He begins to know that pathways and streets lead somewhere. He may name his own street, his village or city, neighboring cities. In time the drug store, the market place, nursery school and kindergarten become part of his "cosmology."

If he could draw a map of his universe we can be pretty sure of what he would include; because his cosmology, up to the age of five, is highly personal.

At six and seven his interests become somewhat more impersonal. He displays at least a picture book interest in foreign places; he makes inquiries about both the astronomical and theological heavens. In his efforts at orientation he tries to ascertain the precise spatial location of an over ruling deity. He is curious about the elements, the earth's crust, fire, the wind, the weather, clouds, the melting of snow and ice, the origins of rivers, lakes and sea, mountains and deserts, flora and fauna. A tree is no longer a mere moving blotch against a background. It is a plant. But how did it get there? Where does the wind come from? Or does the tree make the wind by nodding? What are stones made of? And, Mamma, where did you find me? Where was I when you were at school? And *who* took care of the very first baby? And does Superman make supermen?

With such a welter of questions, one might wonder how the child is ever able to escape confusion. And yet he fashions for himself an orderly universe. To begin with, he doesn't ask the questions all at once. He asks in relation to a specific spot on the frontier of *his* unknown. If you try to tell him too much and too early, you are more likely to bewilder him. He is not lost; he simply wants to take one step; that is the *next* one, and always one at a time. He would not ask the questions at all if there were no immanent order in the universe of which he is a very important fragment. He feels himself in a world of lawful forces, some of which he controls. For this reason his questionings and his thinking take him toward and into the realms of the natural sciences and of cosmogony. In his naivete he may even ask, "Well, who made God?" or "Was God born?" And a 7-year-old skeptic argues, "I have never seen God in school."

When skepticism makes its appearance in a child's thinking, we may be sure that the mind is becoming conscious of itself. This leads the child to an increasingly objective view of Nature. At the same time the sense of self is becoming more defined; and the concepts of Deity undergo corresponding changes. During the earlier pre-school ages, the child's relation with the cosmos is so close, and in Piaget's sense, so egocentric, that he attributes purpose and feeling to the events of Nature. Many of the child's spontaneous notions are then probably colored by animism; and occasionally by magic. Frequently his notions bear a striking resemblance to some phase of primitive mythology.

The tendency toward "dynamistic" as opposed to rational thinking doubtless varies with the temperament of the child, as well as with age and circumstances. An imaginative child is likely to project himself even into lifeless, physical objects for the playful fun of it; because the mind can play as well as work. Edmund Gosse in his autobiographic volume, *Father and Son*, supplies us with an engaging example, at the normatively proper age of six: "What are the resources of a solitary child of six?" he asks. "Being so restricted then, and yet so active, my mind took refuge in an infantile species of natural magic. . . . I formed strange superstitions. . . . I persuaded myself that if I could only discover the proper words to say, or the proper passes to make I could induce the gorgeous birds and butterflies in my Father's illustrated manuals to come to life and fly out of the book, leaving holes behind them."

A pedestrian mind would not have had the wit, though it might have the primitiveness, to indulge in such a fancy. For that matter, it might be pointed out that nothing would have more surprised the 6-year-old Edmund, than to find that his magic worked; and that the engravings came alive, for even at that age he was well grounded in the elementary realities of the physical world.

Within the limits of his intelligence and experience, however, the child of six and younger is capable of drawing rational deductions; and he can think in the non-mystical terms of physical causality. At first he thinks of specific causes. By the age of ten he may think of general, mechanical causes. He is less naive; his errors of interpretation are fewer. His modes of thinking and his attitudes toward cause and effect become truly scientific in their essence. But the most remarkable feature of his intellectual development is not an increase of knowledge and accuracy. More remarkable is his interest in causes, which expresses itself in "Why?" even before the age of three.

Whence this Why? which becomes particularly insistent at the ages of four, five and six. It is an untaught tendency of his growing mind. It is as instinctive as his play and phantasy. It resembles a startle response evoked by new or strange situations, and is based on the inborn capacity to wonder.

The corollary of *"Why"* and *"How"* is *"I don't know"* and *"I can't."* The child's questionings reflect and direct the growth of his critical ability. His sense of self becomes more discriminating. He no longer considers himself all powerful; and gradually, or perhaps suddenly, he perceives that his parents are not all powerful. This necessitates a revolutionary revision of his philosophic outlook. He looks upon the world and upon the household in a changing light.

The disillusionment comes as though it were a natural and necessary mechanism for intellectual, as well as emotional development. Edmund Gosse found it so, and was confirmed "in the opinion that certain leading features in each human soul are inherent to it, and cannot be accounted for by suggestion or training." He relates how the *consciousness of self* came to him as a force and as a companion; and how it came as the result of a household incident, in which his mother corrected his father for saying something which was not quite true. And Father accepted the correction!

"Here was the appalling discovery, never suspected before, that my Father was not as God, and did not know everything. The shock was not caused by any suspicion that he was not telling the truth, as it appeared

to him, but by the awful proof that he was not, as I had supposed, omniscient."

"My Father, as a deity, as a natural force of immense prestige, fell
in my eyes to a human level. In future, his statements about things in
general need not be accepted implicitly. But of all the thoughts which
rushed upon my savage and undeveloped little brain at this crisis, the
most curious was that I had found a companion and a confidant in myself. There was a secret in this world and it belonged to me and to a
somebody who lived in the same body with me. There were two of us,
and we could talk with one another. It is difficult to define impressions
so rudimentary, but it is certain that it was in this dual form that the
sense of my individuality now suddenly descended upon me, and it is
equally certain that it was a great solace to find a sympathizer in my
own breast."

When Edmund Gosse grew up he became an eminent critic. It is not
surprising, therefore, that he had an acute sense of self in his childhood.
But all children, even the less gifted, pass through a comparable ante-
adolescent phase during the crisis of the sixth year or thereabouts.
The dethronement of *Paterfamilias* is, after all, not too drastic. Life with
father goes on. The qualities of omnipotence and omniscience are per-
petuated in the child's developing concepts of a Heavenly Father,—and
also in a popular figure who comes down a chimney once a year. With
good reason Santa Claus is sometimes called Father Christmas. He is a
true folk phenomenon. At his best he remains a jolly and kindly em-
bodiment of a beneficent parenthood.

Perhaps our culture should do more to preserve him, by preventing
over commercialization, and also over multiplication; for the susceptible believer is subject to numerical and other confusions. But usually
a child can assimilate, adore, and in time deny him without suffering
any scars of disillusionment. Indeed this substantial saint, in con-
tributing to the spirit of Christmas, assists the child to attain a more
abstract concept of a spiritual deity.

The prevailing culture and the religion of the household have a marked effect upon the child's ideas of God; but the general character of the ideas is basically determined by developmental factors.

These factors are neatly reflected in the growth gradients for the Santa Claus myth. Up to the age of two-and-a-half years the physical Santa is usually feared. He is a strange and formidable threat to the child's security. A year later he begins to be somewhat meaningful and interesting. Most 3-year-olds are aware of Santa long before they are aware of God. The 4-year-old is a true believer and accepts every detail of the myth. The 5-year-old embraces the realism of Santa's clothes, his laugh, his reindeers. The 6-year-old hears doubtings, but he fiercely repels all suspicion. His belief is more emotional; his enjoyment more intense. If he has a lively mind he images not only old Santa himself, but Santa's wife, home, workshop and the ledger in which the names and deeds of good children are enrolled.

Reflective SEVEN has moments of skepticism; or we should say, moments of constructive criticism. His natural science (which includes the measurement and displacement of physical bodies) does not permit him to believe that Santa comes down the chimney. He may repudiate still other details but he adheres to the core of his faith and of his enjoyment. At age eight, the notion of Santa Claus is more etherealized, but it is by no means surrendered. The spirit of Christmas is taking shape as an observed and felt reality.

By the age of nine or ten, the Santa myth has been generally abandoned; but who can doubt that it may play an enriching role in the development of personality? The child's reactions to the myth reflect at least the mechanisms and the stages by which he reaches the higher levels of religious thought. In the early pre-school period he regards his parents as omniscient, but he admits Santa into his pantheon, and ascribes to him parental attitudes when a philosophical need arises. Coincidently he admits angels and heaven into the gallery of his imagination. (His imagination and interest are particularly rich at the age of six.) Parents, in the child's outgrown belief, once made everything in the world. Now there are other agencies; and even Santa may prove to be a bridge to the concept of God as a creator and governor. The 10-year-old is less naive, more rationalistic. He ascribes natural origins and natural processes to Nature and to Man, and over the cosmos he is erecting a supreme deity. He has attained a preliminary stage of maturity where he can combine science and religion in his philosophic outlook.

One of the great tasks of postwar education is to impart the life sciences and the physical sciences in a manner which will preserve both rational and spiritual values.

GROWTH GRADIENTS

§1. TIME

18 MONTHS—Child lives in the present. Finds it difficult to wait.
  Uses no time words but responds to "now."
  Slight sense of timing: sight of juice and crackers may bring him to the table.

21 MONTHS—Continues to live in the present. His chief time word is "now."
  May consider that a certain event, i.e. father coming in, is the signal for next event (supper). Even though father may have come very early, child expects supper at once.
  Responds to "In a minute."
  Improved sense of timing: may sit at the table and wait for juice.

2 YEARS—Child still lives chiefly in the present, but begins to use words denoting the future: "gonna," "in a minute."
  Will wait in response to: "wait," "pretty soon."
  Has several words indicating present time: "now," "today," "aw day," "dis day."
  No words for the past but begins to use past tense of verbs, often inaccurately.
  Comprehends simple time sequences as implied in, "Have clay after juice."

2½ YEARS—Child may use about twenty different time words.
  Now uses freely words implying past, present and future time. Has several different words for each.
  Words for the present: "day," "morning," "afternoon."
  Future: "Some day," "one day," "tomorrow," "pretty soon."
  Past time is usually designated by "last night."
  Freely uses names of the days of the week although inaccurately.

3 YEARS—Most common basic time words now in child's vocabulary.

More time words added to vocabulary between two-and-a-half and three years than in any other equal period.

Many different words now used for past, present and future. Most for future.

Adult can bargain with the child, can persuade him to wait for things.

Expressions of duration: "all the time," "for two weeks," come in.

Pretense of telling time and spontaneous use of clocktime phrases, usually inaccurate.

Much use of the word "time" alone or in combination: "It's time," "lunchtime."

Child can tell how old he is, when he goes to bed, and what he will do next day.

3½ YEARS—Great variety of expressions indicating past, present and future now used spontaneously, to about an equal extent.

Many complicated expressions of duration: "for a long time," "for years," "a whole week," "in the meantime."

Increase in refinement of expression: "It's almost time," "a nice long time."

Expresses habitual action: "On Fridays."

May refer to future happenings as if in the past: "I'm not going to take a nap yesterday."

Ability to answer questions about time not much increased since three years.

4 YEARS—Spontaneously speedy, but slows down under pressure. If urged to hurry, usually goes more slowly.

Has reasonably clear understanding of when events of the day take place in relation to each other.

Past, present and future words continue to be used freely and about equally.

Many new time words or expressions are added.

The word "month" comes in; also such broad concepts as "next summer," "last summer."

5 YEARS—Child lives in the here and now.

Knows when events of day take place in relation to each other.

Dramatic house play involves sequences in time,—routines of the day.

Most of the time words commonly used by adults now in the child's vocabulary

Free verbal handling of the more common aspects of time.

Can name days of the week, at least in rote fashion.

Can answer questions such as "How old will you be on your next birthday?", "What day is it?"

Cannot conceive of not being alive, of dying, or of anyone living before him.

Interest in clocks. Likes to play with toy clocks.

Interest in calendars; likes to find birthday and holiday dates.

6 YEARS—Child tends to dawdle in most routines.

Increasing knowledge of duration. Can discriminate roughly time intervals; but "You may play for twenty minutes" is not useful unless implemented.

An understanding of the seasons, in terms of activities suitable for each.

If asked, "What is Time?" may say "Time to get out of bed."

Interest in his and/or mother's babyhood.

Can answer questions such as "What time do you go to school?", "How long do you stay in school?", "What do you do in the spring?"

Begins to understand that oldest people usually die first.

Some interest in time being different in different parts of the world.

May be mixed up about past and present. Clings to the old yet scoffs at it, and wants the new.

7 YEARS—Adult needs to be aware of child's natural tempo and give him time for performance.

Child may dawdle almost until deadline then speed up and finish with a spurt.

Interest in school schedule as to what subject follows what.

May be afraid of being late for school.

Can tell what time it is; also how many minutes past, or of, the hour.

Can tell what season it is; what month it is; how many minutes in an hour.

If asked "What is Time?" may answer, "Time is to be ready for school."

Uses concepts such as how many years till some event, spontaneously in thinking and in conversation.

8 YEARS—Child is very "speedy" and likes anything that is speeded up.

"Can't wait" for future events or to be grownup.

Likes to consult bulletin board about school schedule.

Can tell time, but still depends on parent to be told that it is bedtime, etc.

Can tell what day of the month it is.

Can name months; can tell what year it is.

Asked "What is Time?", may reply, "What part of the day it is; what time it is."

Beginning of interest in primitive peoples and in times past.

Not very clear about times past; thus not know whether or not George Washington is mentioned in the Bible.

9 YEARS—Child can tell time but does not as a rule take responsibility of depending on his watch to know when to do things.

Practical time sense not too good. Cannot report in any detail what his daily school schedule is. Can tell when recess is, and when he goes home.

Can telephone home if he is going to be late.

May plan schedule of day, or may plan way ahead to an adult future.

Child may feel pressed for time, he is so busy.

May be challenged competitively by timing of a performance.

Interested in biography: the life sequence of the individual (9-10 years).

Marked interest not only in history but in pre-historic times.

Will do a task if told how much there is to do, and how long it will take.

§2. SPACE

1 YEAR—Wriggles for "down." Gestures for "up."
Plays "peek-a-boo."

15 MONTHS—Says "up."

18 MONTHS—Says "down," "off," "bye-bye," "all gone."
Out for a walk, runs ahead of adult and explores by-ways.
Can obey two directions with ball, putting it on chair or on table or giving it to mother.

21 MONTHS—Says: "on," "all gone," "big," *"here."*
Points; pulls person to show things.

2 YEARS—Says: "up high," "in," "out," *"there,"* "where," "go way," "up here," "fall down," "turn around," "other side."
Likes to walk on curbs and walls.
Can obey four directions with ball: on chair, on table, to mother, to examiner.
In play may use pattern in rug, etc. as road for car.

2½ YEARS—Says: "to," "home," "way up," *"right here," "in here," "in there,"* "fall," "under the table," "around the table," "to New York."
Interested in having things in their places. Helps put things away.
Out for a walk, begins to have thought of destination.

3 YEARS—Says: "in the train," "back," "over," *"over here,"* "fits," "gone away," "around," "in New Haven."
Can tell what street he lives on but usually not the number.
Can carry out commands in regard to: over, crooked, under, big, high, long, tall.
Puts ball on, and under chair.
Out for a walk, definitely has destination in mind. Always likes to follow the same route.

3½ YEARS—Says *"go there,"* "go" meaning belong; "found," "in school," *"over there."*
Puts ball on, under, in back of chair.
Can tell what street he lives on and what city he lives in.
If asked how he gets to a certain place, will answer "on the bus," "in the car."
Cannot tell by what route.

4 YEARS—Uses space words more exactly, and in combinations.
Carries out commands in regard to: on top, behind, bumpy, deep, pointed, shallow.
Puts ball on, under, in front of, behind chair.
Plays hide-and-seek.
Makes road in sand for his car. Dramatic rather than spatial use of "store," "home" etc.

Goes on errands outside home, without crossing street. Visits neighbors.

Out for a walk, runs ahead of adult and can wait at crossing.

Likes to go "different" ways when on walks.

If asked how he gets to a certain place, may try to describe the route. More likely to say "the goat way" or "by the ball place."

5 YEARS—Child is here and now. Very literal and factual. Also focal.

Child remains close to home base; close to mother.

Needs things in close juxtaposition spatially.

Needs parent to be right where he himself is; at his level.

Is interested in his home and in his immediate neighborhood.

Likes to do errands around the house; will go to the store usually accompanied by an adult. Can cross streets with traffic lights. Can learn to go to kindergarten by himself.

Can point out simple routes which he takes between near and familiar points.

Can carry out commands in regard to: few, forwards, backwards, tiny, smooth, high.

Likes to trace journeys on maps and make simple maps indicating the route he takes to school etc. Indicates specific landmarks.

Interested in the space which is here but not so much in spatial relations.

Is interested in distant cities and states if someone he knows is there.

Likes to go on excursions with his mother.

6 YEARS—Environment is expanding. Now includes relationships between home, neighborhood, and an expanding community.

Home and school both very important, but child has trouble orienting to the combination of these two different worlds.

Home interests now include: people, keeping house, pets, animals, outdoors, amusements, sources of food, preparation of food, clothing, books, holidays.

School interests now include: materials, equipment, library, various rooms, playgrounds.

The child himself is the center of his universe, but he is also interested in the sun, moon, planets, the whole world.

A rangy orientation to schoolroom: oriented to the whole room.

A minimal, picture-book type of interest in children of other lands.

Marked interest in Heaven, how you get there, etc. A contrasting interest in the Devil and Hell.

Very undifferentiated in regard to space as in all fields.

Can distinguish left and right on own body, but not on bodies of others.

May be able to tell points of compass from a familiar starting point; can name nearby streets.

May begin to realize that same programs come over other people's radio as over his own.

Some interest in what rest of school is like. Enjoys exploring school *with* his group.

If he goes on shopping excursions, must buy something.

7 YEARS—Somewhat similar to six with deepening of meanings and more understanding of relationships throughout the whole community.

School and home both important.

Community interests include details about: grocer, policeman, fireman, etc.

An interest in the elements: earth's crust, stones, heat, fire, sun, geology.

Not ready for study of far times and places (Indians and foreign countries).

Interest in God in Heaven now more clear and more spatial.

In school is oriented toward the teacher.

Interested in having his "own place."

Interested in the fact that "there are other places than just right here."

Marked improvement in understanding of orientation in regard to cardinal points of the compass.

Can play hide-the-thimble.

Can go from home room to another familiar room, but wants specific directions.

8 YEARS—Definite expansion into deeper understanding of wider community relationships.

Foreign countries and world relationships are better understood.

Beginning of interest in primitive people and times past: Indians, Pilgrims.

Child is expansive and evaluative; adventurous; willing to try new things and new places.

Interest in barriers: likes to set his own barriers.

Out of bounds encroaching on neighbors' property. Likes short cuts.

Child is speedy: covers much ground—in every way.

Interest and apparent understanding (to his own satisfaction) of going to Heaven when he dies.

Can distinguish right and left on bodies of others.

Can go to city on bus if put on and met by someone.

9 YEARS—Can go to familiar places on bus, getting on alone; or go downtown alone.

Interest in expanding community life: community problems of health, life, property; mercantile businesses; manufacturing industries; agricultural industries; transportation; weather; animal and plant life in community; holiday and seasonal activities.

Environment widens to include the whole earth. Studies culture outside his own. Understandings, attitudes and concepts become world wide: China, South America, Russia.

Communication with somewhat distant places through correspondence.

Likes geography (maps) and history. Other countries and other times.

Beginning to like biography, (whole development of one person).

Strong interest in details of life in foreign countries and in primitive times.

§3. LANGUAGE AND THOUGHT

4 WEEKS—Cries.
   Makes small, throaty noises.

16 WEEKS—Laughs aloud.

28 WEEKS—Polysyllabic vowel sounds.
   Crying—"m-m-m."

40 WEEKS—One word. Also "dada" and "mama."
   "Bye-bye" and "pat-a-cake" gestures.

52 WEEKS—Two words besides "dada" and "mama."
   Gives a toy on request.

15 MONTHS—Vocabulary of 4 or 5 words including proper names.
   Begins to use jargon.
   Names object; pats picture.

18 MONTHS—Uses and responds to a few favorite words: "Oh my," "all gone," "bye-bye,"
   "tata."
   Gestures help to reinforce language.
   Jargon predominates. Vocabulary of about ten words.
   Needs to be handled physically more than through words.
   In examination child refuses by shaking head "No," says "No," cries, refusing
   to answer.

2 YEARS—Jargon dropping out; 3-word sentences coming in.
   Vocabulary increasing rapidly. May include from 12 to 1,000 words.
   Verbal handling of child begins to supersede physical handling. Certain words
   can be used effectively: "need," "another," "again."
   Speaks and should be spoken to in short, simple phrases: "Have clay after juice."
   In examination child refuses by shaking head "No," says "no," refuses to answer,
   suggests other materials by gesture.

2½ YEARS—Vocabulary increases rapidly. Language now a useful tool for child.
   Spontaneous language often rhythmical and repetitive.
   Long monologues with fluent use of language.
   Verbally asserts domination over members of family.
   Uses such forms as I, me, you.
   More "time" words appear in next six months than during any other equal period.
   Adult now handles child by words instead of physically.
   Key words effective in handling child: "need," "has to have," "when you are
   finished," "it's time to."

Ritualistic. Likes to hear same story over and over.

In examination child refuses situation by shaking head "No," saying "No," asking verbally for other materials.

3 YEARS—More command of language. Uses language fluently and with confidence.

Can use words to control and can be controlled by words.

Interest in new words. Adult can use key words effectively in handling the child: "surprise," "secret," "could help," "might," "new," "different," "maybe."

Listens when reasoned with.

Listens with interest to adult conversations. Increasing span of interest in listening to stories.

Stuttering (3½ years).

In examination child refuses situations by saying "I don't know." Suggests other materials. Verbal reference to mother.

4 YEARS—Out of bounds verbally: talks a great deal; exaggerates; boasts; tells tall tales.

Talks with and about imaginary companions.

Much questioning: "Why?" "How?" as much to keep conversation going as seeking information.

Profanity, mild obscenities; verbal play about elimination.

Calls names; threatens; uses slang.

Likes nonsense words; silly language and rhyming; new and different words.

Many grammatical mistakes, and misuse of words.

Can listen to stories and being read to with sustained interest.

Less need for key words. Adult can talk to child more in man-to-man fashion. Whispering may be effective and child may be willing to whisper an answer which he will not give aloud.

In examination child refuses situations by saying "I can't," "I don't know." Boasts about irrelevant subjects, questions examiner; says "You tell me," "Hey," "Ow."

May say that he thinks with his mouth or with his tongue.

5 YEARS—Likes to talk and will talk to anyone. Some talk "constantly."

Interest in using new and large words; interest in the meaning of words.

Asks, "What does - - - - - spell?"

Innumerable questions; now really seeks information.

Grammar now reasonably accurate; usually one or two inaccurate forms. Criticizes wrong use of grammar in others.

"Loves" to be read to.

Uses language conformingly: "Is this the way to do it?"

In examination, begins to use language thoughtfully: "I think," "I forgot." Evaluates tasks: "That's hard," "That's easy."

Can define simple words.

Difficulty in distinguishing between fantasy and reality.

"Magic" is an accepted answer to the child's "How" questions.

May believe that everything active is alive; that man made everything.

May say that he thinks with his eyes.

Figures things out for himself. Makes own generalizations after even one occurrence of an event. If both his grandfathers died first he may ask, "Do daddies die first?" If by chance he has been told that two brown dogs were females and two black ones were males, he will conclude that all brown dogs are female and all black ones are male.

6 YEARS—Uses language aggressively: calls names, threatens, contradicts, argues. Slang and mild profanity.

Asks many questions. Very talkative.

Uses telephone. Some can dial.

Likes to use big words.

Usually good pronunciation and fairly accurate grammatical form. Can detect own mistakes and may accept correction.

Considerable stuttering, especially in boys.

In examination, is conscious of multiplicity of tasks: "So many words." Interest in beginnings of tasks: "I can't do it far," "I'll go as far as I can."

Can tell differences between two simple objects.

Increased ability to differentiate fantasy and reality.

Interest in magic strong: child plays that he is magic, has magic ears, etc. Counting is magic. Puts baby teeth under pillow and believes that fairies substitute pennies.

Everything that moves may be thought alive in contrast to that which is inert; child believes that God made everything.

7 YEARS—Uses language complainingly: nobody likes him, people are mean and unfair, he has nothing to play with.

If angry, may retreat into silence instead of, as earlier, into angry verbalization.

Interested in meaning and spelling of words. Some use of pictorial dictionary.

Considerable social telephoning to friends.

Use of slang and clichés.

Variable pitch of voice: voice generally loud, but may speak softly or mutter complaints.

Reading, listening to radio, silent verbal planning.

In examination estimates own ability: "I've never done that." "I guessed it."

Criticizes own performance: "What's the matter with me?" Delays: "Got to think it over." Interest in endings: "I've got all up to here."

Can give similarities between two simple objects.

Now relates thinking to head or mind: "You have to think it up in your head"; "It went out of my mind."

Great interest in magic, wishing stones, tricks.

May play at magic, that he has a magic wand, or that he "is" magic.

May believe that everything which moves is alive and that God made everything.

8 YEARS—Out of bounds verbally (as at 4 years): talks a great deal, exaggerates, boasts, tells tall tales.

[446]

Uses language fluently, almost as adult does.

Much social use of telephone.

Some slang and profanity; raises voice when angry or tired.

Reading and radio interests strong.

Good pronunciation and good grammar, as a rule.

Beginning of code language; use of Pig Latin or Double Dutch; secret pass-words.

Can give similarities and differences between simple objects.

Differentiation between fantasy and reality established.

Less belief in magic but interested in magician's tricks and may like to perform simple card tricks.

Can verbalize ideas and problems.

Begins to understand cause and effect relationships.

Distinguishes between original and acquired movement: to be alive is to move by one's self.

9 YEARS—Language now used more as a tool, less for its own sake.

No longer out of bounds verbalization as at eight years.

May return to many incorrect grammatical uses.

Writes out lists and plans.

Uses language to express subtle and refined emotions: disgust, self-criticism.

Reading and radio interests increase.

Considerable verbal criticism of parent's actions.

Extended use of code language.

Emergence of independent critical thinking.

Increasingly realistic conception of the world; does not like fairy stories.

Less belief in magic but strong belief in luck, and some superstition.

§4. WAR

2 YEARS—No answer to question, "What do soldiers (sailors) do?"

2½ YEARS—If he answers question, "What do soldiers (sailors) do?" will reply, "Dey march," or merely, "March."

3 YEARS—Replies to question, "What do soldiers (sailors) do?" "March all around," "Oh dey - - guns."

3½ YEARS—Replies to question, "What do soldiers do?" "They march—that's all I can figure out," "Wave the flags."
Replies to question, "What do sailors do?" "Sail," "Wear little white hats," "Shoot the Japanese," "Teach the WACS to be Coastguards."

4 YEARS—Replies to question, "What do soldiers do?" "March," "Go to war," "Fight the Japs with guns."
Replies to question, "What do sailors do?" "Sail in boats," "Oh sometimes they're

in sailing boats but when they're not in sailing boats they're walking with girls or somebody."

5 YEARS—Matter of fact questions about war in Europe, soldiers, what soldiers do, about Germans, Japanese, Hitler, the Nazis.

Tells, without emotion, that father is "in the war" or "in the army."

Thoughtful question: "Are there good Japs and bad Japs? You can't tell me all the Jap children are bad."

Plans about how to stop war: "Get up behind Hitler when he isn't looking and shoot him." Three way plan: a) "Put up a red light"; b) "Take from the people the things they need, then they won't be able to fight"; c) "Pass a law, tell them they shouldn't hurt each other."

Only a few seem afraid of bombs and air raids.

6 YEARS—An aggressive, angry response toward Japanese, Germans, Hitler.

Interest in the badness of the Germans.

Much war play in some detail; drill, march, shoot; airplane and gun play.

Aggressive talk, belittling the enemy.

Continued plans, as at five years, for defeating enemy: "Bomb Japs while they're asleep."

Some show interest in globe, maps, atlas—lands where fighting is going on; especially if father is in the armed forces.

A few worry or dream about bombing, or other aspects of war.

7 YEARS—Beginning in many, of worries and fears about the war. Some dreams about the war. One child dreamed that a spy asked her, "Do you like your government?" Much fear of spies.

War play continues stressing guns and airplanes.

Some boys like war movies and war funny books.

Likes to buy defense stamps.

Likes to collect paper, scrap etc. under direction, with whole school class.

8 YEARS—War play continues, elaborately.

Does not seem to worry about war, though interested.

Factual questions: why did the war start? Difference between Democracy and Fascism, etc.

A few listen to news, look at maps.

Interest in war movies, comic books, serious books.

Has ideas of organizing scrap collection clubs, saving for defense stamps.

9 YEARS—Detailed, serious, factual almost adult interest. Listens to news; follows maps.

Boy asked if he followed war said, "I know Russia is gaining and we captured Leyte."

One says he follows European better than Asiatic war.

Some boys think in terms of whether they prefer Army, Navy or Marines.

May ask about slave labor, how can they force people to work for the enemy. Mature approach and realization.

Surprisingly little aggressive talk about enemy.

Helps with war work (collections, saves for defense stamps).

§5. DEATH

1-3 YEARS—Very little or no understanding of the idea of death.

4 YEARS—Very limited concept of death.

Uses the word with some vague notion of its meaning.

No particular emotion related, though may verbalize a rudimentary notion that death is connected with sorrow or sadness.

5 YEARS—Concept becoming more detailed, accurate and factual. Some recognition of the finality of death, "the end." Though may think it is reversible (5½ years).

Recognize the immobility of the dead.

Attitude quite matter of fact and unemotional.

Bodily actions may come in, associated with death: avoids dead things, or may enjoy killing.

Seems to know as a fact, though apparently does not understand or feel emotionally, that death is related to age and that oldest often die first.

6 YEARS—New awareness of death. Beginning of an emotional response to the idea of death.

Worries that mother will die and leave him.

Connects killing, possibly illness and hospitals, as well as old age, with death.

Idea of death as result of aggression or killing.

Some preoccupation with graves, funerals, burial.

Disturbed by pictures and stories of children or animals dead or dying.

Does not believe that he himself will die.

7 YEARS—Similar to six years, but more detailed and realistic; better understanding.

Still looks at appurtenances: coffin, burial rites etc.

Rather marked interest in causes of death: old age, violence, disease.

Interest in visiting cemeteries.

Still thinks of death in terms of specific human experience.

Further connection of old age with death, oldest dying first.

May complain, "I wish I were dead."

Suspects that he himself will die. Denies that he will die.

8 YEARS—Progresses from an interest in graves and funerals to interest in what happens after death.

Usually refers death only to humanity though earlier included other species.

Feels that he understands the concept better.

May accept fact that all people, including himself, die.

9 YEARS—Reference now made to logical or biological essentials: "not living," "When you have no pulse and no temperature and can't breathe."

Now looks straight at death, not just at the periphery: i.e. coffins, graves.

Accepts quite realistically fact that when he is older he will one day die.

Not a marked interest with most at this age.

§6. DEITY

2 YEARS—No appreciable "religious sense."

May enjoy repeating last phrases of prayers.

Some ready for Sunday school if it is run along nursery school lines.

May be afraid of Santa Claus.

3 YEARS—May repeat whole prayers, as they do nursery rhymes.

Greater interest in Sunday school: may enjoy church for part of the service.

Santa Claus meaningful and of some interest.

4 YEARS—Marked interest in and many detailed factual questions about God. The concept is usually introduced by parents in answer to question of "Why" and "How." Comments and questions likely to be extremely "inappropriate."

Has religion of parents: child believes parents to be omniscient, all-powerful, eternal.

Enjoys prayers and elaborates them from the original.

Enjoys Sunday school and may sit through part of church services—as music.

Firmly believes in Santa Claus, in every detail.

5 YEARS—Many continue 4-year-old interest in and questions about God. Some are already losing this marked interest.

Some believe that God is responsible for everything. If child falls, God pushed him.

Enjoys prayers and makes up his own.

Likes Sunday school but may be very restless in church. May enjoy the pageantry.

Realistic approach to God and Santa Claus. Thinks of them as persons living in houses etc.

6 YEARS—Grasps idea of God as creator of the world, of animals, of beautiful things.

Asks to go to Sunday School. Loves story of Little Lord Jesus. Emotional interest in this. Interest in angels.

Enjoys a short ritualistic service. May enjoy Sunday school very much.

Prayers are important and child expects them to be answered.

Feeling of two forces: Heaven and Hell, God and the Devil, good and bad.

Profanity involves name of God.

Very firm about belief in Santa Claus; insistent and emotional. Fiercely denies any hint that he is not real.

7 YEARS—More thoughtful interest in God and Heaven. Questions becoming more "appropriate."

Beginning of slight skepticism and distinguishing what he knows from what he has merely been told.

Less praying as child takes more responsibility for own night routines.

Sunday school interest; and interest in Bible stories continues.

Beginning skepticism about Santa Claus. Denies some aspects, as that he comes down the chimney. Multiplicity of Santa Clauses seen on street may confuse child.

8 YEARS—Interested in information that soul only, not body, goes to Heaven.

May conceive of death as an immediate act of God, result of disease, or as resulting from disease which in turn is a punishment from God.

Not too much preoccupation about God.

Some still believe in Santa Claus. May deny that he is real, but "protest too much." May be able to substitute a "spirit of Christmas" or of "giving" for the more physical Santa Claus.

Likes Bible stories and passages from Bible. Likes to say prayers with mother.

9 YEARS—In general interest in God and religious matters is not strong.

May pray spontaneously on occasion if in great need or danger.

Most do not believe in Santa Claus.

Sunday school may be of continued interest if well taught or if associated with "clubs."

Bible story interest shifts to portions of Old Testament, especially historical books Enjoy memorizing Psalms and passages from Bible, enjoy singing in the choir

A PHILOSOPHIC POSTSCRIPT

Now, having examined the maturing modes of thinking which determine the philosophies of children, perhaps we should say a concluding word about our own philosophy,—and yours as it may bear on problems of child care. For the temper and the techniques of child care depend primarily upon underlying philosophic outlook.

If we wish to do justice to the child's personality, we must think in terms of growth, in terms of his developmental maturity. This means a philosophy which recognizes the relativities of the life cycle.

Developmentalism is the name for such a philosophy. Developmentalism is the very opposite of fascism, for it acknowledges the individuality of the child and wisely concedes that all his behavior is subject to the natural laws of human growth. These natural laws can be comprehended only through science and yet more science. Such science will not conflict with the humanities, because it makes possible an improvement of human relationships. The controls of our culture must be based on a more widely disseminated knowledge of child development.

We live in a technological age; we know something of the precision and the beauty of engines and machines. The rising generation of parents can readily absorb a science of child development which acquaints them with the mechanisms of growth,—with the machinery of behavior. That will be sound self-knowledge. It would make for tolerance and understanding, and a more penetrating appreciation of the meaning of infancy and childhood. Developmentalism is in harmony with the spirit of democracy.

The awesome flash of the atomic bomb has shocked thoughtful men into a realization of the social significance of science in a democratic culture. Even in the first solemn announcement of the new atomic age we were reminded that the proposition which affirms the worth and dignity of man remains "the strongest, most creative force now present in the world."

But propositions do not operate automatically. They must be implemented. We cannot maintain this most creative of all propositions unless we understand the energies of man in relation to the energies locked in the nucleus of the atom.

The nature of man is almost as terrifying as the unleashed atom. Terrifying until we comprehend, and thereby govern, his inner forces. Only through profound self-knowledge can the human mind bring itself nearer to individual and collective control. For such self-knowledge we need vast and even dramatic extensions of science, both basic and applied. We need a new science of man, and we need it urgently, for the flash of the bomb has revealed the face of evil.

In the aftermath of war we have to take a second look at the moral constitution of man as embodied or prefigured in children. Here we get a warning glimpse of the race-made and man-made origins of evil. Children can be rude and aggressive. But it would be sadly gratuitous to infer that the failures of adult ways of life are due to the imperfections of children. Sound inheritance greatly reduces these imperfections; and wise management brings the others under control. *The intrinsic charm and goodness of childhood still constitute the best guarantee of the further perfectibility of mankind.*

The most ameliorative force that can be released in the years of reconstruction which lie ahead is an intensified conservation of the development of infants and children. Such conservation depends upon favorable political and economic arrangements; but these in turn are dependent on scientific knowledge, as well as on the aspirations which come from humane traditions, from the arts and from religion. We cannot conserve the mental health of children, we cannot make democracy a genuine folkway unless we bring into the homes of the people a developmental philosophy of child care rooted in scientific research.

A science of man, accordingly, becomes a most creative force in the atomic age. It will heighten and multiply human values. It will diffuse among peoples, among common men, and among leaders of state that increase of intelligibility which is necessary for mutual understanding. In a more sincerely sustained effort to understand children, men and women of maturity will better comprehend themselves and their fellows.

REFERENCES AND READINGS

Aldrich, C. Anderson and Aldrich, Mary M. Babies are Human Beings. New York: Macmillan, 1938, ix + 128.

Ames, Louise B. The constancy of psychomotor tempo in individual infants. J. genet. Psychology, 1940, 57, 445-450.

Ames, Louise B. Motor correlates of infant crying. J. genet. Psychology, 1941, 59, 239-247.

Ames, Louise B. Early individual differences in visual and motor behavior patterns: a comparative study of two normal infants by the method of cinemanalysis. J. genet. Psychology, 1944, 65, 219-226.

Ames, Louise B. The development of the sense of time in the young child. J. genet. Psychology, 1946, 68, 97-125.

Ames, Louise B. and Learned, Janet. Imaginary companions and related phenomena. J. genet. Psychology, 1947. (In press).

Anderson, Harold H. School-Home Cooperation. Bulletin State Univ. of Iowa, Child Welfare pamphlet no. 15, new series no. 665, 1932, 1-11.

Association for Childhood Education. Portfolio on Materials for Work and Play. Washington, D. C.: 1945.

Bakwin, Ruth M. and Bakwin, Harry. Psychologic Care during Infancy and Childhood. New York: D. Appleton-Century, 1942, xv. + 317.

Baxter, Bernice. Teacher-Pupil Relationships. New York: Macmillan, 1941, 166.

Biber, Barbara, Murphy, Lois B., Woodcock, Louise P., and Black, Irma S. Child Life in School: A Study of a Seven Year Old Group. New York: Dutton, 1942, xii + 658.

Blanchard, Phyllis. A study of subject matter and motivation of children's dreams. J. abnor. and Social Psychology, 1926, 21, 24-37.

Bonte, Eleanor P. and Mary Musgrove. Influences of war as evidenced in children's play. Child Development, 1943, 14, no. 4, 179-200.

Breckenridge, Marian E. and Vincent, E. Lee. Child Development: Physical and Psychological Growth through the School Years. Philadelphia & London: W. B. Saunders Co., 1943, ix + 592. (Excellent list of references.)

Bull, Nina. Towards a clarification of the concept of emotion. Psychosomatic Medicine, 1945, 7, no. 4, 210-214.

Bullen, Adelaide K. A cross-cultural approach to the problem of stuttering. Child Development, 1945, 16, nos. 1-2, 1-88.

California, Elementary Schools of. Tentative Framework for the Social Studies Curriculum in the Elementary Schools of California. Presented in its revised form at the Social Studies Workshop of the 1944 Conference of Supervisors.

Child Study Association. Parents' Questions. New York: Harper, 1936, xiv + 312.

Child Study: A Quarterly Journal of Parent Education. New York: Child Study Association, 221 West 57th Street.

Commission on Teacher Education. Helping Teachers Understand Children. (Daniel A. Prescott, ed.) Washington, D. C.: American Council on Education, 1945, xv. + 468.

Darwin, Charles. The Expression of the Emotions in Man and Animals. New York: D. Appleton & Co., 1897.

Davis, C. M. Self-selection of food by children. American J. Nursing, 1935, 35, 401-410.

de Schweinitz, Karl. Growing Up: The Story of How We Become Alive, Are Born, and Grow up. New York: Macmillan, 1934, 111 pp.

Doll, Edgar A. The Vineland Social Maturity Scale. Vineland, New Jersey: 1941, 30 pp.

Doll, Edgar A. Your Child Grows Up. Boston: John Hancock Mutual Life Ins. Co. 1939.

Ets, Marie Hall. The Story of a Baby. New York: Viking Press, 1939, 63 pp.

Foster, Josephine C. and Headley, Neith E. Education in Kindergarten. New York: American Book Co., 1936, xii + 368.

Freud, A. & Burlingham, D. War and Children. New York: Ernst Willard, 1943, pp. 191.

Garrison, Charlotte G., Sheehy, Emma D., and Dalgliesh, Alice. The Horace Mann Kindergarten for Five-Year-Old Children. New York: Bureau of Publications, Teachers College, Columbia University, 1937, xii + 146.

Gesell, Arnold. How a Baby Grows: A Story in Pictures. New York: Harper, 1945, 78 pp.

Gesell, Arnold et al. The First Five Years of Life: A Guide to the Study of the Preschool Child. New York: Harper, 1940, xiii + 393.

Gesell, Arnold and Amatruda, Catherine S. Developmental Diagnosis: Normal and Abnormal Child Development. New York: Hoeber, 1941, xiii + 447.

Gesell, Arnold (in collaboration with C. S. Amatruda). Embryology of Behavior: The Beginnings of the Human Mind. New York: Harper, 1945, xix + 289.

Gesell, Arnold (assisted by L. B. Ames). Early evidences of individuality in the human infant. Scientific Monthly, 1937, xlv, 217-225.

Gesell, Arnold and Ames, Louise B. The development of directionality in drawing. J. genet. Psychology, 1946, 68, 45-61.

Gesell, Arnold and Ames, Louise B. The ontogenetic organization of prone behavior in human infancy. J. genet. Psychology, 1940, 56, 247-263.

Gesell, Arnold (in collaboration with Louise B. Ames). The Story of Child Development in Motion Pictures. A guide to the study and interpretation of the Yale Films of Child Development. New York: Encyclopaedia Britannica Films Inc.

Gesell, Arnold and Gesell, Beatrice Chandler. The Normal Child and Primary Education. Boston: Ginn & Co., 1912, x + 342.

Gesell, Arnold and Ilg, Frances L. Feeding Behavior of Infants: A Pediatric Approach to the Mental Hygiene of Early Life. Philadelphia: Lippincott, 1937, ix + 201

Gesell, Arnold and Ilg, Frances L. (In collaboration with Janet Learned and Louise B. Ames). Infant and Child in the Culture of Today. New York: Harper, 1943, xii + 399.

Gesell, Arnold and Thompson, Helen. Twins T and C from infancy to adolescence: a biogenetic study of individual differences by the method of co-twin control. Genet. Psychology Monog., 1941, 24, 3-121.

Gilbert, Margaret Shea. Biography of the Unborn. Baltimore, Md.: Williams and Wilkins, 1938, x + 132.

Gosse, Edmund. Father and Son. New York: Scribner, 1907.

Grayson, Alice Barr. Do You Know Your Daughter? New York: D. Appleton-Century, 1944, xxi + 306.

Henry, George H. Can your child really read? Harper's Magazine, January, 1946, 72-76.

Hildreth, Gertrude. Learning the Three R's. Minneapolis: Educational Publishers, Inc. Revised edition, 1946.

Hubbard, Elizabeth Vernon. Your Children at School: How They Adjust and Develop. New York: John Day, 1942, xv + 176.

Hughes, Richard. A High Wind in Jamaica. New York: Modern Library, 1932, ix + 399. (Fiction).

Hunt, J. McV. (Editor). Personality and Behavior Disorders. 2 vols. New York: The Ronald Press, 1944, 1242 pp.

Jersild, Arthur T. Child Psychology. New York: Prentice-Hall, Inc., 1940, xiii + 592.

Junior Reviewers, 241 Greenwood Street, Newton Centre 59, Mass. (A monthly publication which reviews all new children's books.)

Kanner, Leo. Behavior Disorders in Childhood. In Hunt, J. McV. Personality and the Behavior Disorders. New York: The Ronald Press, 1944. Pages 761-793.

Lee, J. Murray and Lee, Doris May. The Child and His Curriculum. New York: D. Appleton-Century, 1940, xv + 652.

Lerrigo, Marion Olive. Children Can Help Themselves. New York: Macmillan, 1943. ix + 219.

Levine, Milton and Seligmann, Jean H. The Wonder of Life. New York: Simon & Schuster, 1940, 114 pp.

Lowenberg, Miriam E. Your Child's Food. New York: McGraw-Hill, 1939, xviii + 299.

Moreno, J. L. Who Shall Survive: A New Approach to the Problem of Human Inter-relations. Nerv. and Mental Disease Monograph Series No. 58, Washington, D. C.: Nervous and Mental Disease Publishing Co., 1934, xvi + 437.

Neterer, Elizabeth and Ewen, Alice M. Portfolio for Primary Teachers. Assoc. for Childhood Education, 1201 16th St., N.W., Washington 6, D.C.

Piaget, Jean. The Language and Thought of the Child. New York: Harcourt, Brace & Co., 1926, xxiii + 246.

Reynolds, Martha May. Children from Seed to Saplings. New York: McGraw-Hill, 1939, x + 337.

Sheldon, William H. (In collaboration with S. S. Stevens.) The Varieties of Tempera-ment: A Psychology of Constitutional Differences. New York: Harper, 1942, x + 520.

Sherbon, Florence B. The Child. His Origin, Development, and Care. New York: McGraw-Hill, 1934, xix + 707.

Simmons, Katherine. The Brush Foundation Study of Child Growth and Development, II. Physical Growth and Development. Monog. Soc. Res. Child Development, 1944, ix, serial no. 37, no. 1, xvii + 87.

Shuttleworth, Frank K. The Physical and Mental Growth of Girls and Boys Age Six to Nineteen in Relation to Age at Maximum Growth. Monog. Soc. Res. Child Development, 1939, iv, serial no. 22, no. 3, vi + 291.

Starch, Daniel, Stanton, Hazel and Koerth, Wilhelmine. Controlling Human Behavior. New York: Macmillan, 1936, xiv + 638.

Strang, Ruth. An Introduction to Child Study. New York: Macmillan, 1938, xv + 681. (Contains tables of height and weight.)

Terman, L. M. & Miles, C. C. Sex and Personality. New York and London. McGraw-Hill Book Co., Inc., 1936, pp. xi + 600.

Thompson, Helen. Physical Growth. In Handbook of Child Psychology (ed. Leonard Carmichael). New York: John Wiley and Sons, (1946). (Survey of the literature on physical growth).

Wolff, George, M.D. Childhood Mortality from Accidents. U. S. Dept of Labor. Children's Bureau, Publication 311, pp. 25.

Woods, L. A. Elementary Education Suggestive Outline. (Revised edition). A Bulletin of the State Department of Education, Austin, Texas: Prepared under the direction of Edgar Ellen Wilson, Director of Elementary Ed., No. 451, September, 1945, 124 pp.

INDEX

* All ages also appear repeatedly in chronological sequence in the growth gradients in Part
III, pp. 231-451.